Tunable Laser Diodes

Tunable Laser Diodes

Markus-Christian Amann
Jens Buus

Artech House
Boston • London

Library of Congress Cataloging-in-Publication Data
Amann, Markus-Christian.
    Tunable laser diodes / Markus-Christian Amann, Jens Buus.
        p.   cm.
    Includes bibliographical references and index.
    ISBN 0-89006-963-8 (alk. paper)
    1. Tunable lasers. I. Buus, Jens. II. Title.
    TA1706.A55   1998
    621.36'6—dc21   98-28218
                                                                       CIP

British Library Cataloguing in Publication Data
Amann, Markus-Christian
    Tunable laser diodes. — (Artech House optoelectronics library)
    1. Diodes, Semiconductor   2. Semiconductor lasers
    I. Title   II. Buus, Jens
    621.3'81522
    ISBN 0890069638

Cover design by Lynda Fishbourne

International Standard Book Number: 0-89006-963-8
Library of Congress Catalog Card Number: 98-28218

10 9 8 7 6 5 4 3 2 1

Contents

Foreword

A wavelength tunable laser diode is a specific device, characterized by its wavelength tunability, and expected to be a key device for advanced optical communication, as well as for a variety of optical measurements. This book is written by two experts in the field of optoelectronics, Dr. Jens Buus and Professor Markus-Christian Amann, who have been doing pioneering work in the development of advanced laser diodes. This book covers tunable laser diodes from fundamentals of laser diodes, basic principles and practice of wavelength tunable lasers, to application areas. Thus, I believe that this book is an excellent text book for final year undergraduate students, graduate students, researchers working on semiconductor lasers, and also for system engineers interested in the application of tunable laser diodes.

A semiconductor laser itself is a key device for optoelectronics owing to its superior performance such as small size, low power consumption, high efficiency, longer device life, flexibility for selecting wavelength, and adaptability for photonic integrated circuits, etc. Efforts have been concentrated on further development. An integrated laser diode with external waveguide was developed with an intention of exploring the possibility of implementing monolithic integration of optoelectronic devices and components. A wavelength tunable laser diode was created as an extension of the laser diode monolithically integrated with tuning sections within the laser cavity, see "Wavelength tunable 1.5 μm GaInAsP/InP bundle-integrated-guide distributed Bragg reflector (BIG-DBR) lasers" by Y. Tohmori, K. Komori, S. Arai, Y. Suematsu, and H. Oohashi, The Transactions of the IECE of Japan, Vol. E68, pp. 788-790, 1985. After the first trials of the electronically wavelength tunable laser, efforts have been made to achieve excellent performance with wider wavelength tuning range. Presently, the wavelength tunable lasers find many application areas as mentioned in this book.

This book covers almost all of the essential subjects on tunable laser diodes, from theory to applications. It covers fundamentals not only of tunable laser diodes, but of modern laser diodes in general. In Chapter 2, "Fundamental Laser Diode Characteristics," basic properties of semiconductor lasers are presented, and in Chapter 3, "Single-Mode Laser Diodes," essential properties for single-mode lasers are summarized together with the basic principles of operation. In Chapters 4 to 7, the principles, design, and practice of tunable laser diodes are described with an emphasis placed on extremely widely tunable lasers. In Chapter 8, "Related Components," optical components related to tunable lasers and non-semiconductor tunable lasers are discussed. In Chapter 9, "Practical Issues and Applications," the description covers application areas such as optical communication, radar, environmental sensing, reflectometry, and circuit analysis. Finally, in the Appendixes, important factors such as the refractive index of semiconductors, optical waveguiding and transfer matrices, and the thermal response of laser diodes are treated.

I hope that this book would be read by people who have been interested in the new and powerful devices in the optoelectronics area.

Yasuharu Suematsu
Spring, 1998

Preface

The objective of this book is to give a complete account, as of early 1998, of the state of the art of monolithic tunable laser diodes. It is the authors' objective to include all relevant material and to provide a balanced presentation of the underlying theoretical aspects and practical issues of tunable laser diodes. We are combining this account with general background material such as basic laser diode properties (Chapter 2 and the Appendices), the physical principles of tunable laser diodes (Chapter 4), and the theories for propagation in structures with contradirectional or codirectional coupling (Chapters 3 and 7, respectively). Device structures and performance are discussed in detail (Chapters 5 to 7) and material on related topics (Chapter 8) and applications (Chapter 9) is provided as well. By including this material, we hope that the book can be used in different ways by different groups of readers: As a textbook in specialized courses for post graduate students, as a reference book for scientists working in this or related areas, and as a handbook for engineers using tunable lasers.

Selection of references is always problematic. We estimate that over 1,000 papers dealing exclusively, or mainly, with tunable laser diodes and related topics have now appeared in the technical literature. Rather than trying to include all of these papers we have adopted the following approach: All references to quoted results (theoretical or experimental) are included, using primary references unless a more detailed description has been published later by the same authors. References to conference papers are generally avoided if the material has been published elsewhere. In addition we include a number of more general references where the reader can find additional details that it has not been possible to include here.

The completion of this book would not have been possible without the direct or indirect help from a number of people including our former colleagues at Siemens, GEC-Marconi Materials Technology, and University of Kassel, as well as the participants in the RACE projects R1010-CMC, R1069-EPLOT, R2069-UFOS and the ACTS project AC065-BLISS. We would also like to thank a number of authors who have given permission for use of their artwork. In a few cases this material has been supplied in electronic form, thereby easing our work significantly.

Chapter 1

Introduction

Laser diodes were first reported in 1962, shortly after the first demonstrations of other laser types. After the development of high-performance AlGaAs/GaAs double-heterostructure lasers around 1970, this laser structure became a commercial product in the late 1970s offering a number of advantages, including size, power-conversion efficiency, direct-current pumping, reliability, and wavelength flexibility. In addition, laser diodes are potentially very cheap. For these reasons, it is now by far the most common laser type, with several million devices being produced every month. The most important laser diode application is compact disc players; the devices used in this area cost just a few dollars each. A representative collection of papers by the pioneers on laser diodes can be found in the June 1987 issue of the *IEEE Journal of Quantum Electronics*. Up to now, over 30 books dealing exclusively, or mainly, with laser diodes have been written [1–32].

     Since a number of performance characteristics (e. g., power, modulation speed, spectral linewidth, operating wavelength) can be optimized for specific applications, laser diodes find a large number of applications. For applications that require wavelength tuning, the wide spectral gain normally available in laser diodes is particularly interesting. After the successful development of InGaAsP/InP single-mode laser diodes around 1,300 nm and 1,550 nm in the early 1980s, therefore, the realization of electronically wavelength-tunable laser diodes became an important issue worldwide of subsequent research [33]. This research has mainly been driven by the increasing demand on transmission capacity in optical communications systems, making the application of advanced transmission techniques necessary. This particularly comprises wavelength division multiplexing (WDM) technique and coherent optical detection schemes [34, 35]. In all these advanced communications techniques, single-mode, single-frequency laser diodes with an electronically tunable wavelength represent indispensable key components on both the transmitter and the receiver side. Besides the optical communication, numerous applications in sensing and measurement also become feasible or rely on the availability of these light sources [36–38].

     From a practical point of view, compact and robust laser diodes with a simple handling are preferred. Therefore tunable lasers that can be provided as monolithically integrated devices are favored. Accordingly, the monolithically integrated tunable lasers made in InGaAsP/InP are the most developed devices available today. It is the objective of this textbook, therefore, to provide the relevant knowledge needed for the understanding

(a)

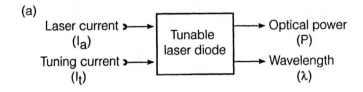

(b)

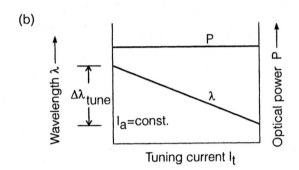

(c)

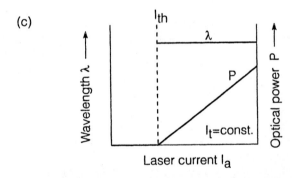

Figure 1.1   Schematic illustration of idealized wavelength-tunable laser diode (a). The ideal relationships between wavelength and power on the one hand, and tuning current and laser current on the other hand, are plotted in (b) and (c). $\Delta\lambda_{tune}$ and I_{th} denote tuning range and threshold current, respectively.

of the operation principles of wavelength-tunable laser diodes as well as to provide guidelines for their implementation in various engineering applications.

A simplified schematic representation of what the user expects from an electronically wavelength-tunable laser is illustrated in Figure 1.1. For most applications, a single-mode light source is required, with two control currents or voltages that define the laser optical power and the laser wavelength separately and independently. Specifically, in Figure 1.1(a) the optical power P should depend only on the control current I_a, where the subscript a stands for active region, while the laser wavelength λ should be dependent only on the wavelength control current I_t, where the subscript t stands for tuning region.

Keeping the laser current constant, the laser wavelength should be a smooth and hysteresis-free function of the applied tuning current as shown in Figure 1.1(b). At constant tuning current, on the other hand, the optical power versus laser current characteristic (Figure 1.1(c)) should show a linear dependence on I_a above the threshold current I_{th} with a constant wavelength.

Experience shows, however, that such an ideal device performance can by far not be obtained with tunable laser diodes. This is because the wavelength tuning mechanisms in laser diodes generally also affect the optical losses, so that the optical power changes during tuning. Equally the optical power control by the laser current affects the device temperature and thus the emission wavelength. Moreover, these deviations from the ideal "orthogonality" between power and wavelength control are usually not the most serious problems associated with wavelength tuning. Instead, the electronic tuning of the laser wavelength may lead to wavelength jumps or hysteresis effects in most device structures [39]. Further, the continuous tunability of the devices may require the precise and simultaneous adjustment of multiple wavelength control currents [40, 41]. Since the latter critically depends on temperature and device ageing, the handling convenience is drastically influenced. As with other electronic components, the device handling in fact is a most important device characteristic of the electronically tunable laser diodes in practice; this may decisively influence their suitability in commercial applications.

In addition to the optical power, most parameters of the laser emission are also affected by introducing the tuning function and show a distinct variation within the tuning range. Unfortunately, most of the laser parameters are usually degraded by the electronic wavelength tuning so that the suitability of the devices may be worsened significantly. Considering the anticipated application, therefore, a proper choice of the laser type may be crucial for achieving the required performance. Hence, it is also a major objective of this book to present the device structures developed so far and to provide an understanding of the different characteristics and application-related suitability of the various laser types. For illustration, an overview of the most important application fields with representative application examples and the specifically demanded device performance is displayed in Figure 1.2.

As can be seen, optical communications, sensing, and measurement are the major areas of application where tunable laser diodes are used. Among the required device characteristics, the continuous tunability, tuning range, optical power, spectral linewidth, and FM modulation bandwidth are most important. Here continuous tunability is understood as the unambiguous and smooth access to any wavelength within the tuning range without mode jumps, hysteresis effects, or any other irregularities. While the continuous tuning is desired in almost any application, it is indispensable in coherent optical detection, optical frequency-modulated continuous wave (FMCW) radar, and optical spectrum analysis.

The tuning range represents the most specific parameter for a tunable laser. Accordingly, the width of the tuning range improves the laser suitability in all practical applications. In most applications, the optical power is also important. This implies a demand for a constant optical power throughout the tuning range.

In many applications such as coherent optical detection, optical FMCW radar and spectrum analysis, where high coherence is required, the spectral purity and linewidth represent an essential issue. It was found very early in the development of the tunable

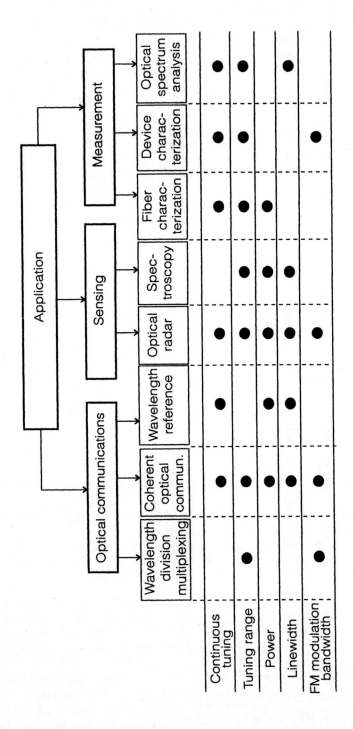

Figure 1.2   Major applications and specific demands on performance of wavelength-tunable laser diodes.

laser diodes that the spectral linewidth is strongly affected by the tuning function [42]. In particular, the continuously tunable laser diodes suffer from a distinct tuning-dependent linewidth broadening.

Finally, the dynamical behavior of the tuning, as determined, for instance, by the FM modulation bandwidth, is important in applications where the tunable lasers are used as FM modulated light sources or where a fast wavelength switching is required. This includes mainly optical communication, but also optical FMCW radar and device characterization.

It can be concluded from this figure that coherent optical communications technique and optical radar are among the most challenging applications for tunable laser diodes. Accordingly, the performance achieved so far with these sophisticated laser diodes is particularly due to the device development for these demanding applications.

Throughout this book, we consider how the requirements of these applications can be met by the devices and evaluate the various device types along these demands.

REFERENCES

[1]   Adams, M. J., *Semiconductor lasers for long wavelength optical fibre communications systems*, London, U.K., Peregrinus, 1987.

[2]   Agrawal, G. P., and Dutta, N. K., *Long-wavelength semiconductor lasers*, New York, NY, Van Nostrand Reinhold, 1986.

[3]   Agrawal, G. P., and Dutta, N. K., *Semiconductor lasers*, New York, NY, Van Nostrand Reinhold, 1993.

[4]   Botez, D. (ed.), *Diode laser arrays*, Cambridge, MA, Cambridge University Press, 1994.

[5]   Butler, J. K., *Semiconductor injection lasers*, New York, NY, IEEE Press, 1980.

[6]   Buus, J., *Single frequency semiconductor lasers*, Bellingham, WA, SPIE, 1991.

[7]   Carlson, N. W., *Monolithic laser diode arrays*, Berlin, Germany, Springer, 1994.

[8]   Casey, H. C., Jr., and Panish, M. B., *Heterostructure lasers—Part A: Fundamental principles*, New York, NY, Academic Press, 1978.

[9]   Casey, H. C., Jr., and Panish, M. B., *Heterostructure lasers—Part B: Materials and operating characteristics*, New York, NY, Academic Press, 1978.

[10] Chow, W. W., Koch, S. W., and Sargent, M., *Semiconductor laser physics*, Berlin, Germany, Springer, 1994.

[11] Chuang, S. L., *Physics of optoelectronic devices*, Chichester, U.K., Wiley, 1995.

[12] Coldren, L. A., and Corzine, S. W., *Diode lasers and photonic integrated circuits*, Chichester, U.K., Wiley, 1995.

[13] Ebeling, K. J., *Integrierte Optoelektronik*, Berlin, Germany, Springer, 1992.

[14] Evans, G. A. (ed.), *Surface emitting semiconductor lasers and arrays*, Boston, MA, Academic Press, 1993.

[15] Fukuda, M., *Reliability and degradation of semiconductor lasers and LEDs*, Norwood, MA, Artech House, 1991.

[16] Ghafouri-Shiraz, H., *Fundamentals of laser diode amplifiers*, Chichester, U.K., Wiley, 1996.

[17] Ghafouri-Shiraz, H., *Distributed feedback laser diodes*, Chichester, U.K., Wiley, 1996.

[18] Ikegami, T., Sudo, S., and Sakai, Y., *Frequency stabilization of semiconductor laser diodes*, Norwood, MA, Artech House, 1995.

[19] Kawaguchi, H., *Bistability and nonlinearities in laser diodes*, Norwood, MA, Artech House, 1994.

[20] Kressel, H., and Butler, J. K., *Semiconductor lasers and heterojunction LEDs*, Boston, MA, Academic Press, 1977.

[21] Morthier, G., and Vankwikelberge, P., *Handbook of distributed feedback laser diodes*, Norwood, MA, Artech House, 1997.

[22] Mroziewich, B., Bugajski, M., and Nakwaski, W., *Physics of semiconductor lasers*, Amsterdam, The Netherlands, North Holland, 1991.

[23] Ohtsu, M., *Highly coherent semiconductor lasers*, Norwood, MA, Artech House, 1992.

[24] Ohtsu, M., *Frequency control of semiconductor lasers*, Chichester, U.K., Wiley, 1996.

[25] Petermann, K., *Laser diode modulation and noise*, Dordrecht, The Netherlands, Kluwer Academic Publishers, 1988.

[26] Sale, T. E., *Vertical cavity surface emitting lasers*, Chichester, U.K., Wiley, 1995.

[27] Suematsu, Y. (ed.), *Handbook of semiconductor lasers and photonic integrated circuits*, London, U.K., Chapman and Hall, 1994.

[28] Thompson, G. H. B., *Physics of semiconductor laser devices*, Chichester, U.K., Wiley, 1980.

[29] Tsang, W. T. (vol. ed.), *Semiconductors and semimetals*, Vol. 22, Parts A to E, New York, NY, Academic Press, 1985.

[30] Vasil'ev, P., *Ultrafast diode lasers*, Norwood, MA, Artech House, 1995.

[31] Yamamoto, Y. (ed.), *Coherence, amplification, and quantum effects in semiconductor lasers*, Chichester, U.K., Wiley, 1991.

[32] Zory, P. S. (ed.), *Quantum well lasers*, Boston, MA, Academic Press, 1993.

[33] Kobayashi, K., and Mito, I., "Single frequency and tunable laser diodes," *IEEE Journal of Lightwave Technology*, Vol. 6, 1988, pp. 1623–1633.

[34] Koch, T. L., and Koren, U., "Semiconductor lasers for coherent optical fiber communications," *IEEE Journal of Lightwave Technology*, Vol. 8, 1990, pp. 274–293.

[35] Kotaki, Y., and Ishikawa, H., "Wavelength tunable DFB and DBR lasers for coherent optical fibre communications," *IEE Proceedings*, Part J, Vol. 138, 1991, pp. 171–177.

[36] Ebberg, A., and Nòe, R., "Novel high precision alignment technique for polarisation maintaining fibres using a frequency modulated tunable laser," *Electronics Letters*, Vol. 26, 1990, pp. 2009–2010.

[37] Schell, M., Huhse, D., and Bimberg, D., "Generation of short (3.5 ps) low jitter (<100 fs) light pulses with a 1.55 μm tunable twin guide laser," *19th European Conference on Optical Communications (ECOC '93)*, pp. 229–232, Montreux, Switzerland, 1993.

[38] Strzelecki, E. M., Cohen, D. A., and Coldren, L. A., "Investigation of tunable single frequency diode lasers for sensor applications," *IEEE Journal of Lightwave Technology*, Vol. 6, 1988, pp. 1610–1618.

[39] Coldren, L. A., and Corzine, S. W., "Continuously-tunable single-frequency semiconductor lasers," *IEEE Journal of Quantum Electronics*, Vol. 23, 1987, pp. 903–908.

[40] Tohyama, M., Onomura, M., Funemizu, M., and Suzuki, N., "Wavelength tuning mechanism in three-electrode DFB lasers," *IEEE Photonics Technology Letters*, Vol. 5, 1993, pp. 616–618.

[41] Ishida, O., Tada, Y., and Ishii, H., "Tuning-current splitting network for three-section DBR lasers," *Electronics Letters*, Vol. 30, 1994, pp. 241–242.

[42] Kotaki, Y., and Ishikawa, H., "Spectral characteristics of a three-section wavelength-tunable DBR laser," *IEEE Journal of Quantum Electronics*, Vol. 25, 1989, pp. 1340–1345.

Chapter 2

Fundamental Laser Diode Characteristics

In Chapter 2, we briefly introduce the fundamental concepts of laser operation in semiconductors as required for the understanding of wavelength tuning and describe the relevant device characteristics. The reader interested in more details on basic semiconductor laser physics is referred to the textbooks [1–4]. Particular background in long-wavelength and single-mode laser diodes can be found in [5–7]. Our starting point is the concept of optical gain in semiconductors and the use of complex refractive indices to take into account both refraction and optical gain or loss. Then, the realization of optical gain by means of semiconductor heterostructures is illustrated and transverse and lateral waveguiding techniques are presented together with the corresponding laser diode structures. Laser threshold, mode spectrum, and modulation behavior are described conveniently by the rate equations approach. Finally, we introduce the quantum well laser structures, which exhibit improved performance with respect to almost any device parameter. Accordingly, these advanced laser diodes represent the state of the art of modern laser diode technology.

2.1 OPTICAL GAIN IN SEMICONDUCTORS

Consider the propagation of a monochromatic plane wave in an isotropic medium characterized by the complex propagation constant (or wave number)

$$\beta = k_0 n = k_0(n' + jn'') \qquad (2.1)$$

where k_0 is the free-space propagation constant for wavelength λ

$$k_0 = \frac{\omega}{c} = \frac{2\pi}{\lambda} \qquad (2.2)$$

$c = 1/\sqrt{\epsilon_0 \mu_0}$ is the free-space speed of light, ϵ_0 and μ_0 are the free-space permittivity and permeability, and n' and n'' are the real and imaginary parts of the complex refractive index (usually $|n''| << n'$). We describe the real electric field vector $e(x, y, z, t)$ in terms of its complex amplitude $\mathbf{E}$ as

$$e(x, y, z, t) = \text{Re}\{\mathbf{E}\exp(j\omega t)\} \qquad \text{(2.3)}$$

where $\mathbf{E}$ in general is a vector, depending on the coordinates x, y, and z.

Assuming a uniform plane wave with field components $\mathbf{E} = (0, E_y, 0)$ and $\mathbf{H} = (H_x, 0, 0)$ (TEM-wave) to propagate along the positive z-axis with no transverse dependencies (i.e., $\partial/\partial x = \partial/\partial y = 0$), we may write

$$E_y(z) = E_0 \exp(-j\beta z) \qquad \text{(2.4)}$$

with E_0 being the amplitude at $z = 0$.

The magnetic field $\mathbf{H}$ is related to $\mathbf{E}$ by Maxwell's equation, which in an isotropic and nonmagnetic ($\mu = \mu_0$) medium reads

$$\nabla \times \mathbf{E} = -j\omega\mu_0\mathbf{H} \qquad \text{(2.5)}$$

so that for the considered TEM-wave

$$H_x = -\sqrt{\frac{\epsilon_0}{\mu_0}}nE_y \qquad \text{(2.6)}$$

The average power per unit area I (intensity) is

$$I = \overline{\mathbf{e} \times \mathbf{h}} = \frac{1}{2}\text{Re}\{E_y \cdot H_x^*\} \qquad \text{(2.7)}$$

Substituting (2.4) and (2.6) in (2.7), we get

$$I = \frac{c\epsilon_0}{2}n'|E_0|^2 \exp(2k_0 n'' z) \qquad \text{(2.8)}$$

Evidently, I increases (decreases) for positive (negative) n'' value, and the corresponding optical gain g, or loss α, respectively, is defined as

$$g = -\alpha = \frac{1}{I}\frac{dI}{dz} \qquad \text{(2.9)}$$

and reads

$$g = 2k_0 n'' \qquad \text{(2.10)}$$

Unless otherwise noted, optical loss and gain are related exclusively to power in this book.

In a semiconductor, optical gain may be achieved if the stimulated emission in a strongly pumped region exceeds the optical losses, which requires population inversion.

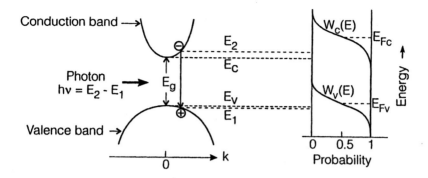

Figure 2.1   Principal band structure and Fermi–Dirac distributions for an inverted semiconductor. Here, k denotes the electron wave vector.

The band structure and Fermi–Dirac occupation probability distributions for electrons

$$W_c(E) = \left[1 + \exp\left(\frac{E - E_{Fc}}{k_B T}\right)\right]^{-1} \tag{2.11}$$

$$W_v(E) = \left[1 + \exp\left(\frac{E - E_{Fv}}{k_B T}\right)\right]^{-1} \tag{2.12}$$

in the conduction (W_c) and valence (W_v) band of an inverted semiconductor are shown in Figure 2.1, where k_B is Boltzmann's constant, T is the absolute temperature, E is the energy and E_{Fc} and E_{Fv} denote the quasi-Fermi levels for conduction and valence band, respectively. Band to band transitions occur only for photon energies $h\nu$ larger than the bandgap energy E_g. At the same time, the photons encounter absorption and amplification by stimulated emission. E_{Fc} and E_{Fv} are determined implicitly by the electron and hole densities

$$N = N_c \frac{2}{\pi} \int_{E_c}^{\infty} Z_c(E) W_c(E) \, dE \tag{2.13}$$

$$P = N_v \frac{2}{\pi} \int_{-\infty}^{E_v} Z_v(E) [1 - W_v(E)] \, dE \tag{2.14}$$

where $N_{c,v}$ and $Z_{c,v}(E)$ are the effective carrier densities and the density of states of conduction and valence band, respectively, and $E_{c,v}$ stand for the band edges ($E_g = E_c - E_v$). In most cases, undoped active regions are used in which $N = P$. Unless otherwise noted, therefore, we will investigate an undoped active region in this chapter.

Depending on the injected carrier density or the occupation probabilities of the valence and conduction band states, respectively, either absorption or gain may dominate. The optical gain by stimulated emission for a photon with energy $h\nu$ dominates the

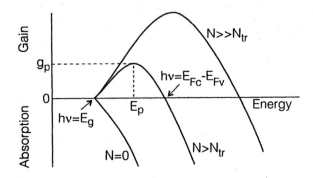

Figure 2.2   Schematic optical gain curves for a semiconductor with various carrier densities below and above the transparency carrier density N_{tr}.

absorption by the band to band transitions if the quasi-Fermi levels separation exceeds the bandgap energy [8]:

$$E_{Fc} - E_{Fv} \geq h\nu = E_2 - E_1 \geq E_g \qquad \text{(Bernard–Duraffourg condition)} \qquad (2.15)$$

Note that by (2.11) to (2.14) the separation of the quasi-Fermi levels requires carrier injection by means of an electric current. The transition from absorption to gain (transparency) occurs at $E_{Fc} - E_{Fv} = 0$, with the injected carrier density denoted N_{tr} (transparency carrier density). Apparently, the probability distribution in Figure 2.1 is inverted because the Bernard–Duraffourg condition is satisfied and optical gain is obtained. Because of the energetic distribution of the occupied electronic states and the smooth transition of the Fermi–Dirac function, the resulting optical gain is spectrally broadened. A schematic plot of principal semiconductor gain curves is displayed in Figure 2.2 for various carrier densities below and above N_{tr} neglecting phonon-assisted indirect transitions and any additional loss mechanisms. As can be seen, optical gain occurs in the energy range $E_{Fc} - E_{Fv} \geq h\nu \geq E_g$ with the gain peak g_p at the gain peak photon energy E_p. Typical values of N_{tr} in GaAs and InGaAsP are between $1 \cdot 10^{18} \text{cm}^{-3}$ and $2 \cdot 10^{18} \text{cm}^{-3}$. In the interesting value range of N around N_{tr}, the peak optical gain in a bulk semiconductor can reasonably be approximated as a linear function of N [9]:

$$g_p(N) = a(N - N_{tr}) \qquad (2.16)$$

where the gain parameter a is typically of the order $3–5 \cdot 10^{-16} \text{cm}^2$ for InGaAsP at a 1,300- to 1,550-nm wavelength [10, 11].

The injected carrier density N is determined by the laser current I and the recombination rate R:

$$I = eR(N)V_a \qquad (2.17)$$

where $V_a = dwL$ is the active region volume with w, L, and d denoting width, length, and thickness of the active region, and e is the elementary charge. Below threshold, the recombination rate $R(N)$ in an undoped gain region can empirically be well approximated by a cubic polynomial [12, 13]

$$R(N) = \frac{N}{\tau_s} + BN^2 + CN^3 \tag{2.18}$$

where τ_s (typ. $\approx 10 - 20$ ns), B (typ. $\approx 10^{-10}$cm^3/s), and C (typ. $\approx 3 - 6 \cdot 10^{-29}$cm^6/s) account for the nonradiative linear, the radiative bimolecular (band to band), and the nonradiative Auger recombination, respectively.

A genuine feature of semiconductors is that gain changes Δg as induced by varying the injected carrier density cause refractive index changes at the peak gain energy. This is due to the strongly asymmetric spectral shape of the gain curves of semiconductors. As gain changes correspond to changes of the imaginary part of the refractive index (2.10) the Kramers–Kronig dispersion relation [1] may be applied to calculate the changes of the real part of the refractive index from Δg:

$$\Delta n'(\omega) = \frac{c}{\pi} P \int_0^\infty \frac{\Delta g(\omega')}{\omega'^2 - \omega^2} \, d\omega' \tag{2.19}$$

where P indicates a principal value integral. Schematic plots of the refractive index changes caused by varying the injected carrier density are shown in Figure 2.3, where the upper plot displays the gain curves for two carrier densities.

As can be seen, the refractive index change at the gain peak wavelength is not vanishing as it would be for a symmetric gain curve. Because lasing usually occurs around the gain peak wavelength, the gain changes inevitably lead to refractive index changes at the laser wavelength, which in turn produce instantaneous frequency changes of the laser emission during relaxation processes. Accordingly, this gain-phase coupling gives rise to an increased spectral linewidth of the semiconductor laser modes. The gain-phase coupling is commonly described by means of the linewidth enhancement (or alpha) factor [14]

$$\alpha_H = -\frac{\partial n'/\partial N}{\partial n''/\partial N} \tag{2.20}$$

Typical values of α_H at a 1,550-nm wavelength are 5 to 7 for bulk InGaAsP [15]. Note that α_H is occasionally defined without the minus sign, yielding negative α_H values in the active region of laser diodes. Besides the radiative transitions between the conduction and valence band, wavelength-dependent absorption mechanisms, such as intervalence band absorption and absorption by free carriers, also contribute to the α_H factor. While the α_H factor is positive for photon energies around the bandgap energy E_g of the considered semiconductor, negative values up to about -20 may appear for photon energies ≈ 200 meV below E_g.

2.2   SEMICONDUCTOR HETEROSTRUCTURES

The concept of the heterostructure laser diode was first proposed by Kroemer [16], and Alferov and Kazarinov [17] in 1963. The corresponding laser diodes incorporate a

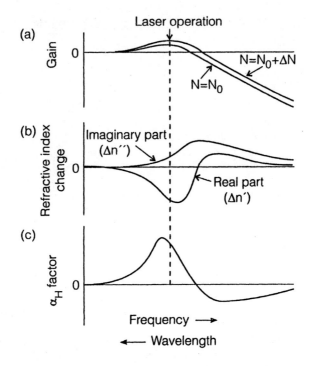

Figure 2.3   Spectral gain curves in a semiconductor for different carrier densities (a), resulting changes in the real and imaginary part of the refractive index (b), and α_H versus frequency (wavelength) (c).

semiconductor heterostructure in which the active layer is surrounded by higher bandgap material, which at the same time enables the transverse confinement of injected carriers and optical field. Because of the paramount progress achieved with the introduction of the double-heterostructure laser diodes, modern laser diodes commonly incorporate a semiconductor double-heterostructure.

The principal energy band diagram of an abrupt heterojunction between two semiconductors with different bandgap energies E_g^A and E_g^B, respectively, is shown in Figure 2.4. The basic model for the description of heterojunctions, which was developed by Anderson [18], assumes that the two semiconductors retain their bulk properties right up to the point where they join each other. Depending on the material parameters, therefore, the difference of the bandgap energies is distributed onto the conduction band (ΔE_c) and the valence band (ΔE_v). On the other hand, however, the Fermi energy E_F must be continuous along the heterojunction. The principal band diagram for a heterojunction between two n-doped semiconductors in thermal equilibrium is shown in Figure 2.4(b). In semiconductor lasers that usually exhibit highly doped confinement layers, the width of the space charge region is of the order of a few nanometers. So electrons may tunnel through the heterojunction and the spikes in the band diagram may be neglected. The essential feature of the heterojunction is that a large potential barrier builds up for the minority

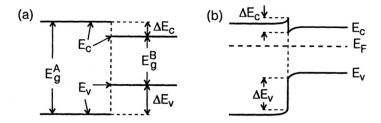

Figure 2.4   Semiconductor heterojunction between two materials of different bandgap energies (a) and principal energy band structure of an abrupt heterojunction (b).

carriers. Consequently, a unipolar injection occurs by the majority carriers of the higher bandgap material.

2.2.1   Carrier Confinement

A schematic illustration of a forward-biased double-heterostructure is shown in Figure 2.5, neglecting the spikes of the bands at the heterojunctions. Electrons are injected into the small-bandgap active region from the n-doped confinement layer with higher bandgap energy, while the holes enter the active region from the p-doped confinement layer on the opposite side. Due to the high-bandgap confinement layers on both sides of the active region, electrons cannot escape into the p-type confinement layer, and holes cannot penetrate into the n-type confinement layer. So the injected carriers are forced to recombine within the active region, almost independently of its thickness. For a large bandgap energy difference of at least $10\,k_BT$ between active and confinement layers,

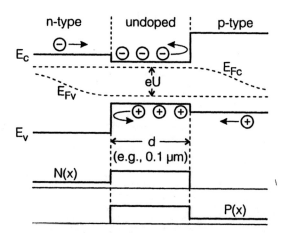

Figure 2.5   Simplified illustration of a semiconductor double-heterostructure under forward bias U, as characterized by the splitting of the quasi-Fermi levels E_{Fc} and E_{Fv}. The bottom plots show the accumulation of the electron and hole densities within the undoped active region ($N = P$).

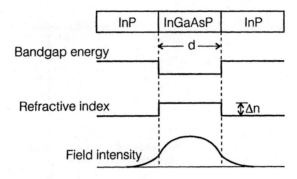

Figure 2.6   Bandgap energy, refractive index, and transverse field intensity of a representative double-heterostructure in InGaAsP/InP.

this *carrier confinement* prevails down to active region thicknesses d of a few nanometers, where quantization effects occur. With the corresponding quantum well (QW) laser diodes, many laser parameters can be improved by a proper design of the layer structure (bandgap engineering). Modern semiconductor lasers, therefore, usually consist of such a QW structure, which are fabricated precisely on an atomic scale with advanced epitaxial techniques such as molecular beam epitaxy (MBE) or metal-organic vapor-phase epitaxy (MOVPE).

2.2.2   Optical Confinement

With few exceptions, semiconductor heterostructures provide the important additional advantage for laser applications that the refractive index at a given wavelength decreases with bandgap energy. As a consequence, an optical waveguide is built by a double-heterostructure providing also *optical confinement* for the photons of the guided waveguide modes as displayed in Figure 2.6. Owing to the refractive index difference Δn, a transverse dielectric waveguide is built with the active layer representing the core layer of thickness d. Each symmetric dielectric slab waveguide with a positive Δn supports at least the fundamental mode for each polarization with an intensity distribution peaking in the active layer as sketched schematically in the bottom plot of Figure 2.6. Therefore, carriers and photons are effectively put together within a double-heterostructure, yielding a strong interaction.

It should further be noted, that bandgap energy in the confinement layers exceeds the photon energy of the light generated in the active region, so that negligible absorption occurs outside the active region.

2.2.3   Material Systems

Semiconductor heterostructures with a high crystalline quality as needed for reliable devices require that the various constituents exhibit the same lattice constant a_0 while the difference in bandgap energy should be as large as possible. The heterostructures are stress-free and can be grown with a high crystalline quality and with no limitations on the layer thickness only in case of lattice-matching.

The requirement of lattice-matching effectively limits the usable material combinations because the epitaxial fabrication of the multilayer structures should start on a binary substrate such as GaAs or InP. This is because the binary III-V compound semiconductors and their lattice constants are unambiguously defined because of stochiometry. Accordingly, various lattice-matched III-V material systems can be distinguished, depending on which binary substrate is used. Thereby semiconductor materials may be employed with three or more compounds, such as the ternary AlGaAs or the quaternary InGaAsP.

By using more compounds, the number of degrees of freedom for the adjustment of lattice constant and bandgap energy increases; however, the epitaxial growth becomes more difficult. For instance, the quaternary compound $In_{1-x}Ga_xAs_yP_{1-y}$ exhibits two parameters x (Gallium mole fraction) and y (Arsenic mole fraction) to adjust the bandgap energy and the lattice constant, while with a ternary compound (e. g., $Al_xGa_{1-x}As$) one usually may not cover a broad range for the bandgap energy by simultaneous lattice-matching. Fortunately, however, as in the case of the ternary $Al_xGa_{1-x}As$, an almost complete lattice-match is obtained for any x-value since AlAs and GaAs exhibit almost the same lattice constant. In general, however, quaternary compound semiconductors are needed if E_g and a_0 are to be varied independently. With modern epitaxial techniques, numerous quaternary semiconductor compounds are now routinely fabricated in the semiconductor industry worldwide.

Among the most important heterostructure material systems for III-V semiconductor lasers are AlGaAs on GaAs substrate and InGaAsP on InP substrate. While AlGaAs/GaAs covers the wavelength range below 900 nm, the InGaAsP/InP material system gained importance for light sources and detectors in the 1,200–1,670 nm wavelength regime. So the wavelengths with minimal dispersion in optical fibers at 1,300 nm and minimal absorption at 1,550 nm may be covered with InGaAsP/InP laser diodes. A diagram displaying the bandgap energies and lattice constants of the quaternary $In_{1-x}Ga_xAs_yP_{1-y}$ and of various binary III-V semiconductors is shown in Figure 2.7. The compositions lattice-matched to the InP substrate are indicated by the broken curve. With Vegard's law [3] one can deduce that lattice-matching to InP ($a_0 = 0.5869$ nm) occurs if the Gallium and Arsenic mole fractions x and y, respectively, are chosen such that [19]

$$x = \frac{0.452y}{1 - 0.031y} \tag{2.21}$$

The bandgap energy of $In_{1-x}Ga_xAs_yP_{1-y}$ depends on x and y in a good approximation as [20]

$$\begin{aligned} E_g \ \text{[in eV]} \ = \ & 1.35 + 0.668x - 1.068y \\ & + 0.758x^2 + 0.078y^2 - 0.069xy - 0.332x^2y + 0.03xy^2 \end{aligned} \tag{2.22}$$

Correspondingly, the bandgap wavelength

$$\lambda_g = \frac{hc}{E_g} \qquad (h: \text{Planck's constant}) \tag{2.23}$$

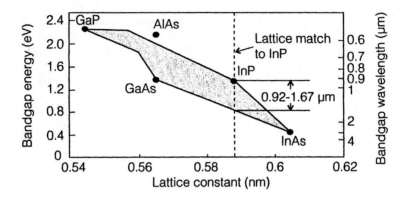

Figure 2.7   Bandgap energy and lattice constant of the quaternary $In_{1-x}Ga_xAs_yP_{1-y}$ and various binary
III-V compound semiconductors.

of $In_{1-x}Ga_xAs_yP_{1-y}$ lattice-matched to InP varies between 920 nm ($y = 0$, $x = 0$) and
1,670 nm ($x = 0.47$, $y = 1$). For the entire composition range of $In_{1-x}Ga_xAs_yP_{1-y}$ lattice-matched to InP neither miscibility gap or indirect semiconductor compounds exist, making this material system ideally suited for optical sources and detectors in the
long wavelength region. The wavelength and composition dependent refractive index of
$In_{1-x}Ga_xAs_yP_{1-y}$ is given in Appendix A.

2.3   WAVEGUIDING AND TRANSVERSE LASER MODES

2.3.1   The Slab Waveguide

The semiconductor double-heterostructures described in the preceding section constitute
transverse dielectric waveguides with one or more guided transverse modes. These modes
may be polarized either transverse electric (TE) or transverse magnetic (TM). They are
characterized by their field component (E or H) into the direction normal to the layer
plane. In the case of the TE or the TM mode only a magnetic or an electric field component, respectively, exists normal to the layer plane. This means for the TE mode that
the dominant component of the electric field lies in the layer plane perpendicular to the
propagation direction. For the TM mode, accordingly, the dominant component of the
magnetic field lies in the layer plane perpendicular to the propagation direction. In practice, TE modes are mostly excited in semiconductor lasers because they are more strongly
guided by the dielectric waveguide and therefore exhibit the higher modal gain. Moreover, the end facet reflectivity is higher for TE than for TM modes of the same order.
Owing to its importance for laser diodes, a detailed description of the fundamental TE
mode of the slab waveguide is given in Appendix B.

A schematic cross-section of a symmetric dielectric waveguide with core layer
thickness d, core layer refractive index n_1, and confinement layer refractive index n_0 is
displayed in Figure 2.8(a). It can be shown [21] that each propagating mode can be

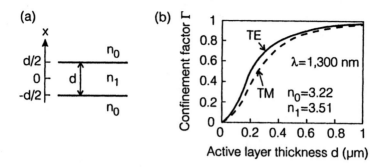

Figure 2.8 Schematic cross-section of symmetric dielectric slab waveguide (a). Optical confinement factor of fundamental TE and TM modes of a symmetric InGaAsP/InP dielectric slab waveguide as used for $\lambda = 1,300$-nm laser diodes (b).

described by a propagation constant β given by

$$\beta = n_{eff}k_0 \tag{2.24}$$

with $n_1 > n_{eff} > n_0$, where n_{eff} is close to n_0 for small d and close to n_1 for large d.

The strength of the mode confinement is usually characterized by means of the so-called (optical) confinement factor Γ, which measures the mode power confined within the active layer relative to the total mode power:

$$\Gamma = \frac{\text{Mode power in the active layer}}{\text{Total mode power}} \tag{2.25}$$

Defining the x-coordinate along the normal direction to the layer plane with the origin in the center of the active (core) layer, Γ reads for the case of TE modes (Appendix B, [22])

$$\Gamma = \frac{\int_{-d/2}^{d/2} |E_y|^2 \, dx}{\int_{-\infty}^{\infty} |E_y|^2 \, dx} \tag{2.26}$$

Gain (or loss) in the active layer is described by allowing n_1 to be complex:

$$n_1 = n_1' + jn_1'' \tag{2.27}$$

where the active layer gain g_a is related to the imaginary part of n_1:

$$g_a = 2k_0 n_1'' \tag{2.28}$$

For the case of a modest ($< 10\%$) relative index difference in the slab, it can be shown [23] by treating n_1'' as perturbation that gain in the active layer gives rise to a modal gain $g_{eff} = 2\text{Im}\{\beta\}$ given by

$$g_{eff} \approx \Gamma g_a \tag{2.29}$$

In general, the confinement factors for the various modes in each layer of a multi-layer dielectric waveguide must be calculated numerically [21, 23]. One then obtains the gain or loss of the transverse modes by adding the products of the gain or loss coefficients of each layer with the corresponding confinement factors.

Calculations of the confinement factor for the fundamental TE and TM modes of a symmetric InGaAsP/InP dielectric slab waveguide as used for typical $\lambda = 1,300$ nm laser diodes are displayed in Figure 2.8(b). The difference between the confinement factors of the two polarizations is sufficient to ensure a stable operation in the TE mode of most laser diodes.

A useful approximation for the confinement factor of the fundamental TE mode in a symmetric dielectric slab waveguide is given in (B.24, App. B) and can be written

$$\Gamma(d) \approx \left[1 + (d_0/d)^2\right]^{-1} \tag{2.30}$$

where the normalization thickness d_0 is given by

$$d_0 = \frac{\lambda}{2\pi} \sqrt{\frac{2}{n_1^2 - n_0^2}} \tag{2.31}$$

Obviously, for small d values $\Gamma \propto d^2$, while for thick active layers Γ asymptotically approaches unity.

Usually the transverse structure of laser diodes is designed such that only the fundamental TE (and TM) mode is guided. In the symmetric dielectric slab waveguide shown in Figure 2.8(a), this is the case for

$$d < \frac{\lambda}{2\sqrt{n_1^2 - n_0^2}} \tag{2.32}$$

For the numerical example in Figure 2.8(b) we find $d < 0.465\,\mu\text{m}$.

At the end facets of a laser diode, the dielectric waveguiding ceases and the optical power is radiated into free space. Depending on the full width at half maximum (FWHM) of the nearfield width $d_{1/2}$, diffraction occurs defining the FWHM angle $\Phi_{1/2}$ of the farfield. Assuming a Gaussian beam, $d_{1/2}$ and $\Phi_{1/2}$ are related by

$$\Phi_{1/2} = \arctan\left(\frac{2\lambda}{\pi d_{1/2}}\right) \tag{2.33}$$

Because $d_{1/2}$ is approximately equal to d/Γ, an effective transverse waveguide providing a narrow spot size exhibits a broad farfield. With typical $d_{1/2}$ values of the order 0.5–$3\,\mu\text{m}$, the farfield width $\Phi_{1/2}$ of common 1,300- to 1,550-nm laser diodes is of the order 10–60°.

2.3.2 Lateral Waveguiding

Up to now, we investigated the transverse (x-direction) waveguiding of a planar slab waveguide and emphasized the advantages of single transverse mode waveguides. Wave-

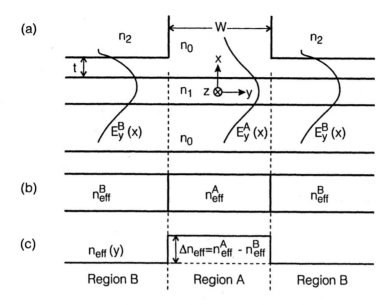

Figure 2.9   The effective refractive index method applied to a ridge-waveguide (a). From the solutions of the transverse (x-direction) wave equation in each lateral region, an effective lateral slab waveguide is deduced (b) with effective refractive index step Δn_{eff} (c).

guide structures to be applied within usual laser diodes, however, require also the waveguiding with respect to the lateral y-direction. This is because a stable and well-defined laser beam may only be obtained by operating the laser diode in one single transverse and lateral mode, which may be achieved by implementing a narrow lateral waveguide structure that supports only one mode of each polarization. In principle, this may be performed equally as in the transverse direction by applying a lateral dielectric waveguide structure as well. Depending on how the lateral index-guiding is accomplished, the corresponding laser structures are referred to either as index-guided (IG) or quasi-index-guided (QIG) laser diodes.

Two-dimensional waveguides can conveniently be treated by means of the effective refractive index method [24, 25], which is illustrated in Figure 2.9 for the case of a QIG ridge waveguide (RW). The RW consists of a transverse dielectric slab, which is laterally modified by replacing part of the upper confinement layer (e. g., InP) with a material of lower refractive index, such as Al_2O_3, ($n_0 > n_2$). If the distance t to the active region is sufficiently small (e. g., $0.2\,\mu m$), then the evanescent optical field becomes noticeably affected. Depending on the confinement factor within the lower index region, the effective refractive index of the transverse mode outside the stripe becomes reduced. Consequently, an effective lateral slab waveguide is built as shown in Figure 2.9(b) with effective refractive indices n_{eff}^A and n_{eff}^B for the stripe and side regions, respectively. The positive effective refractive index difference $\Delta n_{eff} = n_{eff}^A - n_{eff}^B$ (c. f., Figure 2.9(c)) provides the lateral waveguiding.

So the two-dimensional waveguiding problem is solved approximately within the effective refractive index method by first solving the one-dimensional wave equation for the transverse slab waveguides in the stripe and the side regions, and then using the effective refractive indices to build an effective lateral slab waveguide, which is finally treated by solving the one-dimensional lateral wave equation. Because $\Delta n = n_1 - n_0 >> \Delta n_{eff}$, the single-mode condition (2.32) for the lateral direction allows $w >> d$. The two-dimensional optical confinement factor can be approximated by the product of the confinement factors of the transverse slab waveguide in the stripe region A, Γ_{trans}, and the lateral confinement factor of the effective lateral slab waveguide, Γ_{lat}:

$$\Gamma \approx \Gamma_{trans} \cdot \Gamma_{lat} \tag{2.34}$$

where Γ_{lat} may also be well approximated by (2.30) substituting the layer thickness d by the stripe width w and taking for the normalization thickness $w_0 = (\lambda/2\pi)\sqrt{2/[(n_{eff}^A)^2 - (n_{eff}^B)^2]}$.

A third principal lateral waveguiding technique is employed in the gain-guided (GG) laser diodes. These devices abondon any built-in lateral waveguiding technique but rely on the waveguiding introduced by laterally confining the optical gain. The latter is easily accomplished by a simple stripe geometry, in which the injected current is laterally restricted to a few micrometers. Formally, a GG waveguide can be considered as a dielectric waveguide with imaginary or—more usually—complex effective refractive index difference. It can easily be shown (e. g., [5]) that also in this case the wave equation yields solutions for guided lateral modes. In spite of their technological simplicity, in optical communications and most other applications the GG lasers are entirely replaced today by the more powerful IG and QIG laser diodes.

A comparison of the three basic lateral waveguiding techniques is performed in Figure 2.10. The solid and broken curves indicate the idealized and realistic device characteristics. As can be seen, neither of the three waveguiding mechanisms occurs exclusively. In particular, the gain-guiding usually comprises a considerable amount of index-antiguiding because of the index depression by the injected carriers according to (2.20), noting that $\alpha_H > 0$. The index-guided laser diodes also exhibit gain-guiding; however, this can usually be completely neglected with respect to the strong index-guiding efficiency. In the case of the QIG laser diodes, on the other hand, the index depression by the injected carriers and, in the weakly guiding limit, also the gain-guiding mechanism can become significant [26].

2.4 LASER STRUCTURES

The basic IG semiconductor laser comprises an active region of narrow-bandgap material embedded within a semiconductor of larger bandgap energy as shown in Figure 2.11(a). In this so-called buried heterostructure (BH) semiconductor lasers [27], a rectangular dielectric waveguide is built with the refractive index of the active region being largest. Because of the almost complete transverse and lateral carrier confinement by the heterostructure and the strong two-dimensional waveguiding, BH lasers can be made rather narrow with stripe width below 1 μm and may therefore achieve low threshold currents.

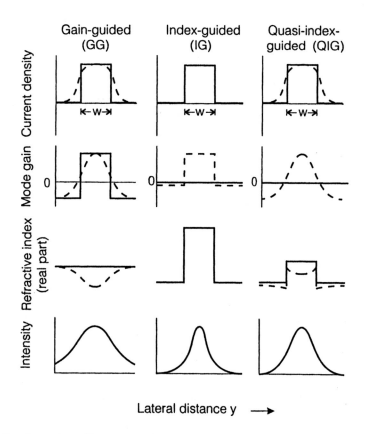

Figure 2.10 Comparison of three principal lateral waveguiding techniques: Gain-guiding, index-guiding, and quasi-index-guiding. The solid and broken curves indicate idealized and realistic characteristics, respectively.

A representative $P(I)$-characteristic of a BH laser at 1,550 nm with a stripe width w of 1.5 μm and a length L of 400 μm is shown in Figure 2.11(b) together with the laser spectra at different currents. Small threshold current ($\approx$ 10 mA), a linear light-current relationship above threshold and considerable optical power around 5 mW at 40 mA are obtained.

Since the fabrication of BH laser diodes requires multiple epitaxial steps interrupted by etching processes to build the active stripe, the device technology is complicated and the reliability may be degraded. This is in contrast to the early GG laser diodes [28] in which the active layer is not being processed and a single epitaxial step is sufficient.

The lateral waveguiding in the GG laser diodes is simply induced by a stripe-contact geometry that weakly confines the injection current and the carrier density in the lateral direction. Because of the varying lateral gain profile, the optical field is weakly

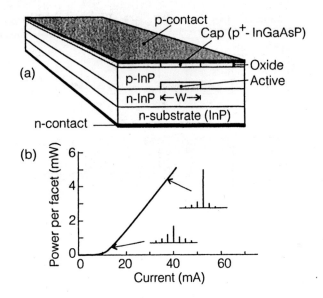

Figure 2.11   Perspective view of device structure (a) and power versus current characteristic (b) of a $\lambda = 1,550$-nm index-guided BH laser in InGaAsP/InP. The insets schematically show the longitudinal mode spectra.

confined to the laser stripe. Besides modal instabilities, the weak lateral confinement prevents the realization of low-threshold laser diodes with the gain-guiding technique.

As a consequence, improved laser diodes exhibiting a small threshold current and high reliability at the same time have been developed by combining most of the advantages of the basic gain- and index-guided laser structures yielding the QIG laser diodes. Common to all QIG lasers is that as with the GG lasers, the active region is not processed between epitaxial growth steps, and that nevertheless, the lateral optical confinement is dominated by the index-guiding (as with the IG lasers).

A representative QIG RW laser structure [29, 30] in InGaAsP/InP is shown schematically in Figure 2.12. In the RW lasers, the carrier confinement is not complete because carrier outdiffusion within the active region is not prevented. With respect to the

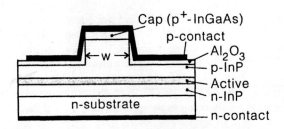

Figure 2.12   Schematic cross-section of a $\lambda = 1,550$-nm QIG RW laser in InGaAsP/InP.

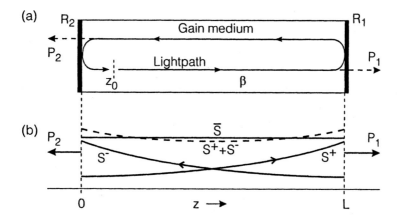

Figure 2.13   Schematic longitudinal view of Fabry–Perot laser with homogeneously distributed gain medium supporting waves with propagation constant $\beta = k_0 n'_{eff} + j g_{net}/2$ (a). Photon density distributions of the forward (S^+) and backward (S^-) propagating waves and the total (broken curve) and average ($\bar{S}$) photon densities in the cavity (b).

lateral carrier distribution, therefore, the effective active region width equals the stripe width w plus approximately one diffusion length (≈ 1–$2\,\mu$m) on each side. The optical confinement, however, can be made rather strong, enabling lateral mode spot sizes down to 2 to $3\,\mu$m .

2.5   THE FABRY–PEROT LASER

The transverse and lateral waveguiding techniques introduced in the two preceding sections are required to define the two-dimensional optical waveguiding in a realistic laser diode. Our objective in this section is to investigate the essential characteristics of an optical resonator, which is made by introducing optical feedback with respect to the longitudinal direction (i. e., the third geometrical dimension). Because of the optical waveguiding, no diffraction occurs for the guided modes during propagation along the laser diode. Regarding the propagation along the laser axis, therefore, the body of the laser diode may be taken as a homogeneous and amplifying medium, the refractive index of which equals the complex effective refractive index of the particular transverse mode under consideration. By limiting our investigations on the practically relevant case of a transverse and lateral single-mode laser, the most simple basic laser configuration is that of a Fabry–Perot resonator with no transverse dependencies as shown schematically in Figure 2.13. The wavelength-dependent mode gain g_{eff} caused by the active medium gain g_a is Γg_a (2.29), while the net mode gain g_{net} is defined as

$$g_{net} = g_{eff} - \alpha_i \tag{2.35}$$

where the internal optical losses in the waveguide (e. g., scattering, absorption) are contained in α_i.

Taking the axial field dependence as $\exp(\pm j\beta z)$, where the positive and negative sign correspond to backward and forward propagating waves, respectively, the propagation constant β within the cavity including the internal gain and loss is

$$\beta = k_0 n'_{\text{eff}} + j\frac{g_{\text{net}}}{2} \tag{2.36}$$

and the photon densities in the active region of the forward and backward propagating waves S^+ and S^-, respectively, are

$$S^+(z) = S^+(0)e^{g_{\text{net}}z} \tag{2.37}$$
$$S^-(z) = S^-(0)e^{-g_{\text{net}}z} \tag{2.38}$$

where $S^+(0) = R_2 S^-(0)$ with R_2 denoting the power reflectivity of the left mirror. The steady-state oscillation condition requires that the field at any axial reference plain $z = z_0$ (see Figure 2.13(a)) reproduces itself in magnitude and phase after one cavity roundtrip along the indicated lightpath. Equivalently, this means that the complex cavity roundtrip gain must be unity, which can be expressed mathematically as

$$r_1 r_2 e^{-2j\beta L} = 1 \tag{2.39}$$

where the cavity length is denoted by L, and the mirror amplitude reflectivities r_1 and r_2 are assumed to be real. In case of the simple Fabry–Perot diode laser shown in Figure 2.13, the end facet reflection of the semiconductor-air interface may be calculated by Fresnel's formula for plane waves, which for the symmetrical case yields:

$$r = r_1 = r_2 = \frac{n'_{\text{eff}} - 1}{n'_{\text{eff}} + 1} \tag{2.40}$$

where we have neglected $n''_{\text{eff}}(= g_{\text{net}}/2k_0)$, because $|n''_{\text{eff}}| << n'_{\text{eff}}$. With typical values of n'_{eff} around 3.5 for InGaAsP and AlGaAs lasers, we find $r \approx 0.55$ and for the power reflectivity $R = r^2 \approx 0.3$. Because practical laser diodes make up a dielectric transverse waveguide, modal effects occur that increase (decrease) the reflectivity of the TE (TM) mode as compared with the Fresnel reflection.

Defining the end loss (or mirror loss, respectively):

$$\alpha_m = \frac{1}{2L} \ln \frac{1}{R_1 R_2} \tag{2.41}$$

and considering the periodicity of the exponential function with respect to the imaginary part of the argument, we may rewrite the oscillation condition (2.39):

$$2j\beta L + \alpha_m L = 2j\pi N \tag{2.42}$$

where N is an integer denoting the longitudinal mode number, which equals the number of half-wavelengths that fit into the laser cavity of length L. Separating (2.42) into real and imaginary parts yields two separate conditions, one on the amplitude and the other on the phase change of the roundtrip field propagation. Introducing the cavity roundtrip gain

$$g_c = g_{net} - \alpha_m \qquad (2.43)$$

and using (2.36) we obtain from the real part of (2.42) the gain condition

$$g_c = 0 \qquad (2.44)$$

or with (2.35):

$$\Gamma g_a - \alpha_i - \alpha_m = 0 \qquad (2.45)$$

Denoting the total cavity loss as the sum of the end loss and the internal loss

$$\alpha_{tot} = \alpha_m + \alpha_i \qquad (2.46)$$

we can write the gain condition (2.44) as

$$g_c = g_{eff} - \alpha_{tot} = 0 \qquad (2.47)$$

The imaginary part of (2.42) defines the phase condition (i. e., the phase change $2\beta'L$ after a complete cavity roundtrip must be an integer multiple of 2π). This leads to a resonance condition for the cavity, defining a set of longitudinal modes:

$$\lambda_N = \frac{2n'_{eff}(\lambda_N)L}{N} \qquad \text{phase condition} \qquad (2.48)$$

Note that the mode wavelengths are essentially reciprocal to the corresponding mode numbers, so that the higher order modes exhibit the shorter wavelengths. In the lasing regime, both (2.44) and (2.48) must be met simultaneously by the lasing modes.

According to the large dimensions of the laser cavity, as compared with the wavelength, the longitudinal mode number of lasers is usually very large. Even for the relatively short edge-emitting InGaAsP and AlGaAs laser diodes ($L \approx 100$ to $1,000\,\mu m$, $n'_{eff} \approx 3.3$) operating at wavelengths between 750 and 1,550 nm, N is of the order 10^3 to 10^4.

Considering a relatively small number (e. g., 10) of longitudinal modes centered on mode N (wavelength λ_N) with a large mode number ($N >> 1$), (2.48) defines a comb-mode spectrum with an almost constant mode spacing:

$$\Delta\lambda_m = \lambda_N - \lambda_{N+1} \simeq \frac{\lambda_N^2}{2n_{g,eff}L} \qquad (2.49)$$

where

$$n_{g,eff} = \frac{d\left(k_0 n'_{eff}\right)}{dk_0}\bigg|_{\lambda_N} = n'_{eff}(\lambda_N) - \lambda_N \frac{dn'_{eff}}{d\lambda}\bigg|_{\lambda_N} \qquad (2.50)$$

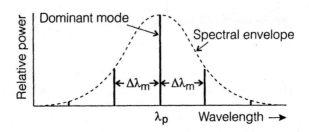

Figure 2.14   Longitudinal emission spectrum of Fabry–Perot laser diode.

is the effective group index, that includes the dispersion of $n'_{eff}(\lambda)$ around λ_N. Typically, $n_{g,eff} \approx 4$, so that with usual laser lengths around 400 μm, the mode spacing $\Delta\lambda_m$ amounts to 0.3–1 nm. Because of the densely spaced modes, the gain curve of the laser-active medium covers many longitudinal modes. In the lasing regime, the essentially homogeneous gain saturation mechanism of semiconductor lasers provides the validity of (2.44); that is, $g_c = 0$. This saturation mechanism is commonly referred to as "gain-clamping" mechanism.

The exact definition of the laser wavelength is performed by the phase condition (2.48). Thereby the lasing mode is selected as the mode from the longitudinal mode set with wavelength nearest to λ_p.

In the Fabry–Perot laser diodes, the laser operation is usually not single-mode but occurs with different amplitudes in many longitudinal modes. The principal emission spectrum of such a laser diode with the gain peak wavelength λ_p equal to λ_N is shown schematically in Figure 2.14. While the longitudinal mode at $\lambda_N = \lambda_p$ exhibits the largest power, the neighboring modes may also carry a significant amount of the total laser emission. The width of the spectral envelope (broken curve) depends on the width of the gain bandwidth of the active medium. Typically, in InGaAsP/InP Fabry–Perot laser diodes at 1,550-nm wavelength, the gain curve is several tens of nanometers wide with the width of the multimode spectrum being a few nanometers and the emission usually occurs in about 4 to 10 longitudinal modes.

2.6   THE RATE EQUATIONS

The simplest way to investigate the basic laser properties is the rate equation approach. Assuming a longitudinal homogeneous laser cavity with equal mirror reflectivities, we may write down the single-mode rate equations for the carrier density $N = P$ and the averaged photon density $\overline{S}$ in the active region

$$\overline{S} = \frac{1}{L} \int_0^L \left(S^+(z) + S^-(z)\right) \, dz \tag{2.51}$$

as

$$\frac{dN}{dt} = \frac{I}{eV_a} - v_g g_{eff} \overline{S} - R(N) \tag{2.52}$$

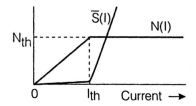

Figure 2.15   Schematic plots of carrier density N and photon density $\overline{S}$ versus laser current.

$$\frac{d\overline{S}}{dt} = v_g g_c \overline{S} + R_{sp} \tag{2.53}$$

where v_g is the group velocity and $R(N)$ is the spontaneous recombination rate (2.18). In (2.52), the first term on the right-hand side is the carrier injection rate, and the second term is the stimulated emission rate, which is proportional to the mode gain and the average photon density. The first term on the right-hand side in (2.53) represents the photon density change by stimulated emission and absorption, which is proportional to the cavity gain g_c, and R_{sp} is the spontaneous emission into the lasing mode, which is related to the mode gain by way of Einstein's relations

$$R_{sp} = v_g g_{eff} n_{sp}/V_a \tag{2.54}$$

with n_{sp} (typ. $\approx 2-3$) being the spontaneous emission coefficient [31]. Note that differing from the approximate treatment in (2.44) and (2.47), where spontaneous emission has been neglected, the cavity gain g_c is not exactly zero, even in the stationary case ($d\overline{S}/dt = 0$), but slightly negative as determined by (2.53). With respect to the magnitudes of g_{eff} and α_{tot}, however, the approximation $g_c = 0$ is reasonable in (2.47).

2.6.1   Stationary Solution of the Rate Equations

In the stationary case, we put $d\overline{S}/dt = dN/dt = 0$, so that the rate equations become a pair of coupled nonlinear algebraic equations. In the regime above threshold, the spontaneous emission term in (2.53) may be neglected in the stationary case. In an analogy to (2.44), we obtain from the photon density rate equation $g_c \cong 0$, which with (2.47) means that also $g_{eff} \cong \alpha_{tot}$, independently of $\overline{S}$. Because with (2.29), the mode gain g_{eff} is the product of confinement factor and active region material gain g_a; also, g_a must be constant above threshold, which finally means that the carrier density is also kept fixed at its threshold value N_{th}. Figure 2.15 schematically shows the N versus I relationship with the clamping of $N = N_{th}$ above threshold from the gain-clamping mechanism. The threshold current is obtained from the rate equation (2.52) for the carrier density, taking $\overline{S} = 0$ as

$$I_{th} = eV_a R(N_{th}) \tag{2.55}$$

Assuming laser operation at the active region gain peak wavelength λ_p and using the linearized carrier density-gain relation of (2.16), we obtain

$$N_{th} = N_{tr} + \frac{\alpha_{tot}}{a\Gamma} \tag{2.56}$$

The photon density above threshold is a linear function of the current I (c. f., Figure 2.15):

$$\bar{S} = \frac{I - I_{th}}{eV_a v_g \alpha_{tot}} \qquad \text{for } I > I_{th} \tag{2.57}$$

which we can deduce from the carrier density rate equation (2.52) considering that N as well as $R(N)$ remain unchanged for $I > I_{th}$ and by using $g_a = \alpha_{tot}/\Gamma$, which results from (2.29) and (2.47). Above threshold, the photon density $\bar{S}$ can be related to the optical power as follows: The total optical energy E in the laser is given by the product of the photon density in the active region, the volume V_a and the energy per photon:

$$E = \bar{S} V_a h\nu \tag{2.58}$$

The optical power per facet P is then given by the energy multiplied by the rate $v_g \alpha_m$ at which energy escapes from the ends:

$$P = \frac{v_g \alpha_m \bar{S} V_a h\nu}{2} \tag{2.59}$$

where the factor 1/2 is included because we have assumed that equal amounts of power are emitted from each end ($R = R_1 = R_2$). Using (2.57), the optical power for each facet is related to the drive current as

$$P = \frac{h\nu}{2e} \frac{\alpha_m}{\alpha_{tot}} (I - I_{th}) \qquad \text{for } I > I_{th} \tag{2.60}$$

and the differential efficiency per facet is

$$\frac{dP}{dI} = \frac{h\nu}{2e} \frac{\alpha_m}{\alpha_{tot}} \tag{2.61}$$

Frequently, use is made of the differential quantum efficiency per facet, which for $R = R_1 = R_2$ reads

$$\eta_d = \frac{dP/h\nu}{dI/e} = \frac{\ln(1/R)}{2\alpha_{tot}L} \tag{2.62}$$

Numerical Example: Given a $\lambda = 1{,}300$-nm laser diode with the following parameters: $L = 400\,\mu m$, $w = 1.5\,\mu m$, $d = 0.1\,\mu m$, $R_1 = R_2 = 0.35$, $\alpha_i = 15\,cm^{-1}$, $a = 3 \cdot 10^{-16}\,cm^2$, $\tau_s \Rightarrow \infty$, $B = 10^{-10}\,cm^3 s^{-1}$, $C = 3 \cdot 10^{-29}\,cm^6 s^{-1}$, and $N_{tr} = 1.2 \cdot 10^{18}\,cm^{-3}$. From Figure 2.8 we find the confinement factor $\Gamma = 0.2$. With these parameters, we obtain $V_a = 6 \cdot 10^{-11}\,cm^3$, $\alpha_m = 26\,cm^{-1}$, $\alpha_{tot} = 41\,cm^{-1}$, $N_{th} = 1.9 \cdot 10^{18}\,cm^{-3}$, $I_{th} = 5.4\,mA$, $\eta_d = 0.32$, and $dP/dI = 0.3\,mW/mA$.

2.6.2   Laser Spectrum and Side-Mode Suppression

The time-averaged power in the laser modes and the side-mode suppression ratio *SSR* can be calculated by means of the multimode rate equations [32]. For the dominant mode N and the second strongest mode, assumed to be mode $N + 1$, these equations read under stationary conditions:

$$\frac{d\overline{S}_N}{dt} = 0 = \dot{R}_{sp}(\lambda_N) + \overline{S}_N v_g g_c(\lambda_N) \tag{2.63}$$

$$\frac{d\overline{S}_{N+1}}{dt} = 0 = R_{sp}(\lambda_{N+1}) + \overline{S}_{N+1} v_g g_c(\lambda_{N+1}) \tag{2.64}$$

where $R_{sp}(\lambda_i)$ and $\overline{S}_i$ are the spontaneous emission rate and the average photon density of the *i*-th mode. The *SSR* equals the photon density quotient of modes N and $N + 1$:

$$SSR = \frac{\overline{S}_N}{\overline{S}_{N+1}} \tag{2.65}$$

With an FWHM of the spontaneous emission spectrum of the order several tens of nanometers and mode spacing $\Delta\lambda_m$ typically below 1 nm, we may neglect the wavelength dependence of R_{sp} between the neighboring modes N and $N + 1$ by putting

$$R_{sp}(\lambda_N) = R_{sp}(\lambda_{N+1}) = R_{sp} \tag{2.66}$$

From (2.64) and (2.66), we obtain the photon density $\overline{S}_{N+1}$ as

$$\overline{S}_{N+1} = -\frac{R_{sp}}{v_g g_c(\lambda_{N+1})} \tag{2.67}$$

We may write

$$g_c(\lambda_{N+1}) = g_c(\lambda_N) - \delta g \tag{2.68}$$

where

$$\delta g >> |g_c(\lambda_N)| \tag{2.69}$$

so that (2.67) can be rewritten as

$$\overline{S}_{N+1} \approx \frac{R_{sp}}{v_g \delta g} \tag{2.70}$$

This is illustrated schematically in Figure 2.16(a) showing the mode gain g_{eff} versus the wavelength with the dominant mode N placed exactly at the wavelength of maximal gain λ_p, so that maximal side-mode suppression is obtained. The total loss α_{tot} in the Fabry–Perot laser diode, on the other hand, can be assumed to be wavelength independent. As can be seen, the gain of mode N is only slightly smaller than the total loss,

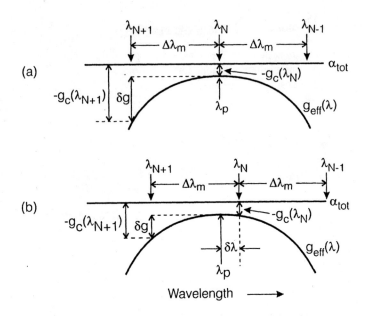

Figure 2.16   Wavelength dependence of mode gain g_{eff} and total mode loss α_{tot} for a Fabry–Perot laser diode. Optimal *SSR* is obtained if the dominant mode N is placed exactly at the center of the gain curve (a). In general, however, the gain peak of the g_{eff} characteristic is displaced with respect to the comb-mode spectrum (b).

revealing a negative but rather small cavity roundtrip gain $g_c(\lambda_N)$. In this symmetrical case, modes $N - 1$ and $N + 1$ attain equal gain, which is smaller than the gain in the dominant mode N by δg (> 0). Even though δg is much smaller than g_{eff} or α_{tot}, it is usually large against $|g_c(\lambda_N)|$, so that (2.70) applies.

In general, however, the spectral position of the gain characteristic relative to the comb-mode spectrum is less favorable and the situation displayed in Figure 2.16(b) is more realistic. Here, mode N is spectrally misplaced by $\delta\lambda$ with respect to λ_p, so that modes $N - 1$ and $N + 1$ attain different gain, and the gain difference δg is reduced as compared with the symmetrical case. In the most unfavorable case, the two strongest modes (i. e., N and $N + 1$) show almost equal gain ($\delta g \approx 0$), so that two-mode operation occurs ($SSR \approx 1$).

Considering the relationship (2.59) between $\bar{S}_N$ and the optical power P_N per mirror in mode N at equal mirror reflectivities $R_1 = R_2$, and taking R_{sp} from (2.54) by inserting $g_{eff} \approx \alpha_{tot}$, we finally obtain after substitution in (2.65):

$$SSR = \frac{2P_N\delta g}{h\nu v_g n_{sp}\alpha_{tot}\alpha_m} \tag{2.71}$$

In dominating single-mode operation, the total optical power of all laser modes together is only slightly larger than the power in the main mode. In this case, we may therefore apply (2.71) with P_N substituted by the total optical power P.

Approximating the mode gain around the wavelength of maximal gain λ_p as parabola

$$g_{\text{eff}}(\lambda_p + \delta\lambda) = g_{\text{eff}}(\lambda_p) - b_g \delta\lambda^2 \qquad (2.72)$$

we obtain

$$\delta g = b_g \Delta\lambda_m (\Delta\lambda_m - 2|\delta\lambda|) \qquad |\delta\lambda| < \frac{\Delta\lambda_m}{2} \qquad (2.73)$$

so that the effect of detuning λ_p with respect to the comb-mode spectrum by $\delta\lambda$ can be included in (2.71) as

$$SSR = \frac{2Pb_g \Delta\lambda_m (\Delta\lambda_m - 2|\delta\lambda|)}{h\nu v_g n_{\text{sp}} \alpha_{\text{tot}} \alpha_m} \qquad |\delta\lambda| < \frac{\Delta\lambda_m}{2} \qquad (2.74)$$

Numerical Example: For illustration we consider now the symmetrical case ($\delta\lambda = 0$) for a typical InGaAsP/InP Fabry–Perot laser diode at $\lambda_N = \lambda_p = 1{,}550\,\text{nm}$ ($h\nu = 0.8\,\text{eV}$) with 5-mW optical power per mirror. The other laser parameters are $L = 500\,\mu\text{m}$, $n_{g,\text{eff}} = 4$, $\Gamma = 0.2$, $n_{\text{sp}} = 2$, $R_1 = R_2 = 0.35$ (yielding $\alpha_m = 21\,\text{cm}^{-1}$), and $\alpha_i = 30\,\text{cm}^{-1}$. The gain difference δg is calculated by approximating the active region material gain characteristic as parabola around λ_p according to

$$g_a = g_a(\lambda_p) - b_a (\lambda - \lambda_p)^2 \qquad (2.75)$$

with $b_a = 0.15\,\text{cm}^{-1}/\text{nm}^2$ for InGaAsP at 1,550-nm wavelength [33]. The parameter b_g, which accordingly applies to the mode gain, is then calculated as $b_g = \Gamma b_a$. Using these parameters in the example above ($P = 5\,\text{mW}$), we obtain a mode spacing $\Delta\lambda_m$ of 0.6 nm, a cavity gain difference δg of 0.011 cm^{-1}, and an SSR of 53 or 17 dB ($= 10\log SSR$), respectively. The cavity gain $g_c(\lambda_N)$ is $-2 \cdot 10^{-4}\,\text{cm}^{-1}$, which is several orders of magnitude smaller than δg (0.011 cm^{-1}) and $g_{\text{eff}} = \alpha_{\text{tot}} \approx 51\,\text{cm}^{-1}$, so that the approximations made in the derivation of the SSR formula (2.71) are justified.

We can conclude that the SSR in Fabry–Perot laser diodes is commonly at most of the order 20 dB, making these devices unsuitable for applications where a high spectral purity is needed. It should be stressed that in most practical applications, where the lasers are being directly modulated, the effective SSR may be substantially smaller. This is because by direct-modulating the laser, the cavity gain characteristic undergoes small changes that temporarily reduce the $|\delta g/g_c(\lambda_N)|$ ratio, which in turn leads to reduced SSR values as compared with the time-averaged stationary operation considered so far.

2.6.3 Small-Signal Modulation Behavior

The modulation behavior of a laser diode may be deduced from the analysis of the rate equations (2.52) and (2.53). In case of analog modulation, the modulation of current and light is small against the bias. In this case, the rate equations can be linearized by applying the small-signal approximation. The derivation of the modulation response will not be given here; the interested reader is referred to [34]. The result of the small-signal

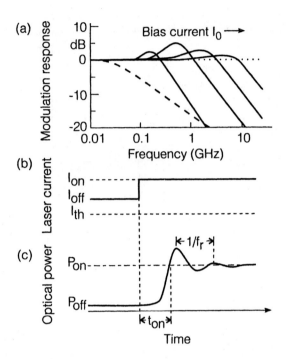

Figure 2.17   Modulation response for small-signal modulation (a) and pulse-modulation characteristic of above-threshold biased laser diode ((b) and (c)). The broken curve in (a) indicates the subthreshold (LED mode) modulation behavior.

approximation is schematically shown in Figure 2.17. The most important features of the small-signal modulation response are the occurrence of a resonance at the relaxation frequency f_r, the slope of -20 dB per decade at high modulation frequencies, and the increase of bandwidth with higher bias current levels. This is also reflected in the pulse response as shown in Figure 2.17(b) and (c). Here, the relaxations manifest themselves by the ringing of the optical output at the relaxation frequency f_r.

Below threshold (LED mode), small carrier density changes ΔN around a stationary value $N_0(I_0)$ are governed by the differential carrier lifetime τ_d:

$$\frac{d\Delta N}{dt} = \frac{\Delta J}{ed} - \frac{\Delta N}{\tau_d} \tag{2.76}$$

where

$$\tau_d = \left(\frac{dR}{dN}\right)^{-1}_{N=N_0} = \frac{1}{1/\tau_s + 2BN_0 + 3CN_0^2} \tag{2.77}$$

It should be noted that N_0 and, hence, τ_d depend on the bias current I_0. The modulation response for this case is displayed in Figure 2.17(a) as a broken curve indicating a rather

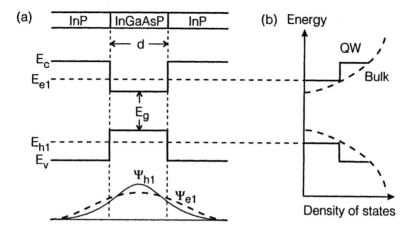

Figure 2.18   InGaAsP/InP single quantum well. Layer structure, energy band diagram, and wave functions of the bound electron and hole ground states (a). Density of states of quantum well (solid curve) and bulk semiconductor (broken curve) (b).

small 3-dB cutoff frequency of the order of several tens of megahertz for undoped active region and a slope of -10 dB per decade above the cutoff frequency. The LED mode is important for wavelength-tunable laser diodes, since the tuning regions are often operated in the LED mode (i. e., without gain-clamping) so that the FM modulation response is determined by τ_d.

2.7   QUANTUM WELL LASER DIODES

With the development of modern epitaxial techniques that allow the controlled growth of semiconductor heterostructures on the atomic scale, it became possible to produce thin layer structures, the so-called quantum well (QW) structures, in which quantization effects of the confined carriers occur. This may not only yield larger optical gain per electron-hole pair and smaller threshold currents than in the bulk lasers, but also enables the fabrication of synthetic semiconductor multilayer structures (superlattices) with new physical properties. QW laser diodes have gained importance for almost every application because of their better performance with respect to the conventional laser diodes. The physics of quantum semiconductor structures and the issue of QW lasers, including their applications, are treated extensively, for instance, in the textbooks [35] and [36].

The principal cross-section of an InGaAsP/InP single QW is shown in Figure 2.18. The QW essentially consists of a double-heterostructure with a thin core layer. The quantization effects occur if the core layer thickness d is of the order of or smaller than the de Broglie wavelength of the carriers, which is about 15 nm, so that typical QW thicknesses are a few nanometers; that is more than an order of magnitude smaller than the active layers in common bulk laser diodes (≈ 0.05–$0.3\,\mu$m).

From the solution of the stationary Schrödinger equation we obtain the discrete eigenenergies E_{ei} and E_{hi} ($i = 1, 2, \ldots$) and wave functions Ψ_{ei} and Ψ_{hi} of the bound states. As can be seen, because of quantization, the effective bandgap energy is increased, as the lowest energy gap between the electron and hole states $E_{e1} - E_{h1}$ is larger than the bandgap energy E_g of the InGaAsP. The quantization in one dimension also modifies the density of states as shown in Figure 2.18(b), indicating a steplike behavior. The modification of the state density leads to an increase in the differential gain dg/dN because the smearing of the injected carriers over a broad energy range is reduced by the quantization. For the realization of low-threshold laser diodes, one designs the QW structure such that under the anticipated operation conditions, only the ground state $i = 1$ becomes significantly populated.

As the thickness of the active layers in a QW structure must be very thin to obtain the quantization effects, the requirement of lattice-matching to the substrate as discussed in Section 2.2 is relaxed. This is because lattice-mismatch is tolerated unless the strain in the mismatched layer leads to a destruction of the crystal. This implies that depending on the mismatch, a strained layer may grow up to its critical thickness without introducing crystal damages. As a consequence, therefore, an additional degree of freedom is provided for the crystal grower, and the strained-layer (SL) QW lasers may considerably improve the performance of InGaAsP/InP lasers [37]. For carrier densities in the $4 - 6 \cdot 10^{18} \, \text{cm}^{-3}$ regime, InGaAsP/InP SL QWs achieve about twice the gain than that of the bulk InGaAsP. It should be noted that the gain versus current density relationship of the QW structure may be well fitted by a logarithmic relation [38]

$$g \propto \ln \frac{J}{J_0} \qquad (2.78)$$

For application in laser diodes, however, it is not the material gain but the mode gain that must be optimized for a given injection current. So the optical confinement is an important matter, particularly in the case of the narrow QWs. Referring to (2.30), we expect unacceptably small confinement factors for active layer thicknesses in the nanometer regime ($\Gamma \propto d^2$ for $d \to 0$) that may entirely cancel the gain improvements by the QW technique. This is schematically illustrated in Figure 2.19(a), where the bandgap energy and the transverse carrier and photon distributions are shown for the case of a single quantum well. As can be seen, a strong confinement of the carrier wavefunction contrasts the weak optical confinement. It is most essential to increase the optical confinement by adding an additional optical waveguide around the QW. The corresponding structures are referred to as *separate confinement heterostructure quantum well* (SCH-QW) structures. The additional layers around the QW may either have constant composition and refractive index (SCH-QW structure) or a graded composition leading to a graded refractive index SCH-QW structure (GRINSCH-QW structure) as shown in Figure 2.19(b). In this way, the optimizations of optical confinement and carrier confinement are effectively decoupled so that the optical confinement factor can significantly be improved for typical QW structures as illustrated in the field plot of Figure 2.19(b). Effective optical confinement and large optical gain may also be achieved by the so-called multiple quantum well (MQW) structure shown in Figure 2.19(c), where the number of quantum wells is typically three to seven.

It should finally be noted that besides the optical gain and the laser threshold current, most other laser parameters may be optimized as well by the application of the

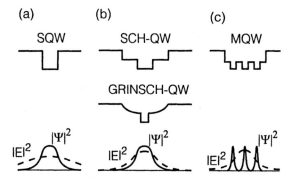

Figure 2.19   Bandgap energies, optical fields, and carrier distributions in a thin single QW (a), in a SCH-QW structure (b), and in an MQW structure (c).

QW technology [39]. In particular, the α_H factor (c. f., Section 2.1) may significantly be reduced in SL QW laser diodes [40].

REFERENCES

[1] Thompson, G. H. B., *Physics of semiconductor laser devices*, Chichester, U.K., Wiley, 1980.

[2] Casey, H. C., Jr., and Panish, M. B., *Heterostructure lasers—Part A: Fundamental principles*, New York, NY, Academic Press, 1978.

[3] Casey, H. C., Jr., and Panish, M. B., *Heterostructure lasers—Part B: Materials and operating characteristics*, New York, NY, Academic Press, 1978.

[4] Kressel, H., and Butler, J. K., *Semiconductor lasers and heterojunction LEDs*, Boston, MA, Academic Press, 1977.

[5] Agrawal, G. P., and Dutta, N. K., *Long-wavelength semiconductor lasers*, New York, NY, Van Nostrand Reinhold, 1986.

[6] Morthier, G., and Vankwikelberge, P., *Handbook of distributed feedback laser diodes*, Norwood, MA, Artech House, 1997.

[7] Buus, J., *Single frequency semiconductor lasers*, Bellingham, WA, SPIE, 1991.

[8] Bernard, M. G. A., and Duraffourg, G., "Laser conditions in semiconductors," *Physica Status Solidi*, Vol. 1, 1961, pp. 699–703.

[9] Ghafoori-Shiraz, H., "Temperature, bandgap-wavelength, and doping dependence of peak-gain coefficient parabolic model parameters for InGaAsP/InP semiconductor laser diodes," *IEEE Journal of Lightwave Technology*, Vol. 6, 1988, pp. 500–506.

[10] Dutta, N. K., "Gain-current relation for $In_{0.72}Ga_{0.28}As_{0.6}P_{0.4}$," *Journal of Applied Physics*, Vol. 52, 1981, pp. 55–60.

[11] Osiński, M., and Adams, M. J., "Gain spectra of quaternary semiconductors," *IEE Proceedings*, Part I, Vol. 129, 1982, pp. 229–236.

[12] Bardyszewski, W., and Yevick, D., "Compositional dependence of the Auger coefficient for InGaAsP lattice matched to InP," *Journal of Applied Physics*, Vol. 58, 1985, pp. 2713–2723.

[13] Olshansky, R., Su, C. B., Manning, J., and Powazinik, W., "Measurement of radiative and nonradiative recombination rates in InGaAsP and AlGaAs light sources," *IEEE Journal of Quantum Electronics*, Vol. 20, 1984, pp. 838–854.

[14] Henry, C. H., "Theory of the linewidth of semiconductor lasers," *IEEE Journal of Quantum Electronics*, Vol. 18, 1982, pp. 259–264.

[15] Osiński, M., and Buus, J., "Linewidth broadening factor in semiconductor lasers—an overview," *IEEE Journal of Quantum Electronics*, Vol. 23, 1987, pp. 9–29.

[16] Kroemer, H., "A proposed class of heterojunction injection lasers," *Proceedings of the IEEE*, Vol. 51, 1963, p. 1782.

[17] Alferov, Z. I., and Kazarinov, R. F., "Author's certificate no. 1032155/26-25 USSR," 1963.

[18] Anderson, R. L., "Experiments on Ge-GaAs heterojunctions," *Solid State Electronics*, Vol. 5, 1962, pp. 341–351.

[19] Nahory, R. E., Pollack, M. A., Johnston, W. D., Jr., and Barns, R. L., "Band gap versus composition and demonstration of Vegard's law for $In_{1-x}Ga_xAs_yP_{1-y}$ lattice matched to InP," *Applied Physics Letters*, Vol. 33, 1978, pp. 659–661.

[20] Moon, R. L., Antypas, G. A., and James, L. W., "Bandgap and lattice constant of GaInAsP as function of alloy composition," *Journal of Electronic Materials*, Vol. 3, 1974, pp. 635–643.

[21] Kapany, N. S., and Burke, J. J., *Optical waveguides*, New York, NY, Academic Press, 1972.

[22] Yariv, A., *Optical Electronics*, New York, NY, Holt–Sounders International Edition, 1985.

[23] Adams, M. J., *An introduction to optical waveguides*, Chichester, U.K., Wiley, 1981.

[24] Knox, R. M., and Toulios, P. P., "Integrated circuits for the millimeter through optical frequency range," *MRI Symposium on Submillimeter Waves*, pp. 497–516, Brooklyn, NY, Polytechnic Press, 1970.

[25] Buus, J., "The effective index method and its application to semiconductor lasers," *IEEE Journal of Quantum Electronics*, Vol. 18, 1982, pp. 1083–1089.

[26] Amann, M.-C., and Stegmüller, B., "Polarization competition in quasi-index-guided laser diodes," *Journal of Applied Physics*, Vol. 63, 1988, pp. 1824–1830.

[27] Mito, I., Kitamura, M., Kobayashi, K., Murata, S., Seki, M., Odagiri, Y., Nishimoto, H., Yamaguchi, M., and Kobayashi, K., "InGaAsP double-channel-planar-buried-heterostructure laser diode (DC-PBH LD) with effective current confinement," *IEEE Journal of Lightwave Technology*, Vol. 1, 1983, p. 195.

[28] Oe, K., Ando, S., and Sugiyama, K., "Lasing characteristics of GaInAsP/InP narrow planar stripe lasers," *Journal of Applied Physics*, Vol. 51, 1980, p. 3541.

[29] Garrett, B., and Glew, R. W., "Low-threshold, high-power zero-order lateral-mode DQW-SCH metal-clad ridge-waveguide (AlGa)As/GaAs lasers," *Electronics Letters*, Vol. 23, 1987, p. 371.

[30] Amann, M.-C., and Stegmüller, B., "Narrow-stripe metal-clad ridge-waveguide laser for 1.3 μm wavelength," *Applied Physics Letters*, Vol. 48, 1986, pp. 1027–1029.

[31] Henry, C. H., "Theory of the phase noise and power spectrum of a single mode injection laser," *IEEE Journal of Quantum Electronics*, Vol. 19, 1983, pp. 1391–1397.

[32] Koch, T. L., and Koren, U., "Semiconductor lasers for coherent optical fiber communications," *IEEE Journal of Lightwave Technology*, Vol. 8, 1990, pp. 274–293.

[33] Westbrook, L. D., "Measurement of dg/dN and dn/dN and their dependence on photon energy in λ=1.5 μm InGaAsP laser diodes," *IEE Proceedings*, Part J, Vol. 133, 1986, pp. 135–142.

[34] Petermann, K., *Laser diode modulation and noise*, Dordrecht, The Netherlands, Kluwer Academic Publishers, 1988.

[35] Weisbuch, C., and Vinter, B., *Quantum semiconductor structures*, Boston, MA, Academic Press, 1991.

[36] Zory, P. S. (ed.), *Quantum well lasers*, Boston, MA, Academic Press, 1993.

[37] Thijs, P. J. A., Tiemeijer, L. F., Kuindersma, P. I., Binsma, J. J. M., and Van Dongen, T., "High-performance 1.5 μm wavelength InGaAs-InGaAsP strained quantum well lasers and amplifiers," *IEEE Journal of Quantum Electronics*, Vol. 27, 1991, pp. 1426–1439.

[38] McIlroy, P. W. A., Kurobe, A., and Uematsu, Y., "Analysis and application of theoretical gain curves to the design of multi-quantum-well lasers," *IEEE Journal of Quantum Electronics*, Vol. 21, 1985, pp. 1958–1963.

[39] Tiemeijer, L. F., Thijs, P. J. A., deWaard, P. J., Binsma, J. J. M., and Van Dongen, T., "Dependence of polarization, gain, linewidth enhancement factor, and K factor on the sign of the strain of InGaAs/InP strained-layer multiquantum well lasers," *Applied Physics Letters*, Vol. 58, 1991, pp. 2738–2740.

[40] Ohtoshi, T., and Chinone, N., "Linewidth enhancement factor in strained quantum well lasers," *IEEE Photonics Technology Letters*, Vol. 1, 1989, pp. 117–119.

Chapter 3

Single-Mode Laser Diodes

In Section 2.6.2, we considered the spectral properties of laser diodes under continuous wave (CW) operation. In the numerical example we found that the gain variation over a wavelength range corresponding to the longitudinal mode spacing was of the order $0.01 \, \text{cm}^{-1}$. Under ideal conditions, the side-mode suppression ratio (*SSR*), given by (2.71), may reach a value of the order of 20 dB. However, in the following cases, sufficiently pure single-mode operation may not be possible:

- If the gain curve deviates from the ideal shape.

- If the gain maximum occurs halfway between two modes.

- If the internal loss or end loss has any wavelength dependence.

- If there are any spectral hole-burning phenomena.

- Under dynamic operation (i.e., when the laser is modulated).

- For applications where the required *SSR* is high.

For a number of applications, single-mode operation is essential. This is, for example, the case in an optical communications system where fiber dispersion may be significant, or in any system using coherent detection techniques. There are several ways of achieving single-mode operation; see, for example [1]; here, we will concentrate on the most widely used method, which involves the use of periodic structures to provide spectral selectivity.

After discussing mode-selectivity requirements, we will develop the coupled-mode theory, which describes wave propagation in a periodic structure. This theory will then be applied to lasers that use periodic structures to provide wavelength-selective feedback. We will also consider the practical issues related to the fabrication of these lasers, thermal properties, as well as the spectral properties of single-mode lasers (linewidth).

3.1 MODE SELECTIVITY REQUIREMENTS

As indicated above, the results derived in Section 2.6.2 are rather optimistic and only valid for CW operation. To investigate the spectral properties of a modulated diode laser, one has to consider multimode rate equations, which in general will have to be solved numerically.

Such investigations indicate [2, 3] that the cavity gain for the lasing mode must exceed that of all other modes by about $5\,\mathrm{cm}^{-1}$, compared with a variation of the modal gain of about $0.01\,\mathrm{cm}^{-1}$ over one mode spacing. In [4], an approximate analytical result is derived for the case of digital modulation. Except for a factor with a value near unity, this result can be written

$$\Delta g_c = SSR \frac{n_{\mathrm{sp}}}{2} h\nu v_g \alpha_m (\alpha_i + \alpha_m) \frac{1}{P_{\mathrm{off}}} \qquad (3.1)$$

where P_{off} is the power in the "off" state (corresponding to a digital "0").

Numerical Example: Using $SSR = 100$, $n_{\mathrm{sp}} = 3$, $h\nu = 0.8\,\mathrm{eV}$, $v_g = c/n_{g,\mathrm{eff}}$, $c = 3 \cdot 10^8\,\mathrm{m/s}$, $n_{g,\mathrm{eff}} = 4$, $\alpha_m = \alpha_i = 30\,\mathrm{cm}^{-1}$, and $P_{\mathrm{off}} = 0.05\,\mathrm{mW}$, gives $\Delta g_c = 5\,\mathrm{cm}^{-1}$ in agreement with the numerical results.

As the spectral variation of the modal gain is weak, we can only achieve a high Δg_c if losses vary strongly from mode to mode. If we ignore the wavelength dependence of the internal loss, the only remaining parameter is the end loss. This means that we require the end loss of the lasing mode to be lower than the end losses of all modes; that is, $\Delta \alpha_m = \alpha_{m,1} - \alpha_{m,0} > 5\,\mathrm{cm}^{-1}$ where $\alpha_{m,0}$ is the end loss of the lasing mode and $\alpha_{m,1}$ is the end loss of the next competing mode.

3.2 WAVE PROPAGATION IN PERIODIC STRUCTURES

Following the original paper by Kogelnik and Shank [5], albeit with a slightly different notation, we consider a structure where the refractive index varies periodically in the direction of propagation. All transverse and lateral variations are neglected. The refractive index is written as

$$n(z) = n'_{\mathrm{eff}} + \frac{\Delta n}{2} \cos(2\beta_0 z) \qquad (3.2)$$

It is assumed that the amplitude of the variation, $\Delta n/2$, is much smaller than n'_{eff}, which represents the real part of the effective refractive index of the structure without the grating. The calculation of the effective refractive index for a slab waveguide is outlined in Appendix B. The parameter β_0 is the Bragg propagation constant, related to the period of the structure Λ.

$$\beta_0 = \frac{M\pi}{\Lambda} = \frac{2\pi}{\lambda_B} n'_{\mathrm{eff}} = k_0(\lambda_B) n'_{\mathrm{eff}} \qquad (3.3)$$

where λ_B is the Bragg wavelength in free space, $k_0(\lambda_B)$ is the free-space propagation constant at the wavelength λ_B, and M is the period order. M can take any integer value,

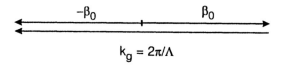

Figure 3.1 Vector diagram for wave coupling in a periodic structure.

but a first-order structure with $M = 1$ is the most common one, and we will restrict the discussion below to this case. For a first-order structure we have

$$\Lambda = \frac{\lambda_B}{2n'_{\text{eff}}} \tag{3.4}$$

which simply means that the period is equal to half a wavelength in the structure.

The effect of the periodic structure is to couple forward (right)-going and backward (left)-going waves in the structure. Introducing the grating vector $k_g = 2\pi/\Lambda$, this is illustrated in Figure 3.1. Suppressing the time factor $\exp(j\omega t)$, and keeping in mind that all transverse and lateral variations are neglected, the equation for the electrical field propagating with a wavelength λ (and free-space propagation constant $k_0 = 2\pi/\lambda$) is

$$\frac{d^2E}{dz^2} + (n(z)k_0)^2 E = 0 \tag{3.5}$$

Neglecting a term containing $(\Delta n)^2$, and using $\beta = n'_{\text{eff}}k_0$, we have

$$(n(z)k_0)^2 = \beta^2 + 4\beta\kappa\cos(2\beta_0 z) \tag{3.6}$$

where we have introduced the parameter κ, known as the *coupling coefficient*, given by

$$\kappa = \frac{\pi\Delta n}{2\lambda} \tag{3.7}$$

We only consider wavelengths λ that are close to the Bragg wavelength λ_B, hence $\beta = \beta_0 + \Delta\beta$ with $\Delta\beta << \beta_0$. Next, we write the field as a sum of right- and left-propagating waves:

$$E(z) = R(z)\exp(-j\beta_0 z) + S(z)\exp(j\beta_0 z) \tag{3.8}$$

The functions $R(z)$ and $S(z)$ vary comparatively slowly with z because we have included the rapidly varying phase-factor in the exponential functions. We now insert (3.6) and (3.8) into the wave equation (3.5), neglect second derivatives of R and S (because they are smaller than the terms containing the first derivatives), use the fact that $\Delta\beta << \beta_0$, and collect terms with identical phase factors ($\exp(-j\beta_0 z)$ and $\exp(j\beta_0 z)$, respectively). This operation gives the coupled-mode equations (the details of the derivation are left as an exercise):

$$\frac{dR}{dz} + j\Delta\beta R = -j\kappa S \tag{3.9}$$

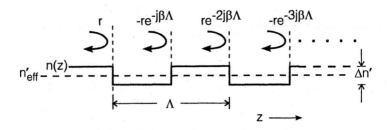

Figure 3.2   Propagation and reflections in a "square" grating.

$$\frac{dS}{dz} - j\Delta\beta S = j\kappa R \tag{3.10}$$

We note that for vanishing coupling ($\kappa = 0$) the two equations become decoupled, yielding the trivial solution $R(z) = R(0)\exp(-j\Delta\beta z), S(z) = S(0)\exp(j\Delta\beta z)$, and hence $E(z) = R(0)\exp(-j\beta z) + S(0)\exp(j\beta z)$. This is just a pair of independent plane waves with constant amplitudes propagating in the $+z$ and $-z$ directions, respectively.

To get a more physical interpretation of the coupling coefficient κ, we now consider a slightly different situation. In Figure 3.2, we show the case of a periodic structure (grating) where the index varies in a stepwise manner between two values, and where each subsection of the structure has a length of half a period. The field reflection coefficient r of the first discontinuity follows from the Fresnel formula

$$r = \frac{\Delta n'}{2n'_{eff}} \tag{3.11}$$

The field reflection of the next discontinuity is $-r$ because we now go from a high to a low index. When the wavelength is equal to the Bragg wavelength the phase change for a roundtrip in a subsection is $\beta_0\Lambda = \pi$ corresponding to a factor -1. Consequently, all reflections add up in phase, and the field reflectivity per unit length (with two reflections per period) is

$$\kappa' = \frac{2r}{\Lambda} = \frac{\Delta n'}{n'_{eff}}\frac{2n'_{eff}}{\lambda_B} = \frac{2\Delta n'}{\lambda_B} \tag{3.12}$$

This deviates by a factor of $4/\pi$ from the definition of κ in (3.7). The reason is that we now consider a square index variation instead of a sinusoidal variation. If we Fourier-expand the index variation for the square grating, we have

$$n(z) = n'_{eff} + \frac{4}{\pi}\frac{\Delta n'}{2}\cos(2\beta_0 z) + \text{higher terms} \tag{3.13}$$

This explains the extra factor $4/\pi$ (compare with (3.2)), and we see that we can interpret the coupling coefficient for a periodic structure as the amount of reflection per unit length.

3.2.1   Alternative Derivation of the Coupled-Mode Equations

Given the number of approximations and discarded terms in the derivation of the coupled-mode equations (3.9) and (3.10), it is somewhat surprising that a more rigorous alternative derivation [6], which avoids some of these approximations, gives the same result because the approximations cancel. Warning: this derivation involves the use of a Green's function and should be skipped by readers who are not familiar with this concept.

We start from (3.5), substituting $n(z)k_0$ by (3.6):

$$\frac{d^2E}{dz^2} + \beta^2 E = -4\beta\kappa \cos{(2\beta_0 z)}E \tag{3.14}$$

using the Green's function

$$G(z, z') = \frac{\exp{(-j\beta \mid z - z' \mid)}}{-2j\beta} \tag{3.15}$$

the solution to (3.14) can be written

$$E(z) = \int_{-\infty}^{\infty} G(z, z')Q(z')\, dz' \tag{3.16}$$

where

$$Q(z') = -4\beta\kappa \cos(2\beta_0 z')E(z') \tag{3.17}$$

By breaking the integral in (3.16) into two parts we have

$$E(z) = R(z)\exp{(-j\beta_0 z)} + S(z)\exp{(j\beta_0 z)} \tag{3.18}$$

where

$$R(z) = \exp{(-j(\beta - \beta_0)z)}\frac{1}{-2j\beta}\int_{-\infty}^{z} \exp{(j\beta z')}Q(z')\, dz' \tag{3.19}$$

$$S(z) = \exp{(j(\beta - \beta_0)z)}\frac{1}{-2j\beta}\int_{z}^{\infty} \exp{(-j\beta z')}Q(z')\, dz' \tag{3.20}$$

Differentiation of these equations then gives

$$\frac{dR}{dz} = -j(\beta - \beta_0)R(z) + \frac{\exp{(j\beta_0 z)}}{-2j\beta}Q(z) \tag{3.21}$$

$$\frac{dS}{dz} = j(\beta - \beta_0)S(z) + \frac{\exp{(-j\beta_0 z)}}{2j\beta}Q(z) \tag{3.22}$$

Substituting $Q(z)$ from (3.17), using $E(z)$ from (3.18), and retaining only the phase-matched terms gives the coupled-mode equations (3.9) and (3.10).

3.2.2   Solution of the Coupled-Mode Equations

The coupled-mode equations constitute a set of two coupled, linear, first-order, ordinary differential equations for the functions $R(z)$ and $S(z)$. Together with (3.8), they describe the field in a structure with a periodic index variation given by (3.2). If we know R and S at a given point, for example $z = 0$ (note that $z = 0$ is not necessarily the start or end point of the periodic structure), we can write the general solution as

$$R(z) = \left(\cosh{(\gamma z)} - \frac{j\Delta\beta}{\gamma} \sinh{(\gamma z)} \right) R(0) - \frac{j\kappa}{\gamma} \sinh{(\gamma z)}S(0) \tag{3.23}$$

$$S(z) = \frac{j\kappa}{\gamma} \sinh{(\gamma z)}R(0) + \left(\cosh{(\gamma z)} + \frac{j\Delta\beta}{\gamma} \sinh{(\gamma z)} \right) S(0) \tag{3.24}$$

where

$$\gamma^2 = \kappa^2 - \Delta\beta^2 \tag{3.25}$$

The proof that this is indeed the solution is carried out by simple substitution of (3.23) and (3.24) into (3.9) and (3.10). The details are left to the reader.

For the case of a periodic structure extending from $z = 0$ to $z = L$, we can relate $R(L)$ and $S(L)$ to $R(0)$ and $S(0)$:

$$R(L) = \left(\cosh{(\gamma L)} - \frac{j\Delta\beta}{\gamma} \sinh{(\gamma L)} \right) R(0) - \frac{j\kappa}{\gamma} \sinh{(\gamma L)}S(0) \tag{3.26}$$

$$S(L) = \frac{j\kappa}{\gamma} \sinh{(\gamma L)}R(0) + \left(\cosh{(\gamma L)} + \frac{j\Delta\beta}{\gamma} \sinh{(\gamma L)} \right) S(0) \tag{3.27}$$

This result can be written in matrix form:

$$\begin{pmatrix} R(L) \\ S(L) \end{pmatrix} = \mathbf{F}_{per}(L) \begin{pmatrix} R(0) \\ S(0) \end{pmatrix} \tag{3.28}$$

where the matrix elements of $\mathbf{F}_{per}(L)$ follow directly from (3.26) and (3.27).

In this way, the periodic structure is described by a transfer matrix that relates the right- and left-propagating waves at one end of the structure to the right- and left-propagating waves at the other end [7]. This description will prove particularly useful in the discussion of DBR (distributed Bragg reflector) and DFB (distributed feedback) lasers in Sections 3.3 and 3.4, as well as for structures consisting of several sections in the longitudinal direction. The general properties of transfer matrices, as well as some important examples of transfer matrices, are described in Appendix C. As an exercise, the reader might want to show that $\mathbf{F}_{per}(L) \cdot \mathbf{F}_{per}(L) = \mathbf{F}_{per}(2L)$.

If we use a periodic structure of length L as a reflector for a right-propagating wave with $S(L) = 0$, the field reflection coefficient follows from (3.27):

$$r_{\text{per}} = \frac{S(0)}{R(0)} = -\frac{\left(\mathbf{F}_{\text{per}}\right)_{21}}{\left(\mathbf{F}_{\text{per}}\right)_{22}} = \frac{-\frac{j\kappa}{\gamma}\sinh\left(\gamma L\right)}{\cosh\left(\gamma L\right) + \frac{j\Delta\beta}{\gamma}\sinh\left(\gamma L\right)} \tag{3.29}$$

For the case where κL, $\Delta\beta L$, and γL are all small compared with unity, we get to first order

$$r_{\text{per}} \approx \frac{-j\kappa L}{1 + j\Delta\beta L} \tag{3.30}$$

This shows the following general trends: $|r_{\text{per}}|$ increases with increasing κL (a higher coupling coefficient leads to a stronger reflection), $|r_{\text{per}}|$ decreases with increasing $\Delta\beta L$ (the reflection becomes smaller when the wavelength deviates from the Bragg wavelength), and the reflection has a $\pi/2$ phase at the Bragg wavelength ($\Delta\beta = 0$). In Section 3.3, we will study the reflection properties further.

It should be noted that in this section the structure has implicitly been assumed to be lossless. Losses can be accounted for by replacing β by $\beta - j\alpha_0$ and $\Delta\beta$ by $(\Delta\beta - j\alpha_0)$, where α_0 is the loss coefficient for the field (this means that the loss coefficient for the power is $2\alpha_0$). With this substitution, all equations and results in this section remain valid. We will return to this situation in Section 3.4.

3.3   DISTRIBUTED BRAGG-REFLECTOR LASERS

In the previous section, we investigated the general properties of periodic structures. The results from the coupled-mode equations show that the reflection coefficient for a periodic structure depends on the wavelength. For wavelengths close to the Bragg wavelength λ_B, the reflections from the individual parts of the grating are in phase (Figure 3.2), and the reflection coefficient can be high. (Its value will depend on the value of the coupling coefficient κ.) For wavelengths well away from λ_B, the reflections do not add up in phase, and the reflection will be low. The wavelength dependence of the reflection can be used to achieve a wavelength-dependent cavity gain for a laser by using a periodic structure as reflector at one (or both) ends of the laser structure. This is the basic principle of the distributed Bragg reflector (DBR) laser.

A number of properties of periodic structures (and therefore of the lasers incorporating these structures) can be expressed in terms of normalized parameters. The "coupling strength" depends on the product of the coupling coefficient κ and the length L. The deviation from the Bragg condition is described by the dimensionless product $\Delta\beta L$. We note that the deviation of the wavelength λ from the Bragg wavelength λ_B is related to the deviation of the propagation constant β from the Bragg propagation constant β_0:

$$\Delta\beta = \beta - \beta_0 = \frac{2\pi n'_{\text{eff}}(\lambda)}{\lambda} - \frac{2\pi n'_{\text{eff}}(\lambda_B)}{\lambda_B} \approx -\frac{2\pi n_g}{\lambda_B^2}\Delta\lambda \tag{3.31}$$

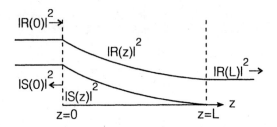

Figure 3.3   Right- and left-propagating waves in reflector.

In this expression, we have allowed for wavelength dependence of n'_{eff}; as a result, the group index n_g (see (2.50)) appears.

3.3.1   Magnitude and Phase of Reflection

We first consider the reflection properties at the Bragg wavelength. Using a periodic structure of length L as a reflector for an incoming wave with amplitude $R(0)$ at $z = 0$, and with no incoming wave and no reflection at $z = L$ (i.e., $S(L) = 0$), we find from the solution (3.26) and (3.27) to the coupled-mode equations (still assuming lossless material):

$$R(z) = \frac{\cosh(\kappa(z - L))}{\cosh(\kappa L)} R(0) \tag{3.32}$$

$$S(z) = \frac{j \sinh(\kappa(z - L))}{\cosh(\kappa L)} R(0) \tag{3.33}$$

This is illustrated in Figure 3.3. We note that $|R(z)|^2 - |S(z)|^2 = |R(L)|^2$. At the Bragg wavelength, the magnitude of the field and power reflection coefficients only depend on κL:

$$|r_{per}| = \tanh(\kappa L) \tag{3.34}$$

$$R_{per} = |r_{per}|^2 = \tanh^2(\kappa L) \tag{3.35}$$

These relations are shown in Figure 3.4. We notice that for values of κL of more than about 0.7, we can get reflectivities similar to (or higher than) what we have for a cleaved facet.

For $\lambda \neq \lambda_B$, we can compute the power reflectivity R_{per} from (3.29). In Figure 3.5, R_{per} is shown as function of $\Delta\beta L$ for several values of κL.

Numerical Example: For $\lambda_B = 1{,}550$ nm, $n_{g,eff} = 4$, $L = 100\,\mu$m, and $\Delta\beta L = 1$, we have $\Delta\lambda \approx 1$ nm.

For $\Delta\beta L > \kappa L$, it is readily shown that the reflectivity is zero for

$$\Delta\beta L = \sqrt{(N\pi)^2 + (\kappa L)^2} \tag{3.36}$$

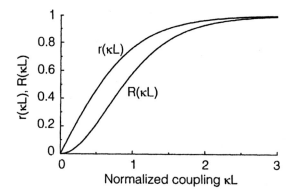

Figure 3.4   Field and power reflectivities at the Bragg wavelength as functions of κL.

with $N = 1, 2, \ldots$, and from Figure 3.5, we see that the width of the range of high reflectivity (i.e., the bandwidth) of a periodic structure with length L is roughly given by $2\kappa L$. Using (3.31) and the relation between κ and the index variation given by (3.7), we can translate this to a bandwidth expressed in terms of wavelength (use $\Delta\beta \approx 2\kappa$ in (3.31)):

$$\frac{\lambda_B^2 \kappa}{\pi n_{g,\text{eff}}} = \frac{\lambda_B \Delta n}{2 n_{g,\text{eff}}} \tag{3.37}$$

which shows that the relative bandwidth is proportional to the relative index variation. We recall from (2.49) that the mode spacing for a laser of length L' is given by

$$\Delta\lambda_m = \frac{\lambda^2}{2 n_{g,\text{eff}} L'} \tag{3.38}$$

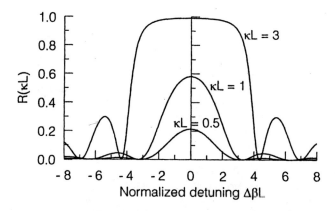

Figure 3.5   Power reflectivity as function of $\Delta\beta L$ with κL as parameter.

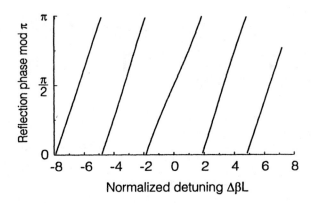

Figure 3.6   The phase of the reflected wave from a structure with $\kappa L = 1$, shown as function of $\Delta\beta L$.

It follows from (3.37) and (3.38) that if we use a periodic structure with a coupling co-efficient κ as a reflector for a laser of length L', and if $\kappa L' < \pi/2$, then there is only one cavity mode within the reflection bandwidth.

We can also find the phase ϕ of the reflected wave from (3.29) using

$$r_{\text{per}} = |r_{\text{per}}|e^{-j\phi} \tag{3.39}$$

An example of a phase calculation is shown in Figure 3.6. From the phase we can define an effective length of the Bragg reflector by

$$2L_{\text{eff}} = \frac{d\phi}{d\beta} \tag{3.40}$$

For the special case $\beta = \beta_0$ (and no loss), we find the simple result

$$L_{\text{eff}} = \frac{\tanh(\kappa L)}{2\kappa} \tag{3.41}$$

This shows that for small values of κL, we have $L_{\text{eff}} = L/2$, and for large values of κL we have $L_{\text{eff}} = 1/(2\kappa)$. For high κL values, the amplitude of the incoming wave has decreased by a factor of $\exp(0.5)$ at the point $z = L_{\text{eff}}$. If we define the penetration depth as the point where the incoming power has decreased by a factor e, we find that the penetration depth is simply given by L_{eff}.

3.3.2   Gratings

So far we have considered periodic structures with no variation in the refractive index in the x- or y- directions. In Figure 3.7, we show a more realistic situation where a grating is formed in a layer in a buried waveguide. If the periodic structure is a first-order

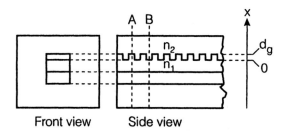

Figure 3.7   Grating structure; A and B indicate "mark" and "space" regions.

rectangular grating with equal length of the mark and space regions, then (c.f., (3.12))

$$\kappa = \frac{2\Delta n'_{\text{eff}}}{\lambda_B} = \frac{2(n'_{\text{eff},A} - n'_{\text{eff},B})}{\lambda_B} \tag{3.42}$$

where $n'_{\text{eff},A}$ and $n'_{\text{eff},B}$ are the effective refractive indices corresponding to the mark and space regions, respectively. If the presence of the grating is considered as a perturbation, it follows from the wave equation that

$$\Delta n'_{\text{eff}} = \Gamma_g(n_1 - n_2) \tag{3.43}$$

where n_1 and n_2 are the refractive indices of the layers forming the grating, and Γ_g is the confinement factor for the grating region of thickness d_g. This confinement factor is calculated for an unperturbed structure where the grating has been replaced by a layer with a refractive index n_{av} given by $n_{\text{av}} = (n_1 - n_2)/2$. It is slightly more accurate to use $n_{\text{av}}^2 = (n_1^2 - n_2^2)/2$, but for low values of $n_1 - n_2$, the difference is not significant. The value of Γ_g depends on the thickness of the grating region, and a typical value is $\Gamma_g = 10^{-3} \cdot d_g/\text{nm}$.

The first-order grating with equal mark and space periods is the one that gives the highest coupling coefficient. For other grating shapes, we can write the coupling coefficient as $\kappa = (2\Delta n'_{\text{eff}}/\lambda_B)f_{\text{red}}$, where $f_{\text{red}} < 1$ is a reduction factor. For a rectangular grating with unequal length of the mark and space (see Figure 3.8), the reduction factor follows from the Fourier coefficient of the grating shape:

$$f_{\text{red}} = \sin\left(\pi\frac{\Lambda_m}{\Lambda}\right) \tag{3.44}$$

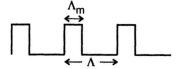

Figure 3.8   Rectangular grating with period Λ and mark length Λ_m.

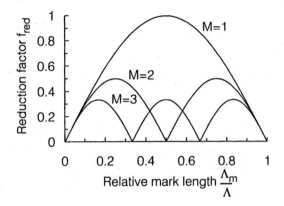

Figure 3.9   Coupling coefficient relative to that for a first-order square grating with equal mark and space regions.

This result can be extended to gratings of higher order, with M denoting the order

$$f_{\text{red}} = \frac{1}{M}\left|\sin\left(\pi\frac{\Lambda_m}{\Lambda}M\right)\right| \qquad (3.45)$$

The results of (3.44) and (3.45) are shown in Figure 3.9. If we consider the case of a square second-order grating, we have $f = 0$ for a mark-to-period ratio of 0.5 because the two reflections from one period are in antiphase. Second-order gratings with mark-to-period ratios of 0.25 or 0.75 correspond to a first-order grating with half the reflections missing, and we have $f = 0.5$. In general, the coupling coefficients for higher order gratings have a more critical dependence on the mark-space ratio. It should also be noted that higher order gratings will have radiation loss. A second-order grating, for example, will provide coupling to a radiation mode, which radiates in a direction perpendicular to the grating. For more details on radiation loss for higher order gratings, the reader is referred to [8–11].

Numerical Example: For $\Gamma_g = 10^{-3} \cdot d_g/\text{nm}$, $d_g = 100\,\text{nm}$, $n_1 - n_2 = 0.2$, $\lambda_B = 1.55\,\mu\text{m}$, and $f_{\text{red}} = 0.7$, we find $\kappa = 90\,\text{cm}^{-1}$. For $L = 100\,\mu\text{m}$ this gives $\kappa L = 0.9$, corresponding to a power reflectivity of 51%.

Other grating shapes can also be analyzed; for example, the triangular grating shown in Figure 3.10. At the top, this corresponds to a rectangular grating with a mark-to-period ratio close to 0; at the bottom the mark-to-period ratio is close to 1. If variations

Figure 3.10   Triangular grating.

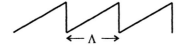

Figure 3.11   Example of blazed grating.

in the optical power distribution across the grating are neglected ($E_y(x)$ constant in the grating), then

$$f_{\text{red}} = \frac{1}{d_g} \int_0^{d_g} \sin\left(\frac{\pi x}{d_g}\right) dx = \frac{2}{\pi} \qquad (3.46)$$

For a sinusoidal grating shape, $n'_{\text{eff}}(z)$ varies sinusoidally, and consequently

$$f_{\text{red}} = \frac{\pi}{4} \qquad (3.47)$$

In general, the coupling coefficient for a grating can be found numerically by the following method: The grating layer is split into sublayers, and the grating in each sublayer is regarded as rectangular with an appropriate value of f_{red}. After multiplying by the confinement factor for the sublayer, this gives a coupling coefficient for the sublayer. Finally, all sublayer contributions are added.

For the case of blazed gratings (see Figure 3.11), the phase of each sublayer contribution must be included.

Examples of calculation of coupling coefficients for several grating shapes can be found in [12].

3.3.3   DBR Laser Structures

The basic principle of a DBR laser is that there is a grating instead of a cleaved facet at one or both ends of the laser structure. To suppress any reflection from the end of the grating an antireflection (AR) coating is applied. Figure 3.12 shows a sketch of a DBR structure with a grating at one end. In practice, the structure is a bit more complicated

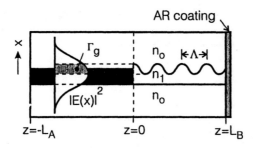

Figure 3.12   Principle of a DBR laser with a grating of length L_B and an active region of length L_A.

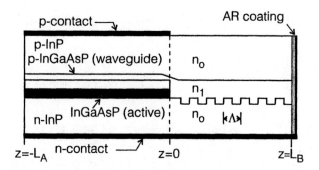

Figure 3.13   "Bundle integrated guide" (BIG) DBR laser structure [13].

as the active layer is only present between $z = -L_A$ and $z = 0$; Figures 3.13 and 3.14 show some examples.   Note that the structure shown in Figure 3.14 requires selective regrowth; more comments on fabrication technology can be found in Section 3.5.

In the design and fabrication of DBR lasers, it is important to ensure a good match of the power distribution profiles at the transition from the active part of the laser to the grating. Any mismatch will lead to a coupling loss and may also give rise to a reflection that will interfere with the reflection from the grating.

If the transition is perfect (100% coupling and no reflection), and if the power reflection at the other end of the active region is R_1, then the gain condition is

$$R_1 R_{per} \exp\left(2g_{net}L_A\right) = 1 \tag{3.48}$$

which gives the required net modal gain in the active region (c.f., (2.42))

$$g_{net} = \frac{1}{2L_A}\left(\ln\left(\frac{1}{R_1}\right) + \ln\left(\frac{1}{R_{per}}\right)\right) \tag{3.49}$$

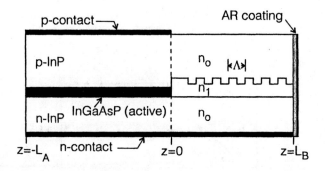

Figure 3.14   "Butt joint" (BJ) DBR laser structure [14].

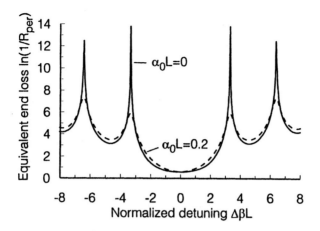

Figure 3.15   Equivalent end loss as a function of Bragg deviation $\Delta\beta L$ for $(\kappa L, \alpha_0 L) = (1,0)$ and $(1,0.2)$. For $L = 100\,\mu\text{m}$, this corresponds to a coupling coefficient of $100\,\text{cm}^{-1}$ and power losses of 0 and $40\,\text{cm}^{-1}$.

The second term in (3.49) represents the power that is leaving the active region at $z = 0$ and can be interpreted as an equivalent end loss. If the grating is lossless, all of that power will be emitted at $z = L_B$. As discussed in Section 3.2.2, losses in the grating can be included by using $\Delta\beta - j\alpha_0$ instead of $\Delta\beta$, where α_0 is the loss coefficient for the field in the grating region, and the power loss is given by $2\alpha_0$. The fact that R_{per} peaks at the Bragg wavelength λ_B leads to the desired wavelength dependence of g_{net}, with g_{net} being lowest at λ_B. This is illustrated in Figure 3.15.

If we neglect variations in material gain and loss, the difference in cavity gain, defined in (2.43), between a mode at (or near) λ_B and a mode at an other wavelength λ, is

$$\Delta g_c = -\frac{1}{2L_A}\ln\left(\frac{1}{R_{\text{per}}(\lambda_B)}\right) + \frac{1}{2L_A}\ln\left(\frac{1}{R_{\text{per}}(\lambda)}\right) = \frac{1}{2L_A}\ln\left(\frac{R_{\text{per}}(\lambda_B)}{R_{\text{per}}(\lambda)}\right) \qquad (3.50)$$

For an active region length of $300\,\mu\text{m}$ and a required cavity gain difference of $5\,\text{cm}^{-1}$, we require $\ln\left(R_{\text{per}}(\lambda_B)/R_{\text{per}}(\lambda)\right) > 0.3$.

The phase condition (i.e., the condition that the phase change after a complete cavity roundtrip must be an integer multiple of 2π) is given by

$$2\beta L_A + \phi = 2N\pi \qquad (3.51)$$

where ϕ is the phase of the reflection from the grating. The mode spacing for wavelengths near λ_B (including dispersion as in Section 2.5) is found using (3.31) and the effective grating length (3.40):

$$\Delta\lambda = \frac{\lambda_B^2}{2\left(L_A n_{g,A} + L_{\text{eff}} n_{g,B}\right)} \qquad (3.52)$$

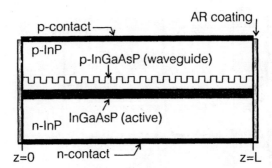

Figure 3.16   Outline of a DFB laser structure. The refractive index of the waveguide region is higher than that of InP, but lower than that of the active region.

where $n_{g,A}$ is the effective group index for the active region, and $n_{g,B}$ is the effective group index for the grating region.

In the simple example discussed above, we could write the gain and phase conditions directly; we could also have derived these results from a transfer matrix analysis, using one matrix for the cleaved facet, one for the active region, and one for the grating. For more complicated situations, the benefits of the use of transfer matrices are more obvious. We can for example include reflections at the transition at $z = 0$ by having one additional matrix. Reflections at the end of the grating can be handled in the same way.

DBR lasers can also have gratings at both ends; see, for example, [2, 15] for further analysis and experimental results for this case.

3.4   DISTRIBUTED FEEDBACK LASERS

In a DBR laser, the active region, which is providing gain, and the grating, which is providing wavelength selectivity, are separated longitudinally. In a distributed feedback (DFB) laser the two functions are combined. A simple sketch is shown in Figure 3.16. DFB lasers are simpler to fabricate than DBR lasers because of the longitudinal uniformity; no longitudinal integration of active and passive region is required. The analysis of a DFB laser, however, is not as simple as for DBR lasers, because the gain and phase conditions do not separate.

3.4.1   DFB Laser With Nonreflecting Facets

The analysis of a DFB laser can be carried out using a transfer matrix. As the DFB laser is a single periodic structure, we use the transfer matrix from (3.26) to (3.28). However, because we are dealing with an active structure, we allow for the presence of gain by replacing $\Delta\beta$ by $(\Delta\beta + jg_0)$, where g_0 represents the gain for the field. Consequently the intensity gain is given by $2g_0$.

The oscillation condition follows from setting element 2,2 of the transfer matrix equal to zero (see Appendix C):

$$\cosh(\gamma L) + \frac{j(\Delta\beta + jg_0)}{\gamma}\sinh(\gamma L) = 0 \tag{3.53}$$

We recall from (3.25) that the parameter γ (including the gain) is given by

$$\gamma^2 = \kappa^2 - (\Delta\beta + jg_0)^2 \tag{3.54}$$

The oscillation condition (3.53) can be written

$$\gamma L \coth(\gamma L) = -j(\Delta\beta L + jg_0 L) \tag{3.55}$$

For a given product of the coupling coefficient κ and the length L, this constitutes a complex transcendental equation, which determines the possible values of $(\Delta\beta L, g_0 L)$. Each solution gives the wavelength (in terms of $\Delta\beta$) and the required gain (in terms of g_0), for the possible lasing modes. In contrast to the situation for Fabry–Perot or DBR lasers, the gain and phase conditions do not separate but are determined together from the complex number $(\Delta\beta L + jg_0 L)$.

The intensity gain $2g_0$ for the mode with the lowest value of g_0 is equal to the net gain $g_{net} = (\Gamma g_a - \alpha_i)$, which must be supplied to compensate for the power emitted from the ends. The quantity $2g_0$ is therefore equivalent to the end loss for a Fabry–Perot laser (c.f., (2.42)). There are solutions to (3.55) with different values of g_0, corresponding to different values for the end loss. For wavelengths far from the Bragg wavelength, the grating does not provide efficient feedback, and the values of g_0 are high. The relation between g_0 and the end loss can be seen using the following argument. Starting from

$$\frac{dRR^*}{dz} = R^*\frac{dR}{dz} + R\frac{dR^*}{dz} \tag{3.56}$$

using a similar expression for S, and the coupled-mode equations (3.9) and (3.10) including the field gain g_0, we find

$$\frac{d(RR^* - SS^*)}{dz} = 2g_0(RR^* + SS^*) \tag{3.57}$$

Integrating (3.57) over the cavity we have

$$\left(|R(L)|^2 - |S(L)|^2\right) + \left(|S(0)|^2 - |R(0)|^2\right) = 2g_0 \int_0^L \left(|R(z)|^2 + |S(z)|^2\right) dz \tag{3.58}$$

The first bracket on the left-hand side of (3.58) is proportional to the power leaving the right end, and the second bracket is proportional to the power leaving the left end. The expression in the integral on the right-hand side is proportional to the energy stored in the cavity.

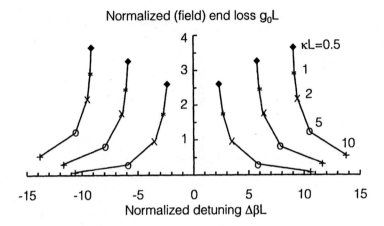

Figure 3.17   Loci of DFB modes in the $(\Delta\beta L, g_0 L)$ plane for various values of κL. For clarity, the points corresponding to the same mode are joined.

In general, the solutions to the oscillation condition (3.55) have to be found numerically. For the case of a high value of κL, there is an asymptotic solution for the mode with the lowest value of $\Delta\beta L$ [5] and the lowest required gain:

$$\Delta\beta L \approx \kappa L \qquad (3.59)$$

and

$$g_0 L \approx \left(\frac{\pi}{\kappa L}\right)^2 \qquad (3.60)$$

In Figure 3.17, we show the results from a numerical solution to (3.55). As expected, an increased feedback (higher κL) leads to a lower end loss (lower $g_0 L$), as the grating becomes more efficient and more power travels round in the cavity. For low values of κL and far from the Bragg wavelength (high values of $\Delta\beta L$), the feedback is less efficient and the end loss is higher (higher $g_0 L$). The symmetry seen in Figure 3.17 follows from (3.54) and (3.55); replacing $\Delta\beta L$ by $-\Delta\beta L$ is equivalent to complex conjugation of (3.54) and (3.55).

For low values of κL we find a normalized modespacing $\delta(\Delta\beta L)$ of π, which is the same as the normalized modespacing for a Fabry–Perot laser of length L. In a Fabry–Perot laser with $R = R_1 = R_2$ and no wavelength dependence of the facet reflectivity, the end loss is the same for all modes, and it is given by $2g_0 L = \ln(1/R)$. For $R = 0.32$, this gives $g_0 L = 0.57$.

Numerical Example: We recall the requirement for single-mode operation $\Delta g_c = 5\,\text{cm}^{-1}$. For $L = 300\,\mu\text{m}$, this gives a required end loss difference of $2\Delta g_0 L = 0.15$ or $\Delta g_0 L = 0.075$. Comparing this result with those shown in Figure 3.17, we see that this degree of loss difference is readily achieved for modes on the same side of the Bragg wavelength.

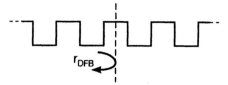

Figure 3.18   Schematic of DFB structure, with the reflectivity r_{DFB} seen from the center toward the end.

The behavior seen in Figure 3.17 is analogous to the formation of stop-bands in solid-state physics, with no propagation exactly at the Bragg wavelength $\Delta\beta L = 0$. We can understand this behavior by looking at the DFB grating structure from its center, as shown in Figure 3.18. With a field gain g_0 at the Bragg wavelength $\Delta\beta L = 0$, we have from (3.54)

$$\gamma^2 = \kappa^2 + g_0^2 \tag{3.61}$$

Consequently, γ is real and positive, and it follows from (3.29) that the field reflection, looking from the center toward the right, r_{DFB}, has a $\pi/2$ phase at the Bragg wavelength. The field reflection looking in the opposite direction also has a $\pi/2$ phase, and the total round trip phase change at the Bragg wavelength is therefore π. Since the round trip phase change must be a multiple of 2π, we cannot satisfy the phase condition at the Bragg wavelength, but there must be a degree of detuning. We have a stop-band between two modes placed symmetrically around the Bragg wavelength, with a width that increases with increasing values of κL. According to (3.59), the asymptotic value of the stop-band width for large values of κL is $2\kappa L$. The results of a numerical calculation of the stop-band width is shown in Figure 3.19. We also note that the stop-band width for a DFB laser is equivalent to the high-reflectivity bandwidth for a DBR laser. The separation between the first zeros of the DBR reflection curve, found from (3.36) with $N = 1$, provides an excellent approximation for the stop-band width as shown in Figure 3.19.

It is clear from this discussion of the "pure" DFB laser structure, such as the one shown in Figure 3.16, that although there is a large degree of mode discrimination for modes on the same side of the Bragg wavelength, modes are placed symmetrically around $\Delta\beta L = 0$. In particular, the mode that has the lowest value of $\Delta\beta L$ and the lowest end loss, has a "partner" at $-\Delta\beta L$ (on the other side of the Bragg wavelength) with the same end loss. The structure will therefore not work as a single-mode laser. In the following sections, we will see how this "degeneracy" can be lifted.

3.4.2   DFB Laser With Reflecting Facets

The simplest way of achieving single-mode operation in a DFB laser is to leave one or both facets as cleaved, rather than using AR-coating. This situation was first studied by Chinn [16] and later in more detail by Streifer, et al. [17]. We first consider the case of one reflecting and one nonreflecting facet, as shown in Figure 3.20. The discrete reflection from the facet will interfere with the distributed reflection in the grating, and the result

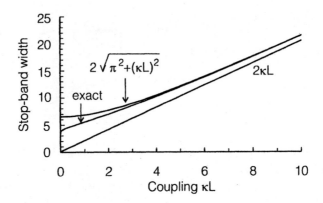

Figure 3.19   Stop-band width $2(\Delta\beta L)_1$ as function of κL, where $(\Delta\beta L)_1$ is the solution closest to the Bragg wavelength.

will depend on the phase angle Θ. The analysis can be carried out using the following transfer matrix:

$$\mathbf{F_{ar-cl}} = \mathbf{F_{dis}}(r_2)\mathbf{F_{hom}}(\Theta)\mathbf{F_{per}}(\kappa L) \qquad (3.62)$$

where the three matrices on the right-hand side represent the discrete reflection r_2 at $z = L$, the phase angle Θ due to the offset ΔL, and the periodic structure with a coupling coefficient κ and a length L, respectively. As discussed in Appendix C, the oscillation condition is found by setting element 2,2 in $\mathbf{F_{ar-cl}}$ equal to zero. The result, neglecting the wavelength dependence of Θ, is

$$\gamma \cosh(\gamma L) + (j(\Delta\beta + jg_0) + j\kappa r_2 \exp(-2j\Theta)) \sinh(\gamma L) = 0 \qquad (3.63)$$

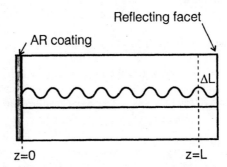

Figure 3.20   Schematic diagram of DFB structure with the left facet AR-coated and the right facet reflecting. The position of the right facet relative to the grating is described by the phase angle $\Theta = \beta\Delta L = 2\pi n'_{\text{eff}}\Delta L/\lambda$.

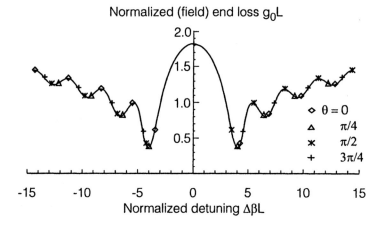

Figure 3.21   Loci of DFB modes for a structure with $\kappa L = 3$ and $r_2 = 0.57$. Notice how the modes move as a function of the phase Θ.

which, as expected, reduces to (3.55) for $r_2 = 0$. The solution to (3.63) for $\kappa L = 3$ and $r_2 = 0.57$, in terms of $(\Delta\beta L, g_0 L)$ with Θ as variable, is shown in Figure 3.21.

From Figure 3.21 and similar results obtained for different values of the coupling coefficient and the facet reflectivity, we can draw the following conclusions: (1) In the presence of a discrete facet reflection the stop-band may be less obvious than that for the "pure" DFB; (2) the lasing mode (i.e., the mode with the lowest value of $g_0 L$) is not always the one closest to the Bragg wavelength; (3) for certain phase angles, there is good mode selectivity (one mode has a lower $g_0 L$ than all the other modes), but for other phase angles, there are two competing modes (modes with similar values of $g_0 L$).

The mode selectivity can be investigated further by plotting the end loss difference $\Delta g_0 L$ as a function of Θ, with $\Delta g_0 L$ defined as the difference in end loss for the two modes with the lowest end losses. An example is shown in Figure 3.22. In practical fabrication, there is no method for controlling the exact facet position relative to the grating, and the phase angles are not equal for lasers from the same wafer. Consequently, the phase angle Θ must be treated as a random variable. This means that only a certain fraction of DFB lasers with a reflecting facet will have an acceptable *SSR*. We define the "single-mode yield" as the probability that the end loss difference exceeds a given value.

Numerical Example: If we require $\Delta g_0 L > 0.075$, as in the numerical example in Section 3.4.1, the example shown in Figure 3.22 gives a single-mode yield of about 55%.

The situation is even more complicated for DFB lasers with two reflecting facets. Again we can use transfer matrices to derive the oscillation condition, but we now need five transfer matrices

$$\mathbf{F}_{\text{cl-cl}} = \mathbf{F}_{\text{dis}}(r_2)\mathbf{F}_{\text{hom}}(\Theta_2)\mathbf{F}_{\text{per}}(\kappa L)\mathbf{F}_{\text{hom}}(\Theta_1)\mathbf{F}_{\text{dis}}(r_1) \qquad (3.64)$$

There are two random phase angles, and the single-mode yield is found by studying $\Delta g_0 L$ as a function of both Θ_2 and Θ_1. The general trends are as follows: For $\kappa L < 1$

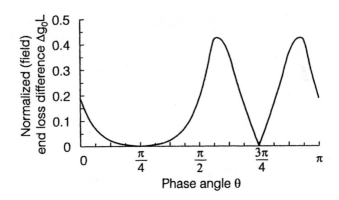

Figure 3.22   End loss difference as function of phase angle for the case $\kappa L = 3$ and $r_2 = 0.57$.

the feedback from the facets dominates and there is very little mode selectivity, the laser looks more like a Fabry–Perot laser, and the single-mode yield is near zero. For very high κL values, the grating dominates, leading to degeneracy and decreasing yield. The yield has a flat maximum for κL values in the range 3 to 5. The exact yield values depend on the required end loss difference; see [18] for specific examples.

It is quite common to use structures with one facet AR-coated and one facet high reflectivity(HR)-coated. For the case of zero reflectivity from one facet and 95% reflectivity from the other, the single-mode yield is high for $0.5 < \kappa L < 2$ and decreases for higher κL values. It is important to note that even a small residual reflectivity from an AR-coated facet may have a significant impact on the mode selectivity. In [19], it is argued that the reflectivity should be under 1%.

All the yield considerations so far apply only to the situation at threshold. For increasing power levels, any nonuniformity in the longitudinal power distribution leads to an increasing nonuniformity in the carrier density, since there is a higher rate of stimulated recombination where the power level is high. This is known as "spatial hole-burning." Because of the dependence of the refractive index on the carrier density, it leads to a nonuniform refractive index, and the Bragg wavelength will vary along the cavity. There may even be situations where the mode that dominates just above threshold becomes unstable, and lasing may switch to another mode [20, 21].

The simplest analysis of the impact of spatial hole-burning on the single-mode yield is carried out by calculating a measure for the uniformity of the power distribution for each phase angle combination. The yield is then defined as the percentage cases where the end loss difference is more than a given value, and the longitudinal power variation is less than a given value. For the DFB laser with two cleaved facets, such a study [22] indicates that the best yield is achieved for values of κL between 1 and 1.5. For higher κL values, the yield decreases because of increasing power nonuniformity.

More detailed calculations require a fully self-consistent calculation of the longitudinal power and refractive index variations, using a nonuniform refractive index in the coupled-mode equations. An early example of such an analysis [23] showed that the best single-mode yield for the AR/cleaved DFB laser was achieved for κL values just under 1.

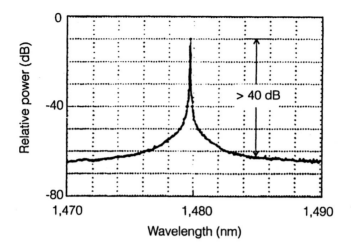

Figure 3.23   Experimental spectrum for a 400-μm-long DFB laser operated at a current giving an optical power of 5 mW. Both facets are cleaved (i.e., no AR-coating is used).

In general, an above-threshold analysis of a DFB laser is carried out by splitting the laser into a number of subsections and describing each subsection by a transfer matrix. In each subsection, the interaction between the photon density and the carrier density is described by rate equations, and the influence of the carrier density on the refractive index is taken into account. For each power level, the oscillation condition is solved by using an iteration scheme; see, for example, [24, 25].

An example of an experimental spectrum for a DFB laser is shown in Figure 3.23.

3.4.3   Phase-Shifted and Gain-Coupled DFB Lasers

It is obvious that it would be desirable to have more reliable methods for ensuring single-mode operation, instead of having to rely on the random facet position relative to the grating. This can be achieved in a number of different ways. One method consists in creating a $\Delta L' = \lambda/(4n'_{eff})$ phase shift in the center of the grating, as shown schematically in Figure 3.24. Such structures were first studied in [26] and later in [27]. For a first-order grating, $\lambda/(4n'_{eff})$ corresponds to half a period, and we can understand why this works by the following argument: At the Bragg wavelength the two reflections shown in Figure 3.24 both have $\pi/2$ phases. A roundtrip over the $\lambda/(4n'_{eff})$ center corresponds to a phase of π; consequently, the round-trip phase at the Bragg wavelength is a multiple of 2π as required.

For a phase-shifted DFB laser with the phase shift placed in the center, and with two AR-coated facets, the lasing condition can again be found from a transfer matrix

$$\mathbf{F}_{ar-\psi-ar} = \mathbf{F}_{per}(\kappa L/2)\mathbf{F}_{hom}(\psi)\mathbf{F}_{per}(\kappa L/2) \qquad (3.65)$$

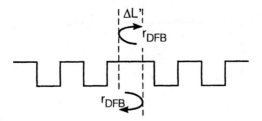

Figure 3.24   Phase-shifted grating.

here, $\psi = \beta \Delta L' = 2\pi n'_{eff} \Delta L' / \lambda$ is the phase corresponding to the physical length $\Delta L'$ of the phase shift. For $\Delta L' = \lambda/(4n'_{eff})$, we have $\psi = \pi/2$. The length of the whole structure is L and the phase shift is placed in the center. Any facet reflectivity (and corresponding phase) can be included by including the appropriate matrices, as in the discussion of the non-phase-shifted DFB laser. To get a high single-mode yield, the residual facet reflectivity should be of the order of 1% or lower [28].

After carrying out the matrix multiplications, the oscillation condition is found by setting element 2,2 equal to zero (the details are left as an exercise):

$$\gamma \coth \left(\frac{\gamma L}{2} \right) + j(\Delta \beta + j g_0) = \pm \kappa \tag{3.66}$$

We can plot this in the same way as we did in Figure 3.17 for the non-phase-shifted structure; the results are shown in Figure 3.25. As γ is real for $\Delta\beta = 0$, it follows from (3.66) that there is now a mode exactly at the Bragg wavelength; this mode has an end loss $g_0 L$ that is lower than that for all the other modes; and it will therefore dominate.

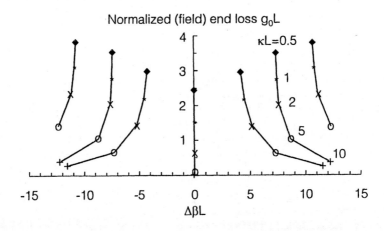

Figure 3.25   Loci of DFB modes for a structure with a $\pi/2$ phase shift in the center, shown in the $(\Delta\beta L, g_0 L)$ plane for various values of κL.

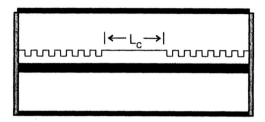

Figure 3.26   DFB laser without a grating in the center.

An examination of the intensity distribution for the dominating mode for a phase-shifted grating shows that for high κL values, the intensity has a pronounced peak in the center, and this may lead to spatial hole-burning problems at high power levels. A closer study has indicated that to achieve a flat intensity distribution, the value of κL should be about 1.25 [29]. Use of multiple phase shifts will also give a more flat intensity distribution [30, 31], or the phase shift can be distributed by using a slightly different grating period in the center part of the laser [32].

Distributed phase shifts can also be fabricated in simpler ways. If a grating is not formed in the center, there will be more high-index material, and the effective refractive index of the center will be higher than the average effective refractive index in the grating regions (see Figure 3.26). The length of the center region L_c can then be adjusted to achieve a total phase shift of $\pi/2$ [33] using

$$(n'_{\text{eff,c}} - n'_{\text{eff,av}})\frac{2\pi}{\lambda}L_c = \frac{\pi}{2} \tag{3.67}$$

Alternatively, an effective index difference can be achieved by changing the width of the active region [34].

As already pointed out in the paper by Kogelnik and Shank [5], a periodic structure with two nonreflecting facets and with a constant refractive index, but a varying gain (or loss), will also have a mode at the Bragg wavelength. According to (3.7), the coupling coefficient is purely imaginary, and at the Bragg wavelength, where γ is real and $\Delta\beta = 0$, the field reflection given by (3.29) becomes real. It has been found that even for structures with reflecting facets, or for structures with mixed index- and gain-coupling, a high single-mode yield can be obtained [22]. More details on the theory for gain-coupled and partly gain-coupled DFB lasers can be found in [35–37].

3.5   LASER FABRICATION AND TOLERANCES

The fabrication of single-frequency lasers, in particular DBR lasers, requires quite sophisticated materials growth and processing technology. Materials growth is often carried out by MOVPE under computer control. As examples we will look at the processing steps involved in the fabrication of the DBR lasers shown in Figure 3.13 [13] and Figure 3.14 [14]. Important steps in the processing sequence for the bundle integrated guide (BIG) DBR laser are shown in Figure 3.27. The butt joint (BJ) DBR laser is using

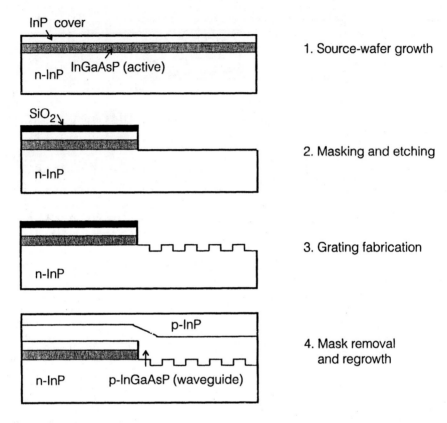

Figure 3.27   Fabrication sequence for BIG DBR laser.

selective regrowth, as shown in Figure 3.28. Notice that the grating seen over the active layer in 4a in Figure 3.28 is "invisible" because the same material is used both below and above the grating.

The processing steps shown in Figures 3.27 and 3.28 are followed by definition of the lateral structure, usually involving stripe masking, etching, and infilling.

DFB lasers are simpler to fabricate than DBR lasers because they do not require the integration of active and passive waveguides. The grating can be formed over the entire wafer, and the processing is very much like that for a more conventional laser. It should be noted that the MBE and MOVPE growth techniques are giving very uniform layer thicknesses over a whole wafer, and the lasers from the wafer will therefore have very similar wavelengths. If a range of wavelengths is desired, or if it is necessary to compensate for design and fabrication tolerances to hit a particular wavelength, gratings with slightly different period can be formed on the same wafer.

The conventional method for grating definition is shown in Figure 3.29. An interference pattern is formed on the surface of the material, which has been coated by a photoresist. The period of the interference pattern is given by $\Lambda = \lambda'/(2 \sin \theta)$, where λ'

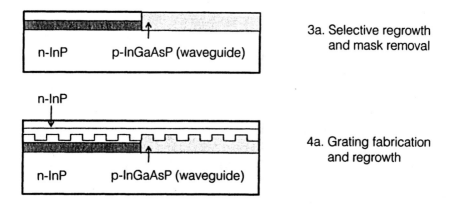

3a. Selective regrowth
and mask removal

4a. Grating fabrication
and regrowth

Figure 3.28   Fabrication sequence for BJ DBR laser; steps 1 and 2 are the same as for the BIG DBR laser.

is the wavelength of the illumination laser used. Developing the photoresist then creates a mask that can be used for grating etching. For a laser diode operating at 1,550 nm, a first-order grating will have a period of about 235 nm. Consequently, the wavelength λ' of the light used to form the interference pattern must be shorter than 470 nm. An alternative method is direct electron beam writing of the grating into the photoresist. This method is much slower but is also more versatile. This is important for the fabrication of more complicated gratings, such as those including one or more phaseshifts.

3.5.1   Wavelength Accuracy

The Bragg wavelength of a grating depends on the grating period and on the real part of the effective refractive index of the mode n'_{eff}, according to (3.3). As a consequence, any changes in the effective refractive index will lead to a change in the Bragg wavelength;

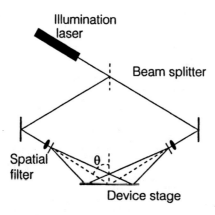

Figure 3.29   Setup for grating definition.

consequently, the deviation of any structural parameter from its design value will lead to a deviation of the lasing wavelength. In general, the sensitivity of the wavelength to a parameter x is given by

$$\frac{d\lambda}{dx} = \frac{\lambda}{n_{g,\text{eff}}} \frac{dn'_{\text{eff}}}{dx} \tag{3.68}$$

The reason for the appearance of the effective group index $n_{g,\text{eff}}$ in (3.68) is that the refractive index is wavelength dependent.

In the following, we consider the case of a DFB laser, using typical parameter values. The most critical parameter is the active layer thickness; we find that the relative wavelength accuracy is related to the relative accuracy of the active layer thickness by

$$\frac{\Delta\lambda}{\lambda} \approx 0.02 \frac{\Delta d_a}{d_a} \cdot \tag{3.69}$$

where the numerical factor is taken from the example in Appendix B. This means that for $\lambda = 1{,}550\,\text{nm}$, a 10% variation in the active layer thickness leads to a wavelength variation of about 3 nm. The impact of a change Δn_a in the refractive index of the active layer is given by

$$\frac{\Delta\lambda}{\lambda} \approx \Gamma \frac{\Delta n_a}{n_{g,\text{eff}}} \tag{3.70}$$

where Γ is the confinement factor. Hence, for $\Gamma = 0.2$, $n_{g,\text{eff}} = 4$, and $\Delta n_a = 0.01$, there is a 0.8-nm wavelength variation. For the sensitivity to the active region width w we find, again using the numerical example in Appendix B, that

$$\frac{\Delta\lambda}{\lambda} \approx 0.01 \frac{\Delta w}{w} \tag{3.71}$$

A 10% width variation will therefore lead to a wavelength variation of about 1.5 nm. If the grating period deviates from the desired value by $\Delta\Lambda$, there will be a wavelength deviation of

$$\Delta\lambda \approx \frac{2n'^2_{\text{eff}}}{n_{g,\text{eff}}} \Delta\Lambda \tag{3.72}$$

giving a 0.05-nm deviation for $\Delta\Lambda = 0.1\,\text{nm}$. Other parameters, such as the thicknesses and compositions of the other layer in the structure, usually have a much smaller impact on the wavelength; some examples are given in [38].

A DFB (or DBR) laser will operate at the wavelength with the highest cavity gain g_c (with $g_c \approx 0$), but because of the wavelength selectivity of the grating and the resulting wavelength variation of the end losses, this is not necessarily the wavelength with the highest gain of the active material. This behavior is in contrast to the behavior of Fabry–Perot lasers, which will always operate near the maximum gain of the active medium because there is little or no wavelength variation in the end loss. This effect can be used deliberately to "detune" the laser away from the gain peak. If the detuning is restricted to about 10 to 20 nm, the impact on the threshold current is limited since the gain is only slightly lower than at the maximum.

The case of "negative detuning" (where the laser is forced to operate at a wavelength shorter than that where the gain has its maximum) is particularly interesting. As indicated in Figure 2.3, the differential gain, defined as the ratio between gain change and carrier density change, is higher if the wavelength is shorter. It can be shown that this leads to a faster dynamic response. Negative detuning is also beneficial for the laser linewidth; we will discuss this point further in Section 3.6.

3.5.2 Thermal Properties Under CW Operation

The thermal time constant for a diode laser is normally in the microsecond range; in a CW analysis, we can therefore neglect thermal transients. Only a part of the electrical power supplied to a laser is converted to optical power, and we first consider the various contributions to the power budget. Consider a laser operated with an average current I, a resistance R, and a photon energy $h\nu$. The voltage drop U over the laser is approximately

$$U = IR + \frac{h\nu}{e} \tag{3.73}$$

We can write the power supplied to the laser as

$$IU = I^2 R + I_{th}\frac{h\nu}{e} + (I - I_{th})(1 - 2\eta_d)\frac{h\nu}{e} + 2(I - I_{th})\eta_d\frac{h\nu}{e} \tag{3.74}$$

where η_d is the differential quantum efficiency per end (2.62) (assuming the end losses to be identical), and I_{th} is the threshold current. The four terms on the right-hand side of (3.74) represent the following contributions: ohmic losses, recombination losses (neglecting the fact that a fraction of this power is emitted from the laser as spontaneous emission), optical losses, and emitted laser power.

Numerical Example: With $I = 30$ mA, $R = 4\,\Omega$, and a photon energy of $0.8\,eV$ (corresponding to a 1,550-nm wavelength), the power supplied to the laser is 27.6 mW, and the ohmic losses account for 3.6 mW. For $I_{th} = 10$ mA and a differential efficiency of 25% per end, we find that the recombination losses are 8 mW, the optical losses are 8 mW, and 4 mW of laser power is emitted from each end. A total of 19.6 mW of the power supplied to the laser is lost, and assuming that the thermal resistance is about 100 K/W, the losses give a temperature increase of about 2°K.

The lasing wavelength depends on the laser temperature, which is given by the ambient temperature plus the temperature increase caused by the losses. There are two important factors to consider—the first is the change in bandgap energy with temperature; the second is the temperature dependence of the refractive index. There is also a change in the cavity length with temperature due to thermal expansion, but this effect can normally be neglected.

The temperature dependence of the bandgap energy leads to a temperature dependence of the wavelength corresponding to the gain peak wavelength, λ_p. A typical value of the temperature coefficient of the bandgap energy for a 1,550-nm laser is $-2.5 \cdot 10^{-4}$ eV/K, leading to a temperature coefficient of λ_p of 0.5 nm/K. The

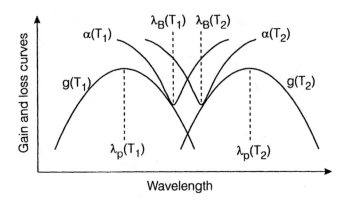

Figure 3.30   Schematic illustration of gain (g) and loss (α) curves for a DFB laser at the temperatures T_1 and T_2, where $T_2 > T_1$.

temperature dependence of the refractive index leads to a temperature dependence of the cavity resonances. For a typical temperature coefficient of the refractive index of about $-2.5 \cdot 10^{-4} \, \text{K}^{-1}$, we get a temperature coefficient of the resonance wavelengths of about 0.1 nm/K.

For a Fabry–Perot laser operating in several longitudinal modes, the envelope of the spectrum will move to longer wavelengths with increasing temperature at a rate of about 0.5 nm/K. The individual modes, however, will only move at a rate of about 0.1 nm/K. For a DFB or DBR laser, the situation is completely different. Here the lasing wavelength is determined by the Bragg wavelength for the grating rather than by the gain peak; we have illustrated this behavior in Figure 3.30. If the gain peak is too far from the Bragg wavelength, the increase in threshold current will be too high, and there is also a risk that the laser may jump to a wavelength close to the gain peak, in particular for lasers with reflecting facets. We should also bear in mind that the threshold current is an increasing function of the temperature. This means that if the Bragg wavelength is longer than λ_p, an increase in temperature only leads to a small change in the threshold current because the inherent temperature dependence of the threshold current is compensated by the improved match between the Bragg wavelength and the gain peak wavelength.

If we assume that we can tolerate a detuning of ± 20 nm, we find, using the temperature coefficients listed above, that we can achieve single-mode operation over a range of 100°K, since the detuning has a temperature coefficient of 0.4 nm/K. According to the numerical example in Section 2.6.2, a 20-nm detuning gives a mode gain that is $12 \, \text{cm}^{-1}$ lower than that at the gain peak wavelength.

3.6   SPECTRAL LINEWIDTH

Even a single-mode laser will have a finite linewidth caused by spontaneous emission into the lasing mode. Whereas photons generated by stimulated emission will add in phase to the lasing field, the phase associated with a spontaneously emitted photon is random. The treatment of laser linewidth is independent of the details of the laser structure, but the

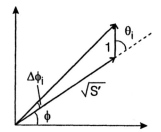

Figure 3.31   Phasor representation of the field in a laser, showing the result of a spontaneous emission event i; note that the figure is not to scale because in reality $S' \gg 1$.

linewidth depends on the number of photons in the laser, and the "translation" of photon number to optical power does depend on the laser structure. We consider a laser operating in a single mode with an average photon density $\bar{S}$ and an active volume V_a. The number of photons in the laser is then

$$S' = V_a \bar{S} \tag{3.75}$$

The situation when one photon with a random phase is added to the field is shown in Figure 3.31. From Figure 3.31, we find the change in the phase:

$$\Delta \phi_i = \frac{1}{\sqrt{S'}} \sin(\Theta_i) \tag{3.76}$$

The accumulated phase change over a time t, when the spontaneous emission rate is R_{sp}, is then

$$\Delta \phi(t) = \sum_{i=1}^{R_{sp}t} \frac{1}{\sqrt{S'}} \sin \Theta_i \tag{3.77}$$

Because we are dealing with a random process we cannot give a definite value for $\Delta \phi(t)$ —we can only make statements about the statistical properties. The phase change due to spontaneous emission has the same properties as a random walk process, with the average phase change over a given time being zero. If the vector addition shown in Figure 3.31 leads to the phasor representing the lasing field making a complete turn over a time of one second, it corresponds to the frequency deviating from its average by one hertz. By equating the variance per time of $\Delta \phi(t)$ to a change in angular frequency:

$$\frac{var(\Delta \phi(t))}{t} = \frac{<(\phi(t) - \phi(0))^2>}{t} = \frac{R_{sp}}{2S'} = \Delta \omega \tag{3.78}$$

we find an expression for the laser linewidth $\Delta \nu$ (see [39] for a more rigorous analysis, which gives the same result);

$$\Delta \nu = \frac{\Delta \omega}{2\pi} = \frac{R_{sp}}{4\pi S'} \tag{3.79}$$

Because the number of spontaneous emission events is large, the distribution of $\Delta\phi(t)$ is Gaussian. It can be shown that this leads to a Lorentzian lineshape.

By using the expression (2.54) for the spontaneous emission rate and (2.59) for the relation between photon density and optical power per end P and assuming that equal amounts of power are emitted from the two ends, we can write the linewidth as

$$\Delta\nu = \frac{h\nu v_g^2(\alpha_i + \alpha_m)\alpha_m n_{sp}}{8\pi P} \tag{3.80}$$

where $h\nu$ is the photon energy, v_g is the group velocity, α_i is the internal loss, α_m is the end loss, and n_{sp} is the spontaneous emission coefficient. The result given in (3.80) is the well-known Shawlow-Townes expression for the linewidth of a laser.

It was realized by Henry [39] that for diode lasers a significant correction factor is required in the linewidth expression. This correction is due to the following process: After a spontaneous emission event, the laser has a photon "surplus": when it relaxes back to its steady state, the carrier density will change because of the interaction between carriers and photons described by the rate equations. A change in the carrier density leads to a change in the refractive index and, hence, the phase. The analysis in [39] shows that this phase change can be written

$$\Delta\phi_i' = \frac{\alpha_H}{\sqrt{S'}}\cos\Theta_i \tag{3.81}$$

where α_H is the linewidth enhancement factor discussed in Section 2.1.

As this process is statistically independent of the initial phase change, we can use the same arguments as above to work out its impact on the laser linewidth. It follows that the linewidth including both contributions can be written

$$\Delta\nu_{STH} = \frac{h\nu v_g^2(\alpha_i + \alpha_m)\alpha_m n_{sp}}{8\pi P}(1 + \alpha_H^2) \tag{3.82}$$

which is referred to as the Schawlow-Townes-Henry linewidth.

A more detailed analysis, taking account of the laser dynamics, has been carried out in [40]. This shows that the laser lineshape is mainly a Lorentzian, but there are small satellite peaks at $\pm f_r$ relative to the linecenter, with f_r being the laser resonance frequency.

Numerical Example: Using $h\nu = 0.8\,\text{eV}$, $v_g = c/n_g$, $c = 3\cdot 10^8\,\text{m/s}$, $n_g = 4$, $\alpha_m = \alpha_i = 30\,\text{cm}^{-1}$, $n_{sp} = 2.5$, $\alpha_H = 6$, and $P = 1.0\,\text{mW}$ in (3.82) gives a linewidth of about 50 MHz.

It is obvious that the linewidth enhancement factor has a dominating impact on the value of the linewidth and that significant improvements can be made if α_H can be reduced. As indicated in Figure 2.3 α_H is a decreasing function of the photon energy (i.e., an increasing function of the wavelength) In a Fabry–Perot laser, the wavelength is determined by the gain peak, but in a DFB or DBR laser, detuning to a shorter wavelength can give a lower value of α_H, and thus a narrower linewidth. This behavior has been demonstrated experimentally [41].

The narrowest reported linewidth to date is 3.6 kHz [42]. This result is achieved using a DFB laser with a distributed phase shift (to reduce spatial hole-burning and thereby allow single-mode operation at a high optical power level) and a high value of κL (giving a low end loss). High optical power is also due to the high efficiency (low internal loss), and the value of α_H is reduced by the combination of detuning and use of SQW material. The reported result is consistent with the following parameter values: internal loss $\alpha_i = 6\,\mathrm{cm}^{-1}$, end loss $\alpha_m = 6\,\mathrm{cm}^{-1}$, efficiency $\eta_d = 25\%$ per end, power $P = 50\,\mathrm{mW}$ per end, and $n_{sp}(1 + \alpha_H^2) = 9$.

REFERENCES

[1] Buus, J., *Single frequency semiconductor lasers*, Bellingham, WA, SPIE, 1991.

[2] Koyama, F., Suematsu, Y., Arai, S., and Tanbun-Ek, T., "1.5–1.6 μm dynamic-single-mode (DSM) lasers with distributed Bragg reflector," *IEEE Journal of Quantum Electronics*, Vol. 19, 1983, pp. 1042–1051.

[3] Cartledge, J. C., and Elrefaie, A. F., "Threshold gain difference requirements for nearly single-longitudinal-mode lasers," *IEEE Journal of Lightwave Technology*, Vol. 8, 1990, pp. 704–715.

[4] Petermann, K., *Laser diode modulation and noise*, Dordrecht, The Netherlands, Kluwer Academic Publishers, 1988.

[5] Kogelnik, H., and Shank, C. V., "Coupled-wave theory of distributed feedback lasers," *Journal of Applied Physics*, Vol. 43, 1972, pp. 2327–2335.

[6] Hall, D. G., "A comment on the coupled-mode equations in guided wave optics," *Optics Communications*, Vol. 82, 1991, pp. 453–455.

[7] Yamada, M., and Sakuda, K., "Analysis of almost-periodic distributed feedback slab waveguides via a fundamental matrix approach," *Applied Optics*, Vol. 26, 1987, pp. 3474–3478.

[8] Streifer, W., Scifres, D. R., and Burnham, R. D., "Analysis of grating-coupled radiation in GaAs:GaAlAs lasers and waveguides," *IEEE Journal of Quantum Electronics*, Vol. 12, 1976, pp. 422–428.

[9] Streifer, W., Burnham, R. D., and Scifres, D. R., "Analysis of grating-coupled radiation in GaAs:GaAlAs lasers and waveguides – II: Blazing effects," *IEEE Journal of Quantum Electronics*, Vol. 12, 1976, pp. 494–499.

[10] Streifer, W., Scifres, D. R., and Burnham, R. D., "Coupled wave analysis of DFB and DBR lasers," *IEEE Journal of Quantum Electronics*, Vol. 13, 1977, pp. 134–141.

[11] Kazarinov, R. F., and Henry, C. H., "Second-order distributed feedback lasers with mode selection provided by first-order radiation losses," *IEEE Journal of Quantum Electronics*, Vol. 21, 1985, pp. 144–150.

[12] Streifer, W., Scifres, D. R., and Burnham, R. D., "Coupling coefficients for distributed feedback single- and double-heterostructure diode lasers," *IEEE Journal of Quantum Electronics*, Vol. 11, 1975, pp. 867–873.

[13] Tohmori, Y., Jiang, X., Arai, S., Koyama, F., and Suematsu, Y., "Novel structure GaInAsP/InP 1.5–1.6 μm bundle integrated guide (BIG) distributed Bragg reflector laser," *Japanese Journal of Applied Physics*, Vol. 24, 1985, pp. L399–L401.

[14] Tohmori, Y., and Oishi, M., "1.5 μm butt-jointed distributed Bragg reflector lasers grown entirely by low-pressure MOVPE," *Japanese Journal of Applied Physics*, Vol. 27, 1988, pp. L693–L695.

[15] Utaka, K., Kobayashi, K., and Suematsu, Y., "Lasing characteristics of 1.5–1.6 μm GaInAsP/InP integrated twin-guide lasers with first order distributed Bragg reflectors," *IEEE Journal of Quantum Electronics*, Vol. 17, 1981, pp. 651–658.

[16] Chinn, S. R., "Effects of mirror reflectivity in a distributed-feedback laser," *IEEE Journal of Quantum Electronics*, Vol. 9, 1973, pp. 574–580.

[17] Streifer, W., Burnham, R. D., and Scifres, D. R., "Effect of external reflectors on longitudinal modes of distributed feedback lasers," *IEEE Journal of Quantum Electronics*, Vol. 11, 1975, pp. 154–161.

[18] Buus, J., "Dynamic single-mode operation of DFB lasers with phase shifted gratings and reflecting facets," *IEE Proceedings*, Part J, Vol. 133, 1986, pp. 163–164.

[19] Kamite, K., Soda, H., Kihara, K., Nishimoto, H., and Ishikawa, H., "Effect of front facet reflectivity on transmission characteristics of asymmetric reflectivity DFB lasers," *Electronics Letters*, Vol. 24, 1988, pp. 1228–1229.

[20] Schatz, R., "Longitudinal spatial stability in symmetric semiconductor lasers due to spatial holeburning," *IEEE Journal of Quantum Electronics*, Vol. 28, 1992, pp. 1443–1449.

[21] Olesen, H., Tromborg, B., Pan, X., and Lassen, H. E., "Stability and dynamic properties of multi-electrode lasers using a Green's function approach," *IEEE Journal of Quantum Electronics*, Vol. 29, 1993, pp. 2282–2301.

[22] David, K., Morthier, G., Vankwikelberge, P., Baets, R. G., Wolf, T., and Borchert, B., "Gain-coupled DFB lasers versus index-coupled and phase-shifted DFB lasers: A comparison based on spatial hole-burning corrected yield," *IEEE Journal of Quantum Electronics*, Vol. 27, 1991, pp. 1714–1723.

[23] Soda, H., Ishikawa, H., and Imai, H., "Design of DFB lasers for high-power single-mode operation," *Electronics Letters*, Vol. 22, 1986, pp. 1047–1049.

[24] Kinoshita, J-I., and Matsumoto, K., "Yield analysis of SLM DFB lasers with an axially-flattened internal field," *IEEE Journal of Quantum Electronics*, Vol. 25, 1989, pp. 1324–1332.

[25] Vankwikelberge, P., Morthier, G., and Baets, R., "CLADISS—a longitudinal multimode model for the analysis of the static, dynamic, and stochastic behaviour of diode lasers with distributed feedback," *IEEE Journal of Quantum Electronics*, Vol. 26, 1990, pp. 1728–1741.

[26] Haus, H. A., and Shank, C. V., "Antisymmetric taper of distributed feedback lasers," *IEEE Journal of Quantum Electronics*, Vol. 12, 1976, pp. 532–539.

[27] Utaka, K., Akiba, S., Sakai, K., and Matsushima, Y., "Analysis of quarter-wave-shifted DFB laser," *Electronics Letters*, Vol. 20, 1984, pp. 326–327.

[28] Okai, M., Tsuji, S., and Chinone, N., "Stability of the longitudinal mode in $\lambda/4$-shifted InGaAsP/InP DFB lasers," *IEEE Journal of Quantum Electronics*, Vol. 25, 1989, pp. 1314–1319.

[29] Soda, H., Kotaki, Y., Sudo, H., Ishikawa, H., Yamakoshi, S., and Imai, H., "Stability in single longitudinal mode operation in GaInAsP/InP phase-adjusted DFB lasers," *IEEE Journal of Quantum Electronics*, Vol. 23, 1987, pp. 804–814.

[30] Ogita, S., Kotaki, Y., Ishikawa, H., and Imai, H., "Optimum design for multiple-phase-shift distributed feedback laser," *Electronics Letters*, Vol. 24, 1988, pp. 731–732.

[31] Agrawal, G. P., Geusic, J. E., and Anthony, P. J., "Distributed feedback lasers with multiple phase-shift regions," *Applied Physics Letters*, Vol. 53, 1988, pp. 178–180.

[32] Okai, M., Chinone, N., Taira, H., and Harada, T., "Corrugation-pitch-modulated phase-shifted DFB laser," *IEEE Photonics Technology Letters*, Vol. 1, 1989, pp. 200–201.

[33] Koyama, F., Suematsu, Y., Kojima, K., and Furuya, K., "1.5 μm phase adjusted active distributed reflector laser for complete dynamic single mode operation," *Electronics Letters*, Vol. 20, 1984, pp. 391–393.

[34] Soda, H., Wakao, K., Sudo, H., Tanahashi, T., and Imai, H., "GaInAsP/InP phase-adjusted distributed feedback lasers with a step-like nonuniform stripe width structure," *Electronics Letters*, Vol. 20, 1984, pp. 1016–1018.

[35] Kapon, E., Hardy, A., and Katzir, A., "The effects of complex coupling coefficients on distributed feedback lasers," *IEEE Journal of Quantum Electronics*, Vol. 18, 1982, pp. 66–71.

[36] David, K., Buus, J., and Baets, R. G., "Basic analysis of AR coated, partly gain-coupled DFB lasers: the standing wave effect," *IEEE Journal of Quantum Electronics*, Vol. 28, 1992, pp. 427–433.

[37] Baets, R. G., David, K., and Morthier, G., "On the distinctive features of gain coupled DFB lasers and DFB lasers with second-order grating," *IEEE Journal of Quantum Electronics*, Vol. 29, 1993, pp. 1792–1798.

[38] Y, Kotaki, and Ishikawa, H., "Wavelength tunable DFB and DBR lasers for coherent optical fibre communications," *IEE Proceedings*, Part J, Vol. 138, 1991, pp. 171–177.

[39] Henry, C. H., "Theory of the linewidth of semiconductor lasers," *IEEE Journal of Quantum Electronics*, Vol. 18, 1982, pp. 259–264.

[40] Henry, C. H., "Theory of the phase noise and power spectrum of a single mode injection laser," *IEEE Journal of Quantum Electronics*, Vol. 19, 1983, pp. 1391–1397.

[41] Ogita, S., Yano, M., Ishikawa, H., and Imai, H., "Linewidth reduction in DFB laser by detuning effect," *Electronics Letters*, Vol. 23, 1987, pp. 393–394.

[42] Okai, M., Suzuki, M., and Taniwatari, T., "Strained multiquantum-well corrugation-pitch-modulated distributed feedback laser with ultranarrow (3.6 kHz) spectral linewidth," *Electronics Letters*, Vol. 29, 1993, pp. 1696–1697.

Chapter 4

Basic Concepts for Tunable Laser Diodes

In Chapter 4, we examine which techniques the wavelength of a semiconductor laser diode may be tuned by, which physical effects may be exploited for the electronic wavelength control, what the physical limitations are, and how other laser parameters become affected by the tuning function. Referring to the oscillation condition in a multimode optical cavity as derived in Chapters 2 and 3, we investigate the laser spectrum if either the peak cavity gain or the comb-mode spectrum or both together are spectrally shifted. From these investigations, we deduce the basic tuning schemes of lasers in general and present their principal realization in the special case of the semiconductor laser. The resulting laser structures represent some kind of integrated photonic devices, the integration techniques of which are also discussed in this chapter. The relevant physical mechanisms for the electronic wavelength control are presented, and their dynamic behavior is investigated. Finally, we investigate the dynamic behavior of the various physical mechanisms used for the electronic wavelength control.

4.1 CONTINUOUS, DISCONTINUOUS, AND QUASICONTINUOUS TUNING SCHEMES

Unlike oscillators in the radio frequency domain, laser oscillators usually tend toward the simultaneous operation in many closely spaced longitudinal modes yielding a comb-mode emission spectrum. This is because of the small mode spacing (typically below 1 nm) that is due to the relatively large dimension, particularly in longitudinal direction, of the laser cavity with respect to the wavelength and the wide gain spectrum (typically several tens of nanometers) that is due to the band to band optical transitions. As described already in Chapter 2, typically several thousand wavelengths fit even into the sub-millimeter-long cavities of semiconductor laser diodes. So the mode spacing is small compared with the laser wavelength and the mode characteristics are rather similar so that it is difficult to select and maintain a certain longitudinal mode during tuning over more than one mode spacing, particularly in the case of fabrication tolerances or device inhomogeneities. Nevertheless, the discussion in Chapter 3 showed that single-mode DFB or DBR lasers may operate well under these conditions. So a main issue of wavelength-tunable laser diodes is the unambiguity and reproducibility of the wavelength tuning.

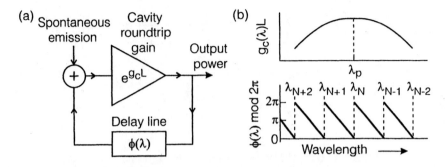

Figure 4.1   Simplified equivalent circuit of a laser oscillator (a) and plots of normalized wavelength-dependent cavity roundtrip gain g_cL and phase shift ϕ (b).

A simplified equivalent circuit for a laser oscillator is shown in Figure 4.1, comprising the cavity roundtrip gain, the phase-shifting function by the cavity transit time, and the spontaneous emission input. The oscillator amplitude and phase conditions as derived in Chapter 2 are represented graphically in Figure 4.1(b) indicating that the wavelength of the dominant laser mode is roughly defined to within $\Delta\lambda_m/2$ by the gain peak wavelength λ_p of the cavity roundtrip gain $g_c(\lambda)$. The exact definition of the laser wavelength is due to the phase condition (2.48) selecting the wavelengths with phase shifts ϕ being an integer multiple of 2π or, mathematically, $\phi(\lambda)$ mod $2\pi = 0$. In the particular case of Figure 4.1, the dominant laser mode is mode N with wavelength λ_N. Inspecting the equivalent circuit in Figure 4.1(a), tuning of the laser wavelength can be done either by varying the cavity roundtrip gain characteristic (i. e., changing λ_p), or by adjusting the cavity transit time (i. e., the phase shift $\phi(\lambda)$), or by varying both parameters. Depending on how the tuning is performed, and which device structure is used, we may distinguish between three basic tuning schemes: continuous, discontinuous, and quasicontinuous tuning. Their principal wavelength versus control current (or voltage) characteristics are displayed in Figure 4.2.

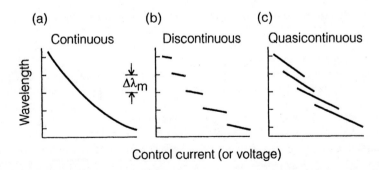

Figure 4.2   Emission wavelength versus control current (or voltage) of continuously (a), discontinuously (b), and quasicontinuously (c) tunable laser diodes. $\Delta\lambda_m$ denotes the longitudinal mode spacing.

The ideal tuning scheme for most practical applications is the continuous tuning [1, 2] as shown in Figure 4.2(a). In this tuning scheme, the laser wavelength is tuned smoothly in arbitrarily small steps[1] without mode changes while all other laser parameters are kept constant as far as possible. Thereby a stable and predominant single-mode operation may be achieved with the side-mode suppression remaining above a reasonable value (e. g., 30 dB in the case of a tunable DFB laser) throughout the entire tuning range. In addition, from the practical viewpoint it is highly desirable to enable the tuning function with only a single control current or voltage. This feature is not obvious for practical tunable laser diode structures [3], because continuous tuning requires the simultaneous mutual adjustment of the cavity gain peak wavelength and the comb-mode spectrum during tuning [4]. Owing to the stringent requirements, the tuning range is smallest in the continuous tuning scheme and seems to be limited to about 15 nm at a 1,550-nm wavelength [5].

Larger tuning ranges may be achieved by allowing for longitudinal mode changes during tuning, as shown in Figure 4.2(b). In this case, the tunability of the comb-mode spectrum represents no limitation on the total tuning range, which is now determined solely by the tuning range of the cavity gain characteristic. In this discontinuous tuning scheme, therefore, tuning ranges of up to about 100 nm at a 1,550-nm wavelength have been obtained [6]. Unfortunately, it is impossible with this tuning scheme to access all wavelengths within the tuning range.

An intermediate tuning behavior may be achieved in the so-called quasicontinuous tuning scheme as plotted in Figure 4.2(c). This is acomplished by joining overlapping small regimes being continuously tunable by each a single longitudinal mode to achieve a large wavelength coverage. Here the total tuning range is finally limited by the tunability of the cavity gain characteristic, while the tuning of the comb-mode spectrum occurs only over about one longitudinal mode spacing.

As outlined above, we can tune the laser wavelength in practice either by changing the cavity gain characteristic or the postition of the comb-mode spectrum alone, or by a simultaneous variation of both parameters. In the next three sections, we describe how the three basic tuning schemes may be accomplished by the variation of these parameters and discuss their performance with respect to wavelength control and handling.

4.2   TUNING OF CAVITY GAIN CHARACTERISTIC

Tuning of the laser wavelength may be done by a spectral shift of the cavity gain curve $g_c(\lambda)$ from its initial state $g_c^0(\lambda)$ as shown in Figure 4.3, where $g_c(\lambda) = \Gamma g_a(\lambda) - \alpha_i - \alpha_m(\lambda)$ is plotted versus the wavelength. Tuning of the g_c characteristic means that the gain peak wavelength λ_p is shifted either by varying the wavelength dependence of the active medium gain $g_a(\lambda)$ or by using laser mirrors with a tunable wavelength-selective mirror loss $\alpha_m(\lambda)$. In both cases, the changes of λ_p may be described as

$$\lambda_p = \lambda_p^0 + \Delta\lambda_p \tag{4.1}$$

---

[1]Since the wavelength of a single-mode laser can be determined only with an accuracy of the spectral linewidth, the wavelength is adjustable in the continuous tuning scheme down to about the spectral linewidth.

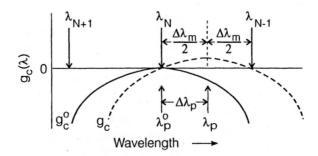

Figure 4.3   Wavelength tuning via shifting the gain peak wavelength λ_p by $\Delta\lambda_p$. The cavity roundtrip gain without tuning, $g_c^0(\lambda)$, is represented by the solid curve. Tuning by $\Delta\lambda_p = \Delta\lambda_m/2$ is represented by the cavity roundtrip gain, $g_c(\lambda)$ (broken curve).

where λ_p^0 is the gain peak wavelength without tuning and $\Delta\lambda_p$ denotes the wavelength shift of the $g_c(\lambda)$ characteristic by the tuning. The tuning range of λ_p is denoted as $\Delta\lambda_{\text{tune},p}$ so that $|\Delta\lambda_p| \leq \Delta\lambda_{\text{tune},p}$. Depending on the mode spacing, $g_c(\lambda)$ further exhibits slight amplitude variations during tuning owing to the gain-clamping mechanism keeping $g_c \approx 0$ at the dominant laser mode(s) but not at λ_p. As can be seen in Figure 4.3, the laser wavelength remains constant at λ_N as long as $|\lambda_p - \lambda_N| < \Delta\lambda_m/2$, since mode N exhibits the largest gain. Exactly at $\lambda_p = \lambda_N + \Delta\lambda_m/2$ or $\Delta\lambda_p = \Delta\lambda_m/2$, respectively, lasing in mode N ceases and mode $N-1$ becomes the dominant mode with wavelength λ_{N-1}. Again, the lasing wavelength remains unchanged until λ_p moves further by $\Delta\lambda_m$ approaching $\lambda_{N-1} + \Delta\lambda_m/2$ (i. e., $\Delta\lambda_p = 3\Delta\lambda_m/2$). Here, mode $N-1$ ceases lasing and mode $N-2$ becomes the dominant mode. This sequence of periods of width $\Delta\lambda_m$ with constant wavelengths separated by wavelength jumps of magnitude $\Delta\lambda_m$ continues with increasing $\Delta\lambda_p$.

The tuning behavior obtained this way is plotted in Figure 4.4, displaying the laser wavelength versus $\Delta\lambda_p$. Taking $\lambda_p^0 = \lambda_N$, the shift of the laser wavelength $\lambda - \lambda_N$ versus the gain peak wavelength shift $\Delta\lambda_p$ relation reads

$$\lambda - \lambda_N = \left(\Delta\lambda_p + \frac{\Delta\lambda_m}{2}\right) - \left(\Delta\lambda_p + \frac{\Delta\lambda_m}{2}\right) \bmod \Delta\lambda_m \tag{4.2}$$

As can clearly be seen, the wavelength is tuned extremely discontinuous, even though $\Delta\lambda_p$ and, consequently, λ_p are varied smoothly. This means that this tuning scheme does not enable the access to any wavelength within the covered wavelength range. Instead, only discrete wavelengths spaced by $\Delta\lambda_m$ can be individually adressed. The total number of accessible modes or wavelengths, respectively, N_w amounts to

$$N_w = \frac{\Delta\lambda_{\text{tune},p}}{\Delta\lambda_m} + 1 \tag{4.3}$$

The principal longitudinal mode spectra for various $\Delta\lambda_p$ values are plotted in Figure 4.4(b). Because the comb-modes are spectrally fixed, tuning may occur solely by the hopping from one longitudinal mode to the next. Accordingly, this figure clearly

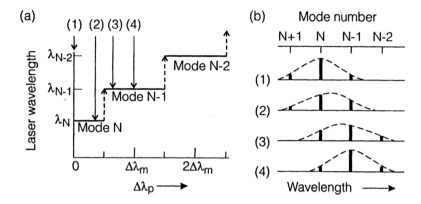

Figure 4.4   Laser wavelength versus gain peak wavelength shift $\Delta\lambda_p$ with $\lambda_p^0 = \lambda_N$ (a). Spectral positions of the comb-modes and principal longitudinal mode spectra at the indicated $\Delta\lambda_p$ positions (b).

illustrates the strong discrete nature of this tuning scheme and the issues of single-mode operation and wavelength ambiguity during tuning.

Referring to (2.74) the *SSR* is strongly affected by the detuning of λ_p relative to the dominant mode wavelength that is due to the gradual decrease of the gain difference δg between the two strongest modes. Because the detuning $\delta\lambda$ of λ_p versus the comb-mode spectrum is related to the gain peak wavelength shift as

$$\delta\lambda = \Delta\lambda_p \bmod \Delta\lambda_m \qquad (4.4)$$

the *SSR* can be calculated by (2.74). Using the laser parameters of the numerical example in Section 2.6.2, the *SSR* is shown in a logarithmic scale versus $\Delta\lambda_p$ in Figure 4.5. Since δg changes from its maximal value, corresponding to the coincidence of λ_p with one of the comb-modes ($\lambda_p = \lambda_N$), down to zero, where λ_p is displaced exactly by $\Delta\lambda_m/2$ from the comb-modes ($\lambda_p = \lambda_N + \Delta\lambda_m/2$), the *SSR* varies strongly during tuning. For this exemplary laser diode, the *SSR* covers the value range between 0 and 17 dB, revealing that a fairly reasonable *SSR* is achieved only near the symmetrical cases, where the gain peak wavelength λ_p coincides with one of the comb-modes. Since (2.71) is valid only for a distinct single-mode operation, the *SSR* values below about 10 dB are less accurate, which is indicated in the figure by the broken curves.

4.3   TUNING OF COMB-MODE SPECTRUM

A completely different tuning behavior may be obtained by keeping λ_p fixed but shifting the comb-mode spectrum. Thereby, the shift of the comb-modes can be described as

$$\lambda_i = \lambda_i^0 + \Delta\lambda_i \qquad (i = \text{mode number}) \qquad (4.5)$$

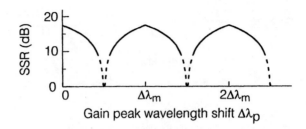

Figure 4.5   *SSR* in decibels versus gain peak wavelength shift for the laser of Figure 4.4.

where λ_i^0 is the initial position of the comb-modes without tuning. This is illustrated in Figure 4.6 for the case of $\lambda_p = \lambda_N^0$. As can be seen, the gain-clamping mechanism provides zero cavity gain at the lasing mode only. As a consequence, the total cavity gain characteristic undergoes small amplitude modulations during tuning.

Referring to (2.48), this tuning method can be induced by changing the optical length ($n'_{\text{eff}}L$) of the laser cavity as done in accordance with the external cavity tunable laser diodes [7]. As the cavity length of monolithic semiconductor lasers is hardly variable, this means that the real part of the effective refractive index in the laser cavity (n'_{eff}) must be changed. The shifts of the mode wavelengths corresponding to an index change of $\Delta n'_{\text{eff}}$ are $\Delta \lambda_i = \lambda_i \Delta n'_{\text{eff}}/n_{g,\text{eff}}$, where $n_{g,\text{eff}}$ is the effective group index (2.50) accounting for the wavelength dependence of n'_{eff}. Because the gain curve is relatively narrow with respect to the wavelength, the relative wavelength differences between the comb-modes are rather small, so that the $\Delta \lambda_i$'s can be taken equal as $\Delta \lambda_i \approx \Delta \lambda_c = \lambda_N^0 \Delta n'_{\text{eff}}/n_{g,\text{eff}}$. Therefore, all comb modes can be considered to be shifted by an equal amount within the wavelength range of interest. The tuning range of the comb-mode spectrum is denoted as $\Delta \lambda_{\text{tune},c}$ so that $|\Delta \lambda_c| \leq \Delta \lambda_{\text{tune},c}$.

Again, lasing occurs in mode i if $|\lambda_p - \lambda_i| < \Delta \lambda_m/2$, defining successive wavelength intervals of width $\Delta \lambda_m$ in which the lasing mode, as identified by its longitudinal mode number i, does not change. In contrast to the previous tuning technique,

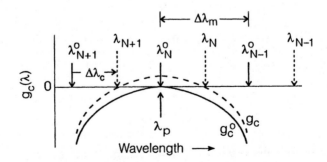

Figure 4.6   Wavelength tuning via shifting the comb-mode spectrum as $\lambda_i = \lambda_i^0 + \Delta \lambda_c$. The cavity gain curves $g_c^0(\lambda)$ (solid curve) and $g_c(\lambda)$ (broken curve) correspond to $\Delta \lambda_c = 0$ (no tuning) and $\Delta \lambda_c = \Delta \lambda_m/2$.

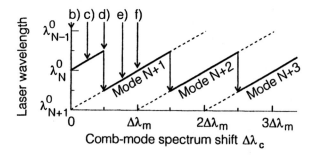

Figure 4.7   Laser wavelength versus comb-mode spectrum shift $\Delta\lambda_c$ for λ_p being kept constant at λ_N^0.

however, the mode wavelengths linearly change with $\Delta\lambda_c$ within each period, so that stepwise continuous tuning regimes are obtained. At the boarders of these regimes (i. e., $\Delta\lambda_c = \Delta\lambda_m/2, 3\Delta\lambda_m/2, \ldots$), a mode jump always occurs to the next-higher-order mode, each yielding a wavelength jump downward by $\Delta\lambda_m$. Keeping λ_p fixed at λ_N^0, the laser wavelength shift depends on $\Delta\lambda_c$ as

$$\lambda - \lambda_N^0 = \left(\Delta\lambda_c + \frac{\Delta\lambda_m}{2}\right) \bmod \Delta\lambda_m - \frac{\Delta\lambda_m}{2} \tag{4.6}$$

The resulting tuning behavior is displayed in Figure 4.7 showing the periodic regimes of a continuous tuning with a wavelength shift equal to the mode spacing $\Delta\lambda_m$, separated by successive mode jumps that exactly cancel the wavelength shift. Accordingly, a periodic continuous tuning range equal to the longitudinal mode spacing $\Delta\lambda_m$ and centered on λ_N^0 can be achieved in this way. The single-mode operation as characterized by the *SSR* exhibits exactly the same behavior as in the case of the λ_p-tuning (c. f., Figure 4.5).

A schematic illustration of the longitudinal mode spectra in this tuning scheme is presented in Figure 4.8. While the fixed cavity gain characteristic is displayed in Figure 4.8(a), the amplitudes of the longitudinal modes at different shifts ($\Delta\lambda_c$) of the comb-mode spectrum are shown in Figure 4.8(b–f). For the sake of clarity, the corresponding tuning positions are labeled as in Figure 4.7. As can be seen, the initial laser spectrum at $\Delta\lambda_c = 0$ (Figure 4.8(b)) is reproduced after tuning by exactly one mode spacing ($\Delta\lambda_c = \Delta\lambda_m$) as shown in Figure 4.8(f). Further, these plots clearly show that even though the tuning is stepwise continuous over a tuning range equal to the longitudinal mode spacing $\Delta\lambda_m$, the spectral performance is rather weak and a reasonable single-mode operation is possible only over a part of the continuous tuning regime.

4.4   SIMULTANEOUS TUNING OF CAVITY GAIN AND COMB-MODE SPECTRUM

Up to now, the tuning behavior has been studied by varying either $\Delta\lambda_c$ or $\Delta\lambda_p$ alone. Thereby a continuous tuning up to at most the longitudinal mode spacing $\Delta\lambda_m$ can be achieved, while the discontinuous tuning covers a wavelength regime up to the tuning

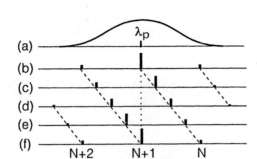

Figure 4.8   Schematic illustration of the fixed cavity gain characteristic (a) and longitudinal mode spectra for the stepwise continuous $\Delta\lambda_c$-tuning in Figure 4.7 (b–f). The various tuning positions are labeled identically in both figures.

range of the total roundtrip gain, $\Delta\lambda_{tune,p}$; in the latter case, however, only a few discrete wavelengths can be accessed within the tuning range. A considerably improved tuning performance can be achieved by a simultaneous shift of the comb modes and the total roundtrip gain curve. This means that a certain relationship is established between $\Delta\lambda_c$ and $\Delta\lambda_p$.

First of all, by keeping $\Delta\lambda_c = \Delta\lambda_p = \Delta\lambda$ and choosing $\lambda_p^0 = \lambda_N^0$, the wavelength is tuned in a continuous manner as $\lambda = \lambda_N^0 + \Delta\lambda$. The laser wavelength versus $\Delta\lambda$ relationship is plotted for this tuning scheme in Figure 4.9(a), while the schematic longitudinal mode spectra are shown in Figure 4.9(b). Apparently, a stable spectrum can in principle be maintained over the entire tuning range, and any wavelength within the tuning range may be accessed. The continuous tuning range $\Delta\lambda_{tune}$ thereby equals the smaller one of $\Delta\lambda_{tune,c}$ and $\Delta\lambda_{tune,p}$. Usually, $\Delta\lambda_{tune}$ is determined by $\Delta\lambda_{tune,c}$, which

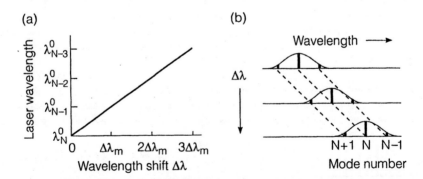

Figure 4.9   Laser wavelength versus wavelength shift characteristic (a) and schematic longitudinal mode spectra (b) for the continuous wavelength tuning by varying $\Delta\lambda_c$ and $\Delta\lambda_p$ equally.

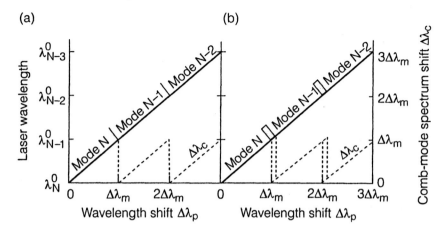

Figure 4.10 Quasicontinuous wavelength tuning by a simultaneous variation of $\Delta\lambda_p$ and $\Delta\lambda_c$. The two cases of nonoverlapping (a) and overlapping (b) continuous tuning ranges are considered.

nevertheless can be much larger than the mode spacing $\Delta\lambda_m$ depending on the laser geometry and the magnitude of the employed tuning mechanism (c. f., Section 4.5).

For $\Delta\lambda_{tune,p} > \Delta\lambda_{tune,c}$ and $\Delta\lambda_{tune,c} \geq \Delta\lambda_m$ a quasicontinuous tuning can be performed over a wavelength range equal to $\Delta\lambda_{tune,p}$. This tuning scheme is illustrated in Figure 4.10. Figure 4.10(a) shows the quasicontinuous tuning for $\Delta\lambda_{tune,c} = \Delta\lambda_m$. Thereby $\Delta\lambda_p$ is varied monotonically, while $\Delta\lambda_c$ is varied stepwise continuous each over a wavelength range $\Delta\lambda_m$ and is then reset to zero. In this way, the laser wavelength also monotonically increases as in the continuous tuning scheme. However, after a shift of $\Delta\lambda_m$, the longitudinal mode number N changes to $N-1$, that is, the next lower-order longitudinal mode becomes the lasing mode. These mode changes make this tuning technique completely different from the continuous tuning scheme described above. This is because the mode jumps let the transition regions between modes be undefined with respect to phase and wavelength, even if the transition regions can be made very small. Because of the discontinuity, this tuning scheme is not suited for many applications. Particularly in frequency-modulated optical radar systems [8, 9] or in a coherent optical receiver [10], the continuous tuning scheme is required.

Schematic tuning spectra are plotted in Figure 4.11, showing the mode numbers and intensity distributions for the longitudinal modes at the critical tuning positions. Without tuning, the laser spectrum is assumed to be symmetrical around mode N as shown in Figure 4.11(a). Tuning over one longitudinal mode spacing by putting $\Delta\lambda_p = \Delta\lambda_c = \Delta\lambda_m$ is shown in Figure 4.11(b). Next, the comb-mode spectrum shift $\Delta\lambda_c$ is reset to zero as shown in Figure 4.11(c). Obviously, the longitudinal mode spectrum in the wavelength domain equals that of Figure 4.11(b). However, the mode numbers changed by -1, so that the dominant laser mode is now the longitudinal mode $N-1$. As two different longitudinal modes represent two independent optical oscillators, the transition from Figure 4.11(b) to Figure 4.11(c) is not unambiguously defined neither with respect to the field phase nor with respect to the wavelength. This sequence of first

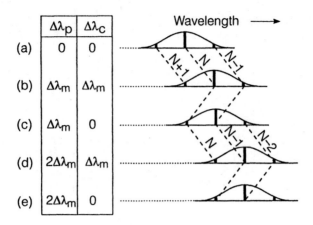

Figure 4.11   Longitudinal mode spectra for the quasicontinuous wavelength tuning over two mode spacings according to Figure 4.10(a). The various tuning positions (a–e) are labeled by the corresponding $\Delta\lambda_p$ and $\Delta\lambda_c$ values and the longitudinal mode numbers.

increasing $\Delta\lambda_p$ and $\Delta\lambda_c$ by $\Delta\lambda_m$ and then resetting $\Delta\lambda_c$ to zero can be continued until $\Delta\lambda_p$ reaches its limiting value $\Delta\lambda_{tune,p}$. Even though the spectral output of this tuning scheme, including the fixed *SSR*, at first glance seems to equal that of the continuous tuning (c. f., Figure 4.9), the periodic mode changes strongly limit the practical use of this technique.

A certain improvement can be obtained if $\Delta\lambda_{tune,c} > \Delta\lambda_m$. In this case, an overlap of the modes exists with respect to the laser wavelength in the transition regions as shown in Figure 4.10(b) by the shaded areas. Therefore, the spectral locations of the mode jumps can be varied over a certain wavelength range, making the wavelength control in the transition regions easier. Accordingly, for instance, a frequency or phase control loop with a sufficient wavelength span can be established at any wavelength within the entire tuning range. From the practical point of view, however, this tuning scheme suffers from the considerable effort required for the wavelength control and from the possible occurrence of a hysteresis in the tuning characteristic.

4.5   ELECTRONIC WAVELENGTH CONTROL

In the past three sections, we demonstrated that the wavelength tuning of laser diodes requires the electronic control of the gain peak wavelength of the cavity roundtrip gain, λ_p, and/or the comb modes' positions λ_i. In this section, we study the physical effects that enable the electronic control of the wavelengths λ_i and λ_p. Investigating the phase condition of the laser oscillator (2.48), we find that the comb modes in a laser diode may be tuned by the electronic control of the real part of the effective refractive index. Accordingly, a waveguide section of length L with an electronically controllable effective refractive index, as shown schematically in Figure 4.12(a), may serve as the basic tuning element to perform the shift of the comb-mode spectrum. As the (double-pass) phase

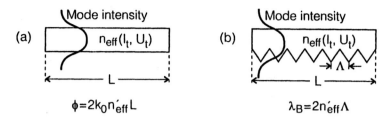

Figure 4.12   The two basic tuning elements for laser diodes exploiting the electronic refractive index control: (a) tunable phase shifter and (b) tunable Bragg reflector. Electronic control of n_{eff} occurs via application of a tuning current I_t or tuning voltage U_t, respectively.

shift of this element $\phi = 2k_0 n'_{eff} L$ is proportional to the product of effective refractive index and length, it is important for a strong tuning effect to extend this element over a major part of the laser cavity.

As already discussed in Chapter 2 (c. f., Figure 2.2), the gain peak wavelength of an inverted semiconductor is not kept fixed at atomic or molecular resonances as with most other laser types but depends on the injected carrier density. Above threshold, however, the gain-clamping mechanism prevents significant carrier changes so that the variation of the semiconductor gain curve by changing the injection current has to be ruled out for widely tunable laser diodes. Moreover, the investigations of the side-mode suppression in Chapter 2 revealed that the spectral selection of the semiconductor gain characteristic is not sufficient to provide a reasonable single longitudinal mode operation, particularly if the mode wavelength is being tuned. Nevertheless, wavelength tuning was demonstrated by varying the gain curve of a multisection laser diode using inhomogeneous current injection (gain-levering effect) [11].

For the realization of a tunable single-mode DFB or DBR laser, the tuning of the cavity roundtrip gain must be done by an electronic control of the wavelength-selective filtering element, namely the Bragg reflector. Inspecting the Bragg condition (3.4) shows that besides the grating pitch, which is built in by the fabrication process, only the effective refractive index of the grating region is left as an adjustable parameter. The effective refractive index of the multilayer laser structure is a function of the refractive indices and thicknesses of the various layers. So the electronic variation of the refractive index of any of these layers yields changes of the effective refractive index as determined by the confinement factor of the corresponding layer (c. f., (2.25)) and may thus be employed to accomplish the tuning of the cavity gain characteristic by tuning of the wavelength-dependent end loss $\alpha_m(\lambda)$. The electronically tunable Bragg reflector as shown schematically in Figure 4.12(b) therefore represents the second basic tuning element to perform the elementary tuning functions described in the previous sections.

The wavelength tuning achieved with a certain effective refractive index change may easily be estimated for the case of the continuous tuning. In this tuning scheme, the laser emits in the same longitudinal mode within the entire tuning range, and mode changes or jumps do not contribute to the tuning effect. As a consequence, the tuning range $\Delta\lambda_{tune}$ cannot be larger than the tuning range of a longitudinal laser mode. The latter is determined by the real part of the maximal change $\Delta n'_{eff}$ of the effective refractive index

n_{eff} as achievable by the electronic control current or voltage. Considering, for example, a DFB laser operating exactly at the Bragg wavelength ($\lambda_0 = \lambda_B$), the tuning range for continuous tuning is given with (3.4) and (2.50) as

$$\frac{\Delta\lambda_{\text{tune}}}{\lambda_0} = \frac{|\Delta n'_{\text{eff}}|}{n_{g,\text{eff}}} \tag{4.7}$$

In the less favorable, discontinuous tuning scheme, on the contrary, tuning is done essentially by mode jumps from one longitudinal mode to the other, so that this limitation does not exist. Accordingly, the ultimate limitation of the tuning range in the discontinuous tuning scheme is set by the spectral width of the active region gain function.

The electronic wavelength tuning of semiconductor laser diodes thus depends on the availability and exploitation of physical effects that enable the refractive index control either by carrier injection (free-carrier plasma effect) [12–14], application of an electric field [15–17], as with the quantum confined Stark effect (QCSE), or by temperature control (thermal tuning) [18, 19]. While the QCSE does the refractive index control without power consumption, the free-carrier plasma effect and the thermal tuning usually exhibit the essential disadvantage that electrical power must be supplied, which heats up the devices and deteriorates most other laser parameters such as optical power, threshold current, and efficiency. On the other hand, the largest refractive index changes and, consequently, tuning ranges have been achieved so far with the free-carrier plasma effect that requires a sustained electric power supply.

4.5.1   The Free-Carrier Plasma Effect

As the free-carrier plasma effect is the most frequently used physical mechanism for tuning and so far has yielded the largest tuning ranges, this important effect deserves a detailed investigation in this section. The refractive index change Δn caused by the injected electron-hole plasma into a semiconductor is mainly due to the polarization of the free carriers but also the spectral shift of the absorption edge yields a contribution to Δn [20, 21]. The effect of the carrier polarization on Δn dominates in the common case of a passive tuning region that exhibits a bandgap energy significantly (e. g., 0.1 eV) larger than the photon energy. In this case, the real part of the refractive index change for the carrier injection $N = P$ into an undoped semiconductor is given by [20]

$$\Delta n' = -\underbrace{\frac{e^2\lambda^2}{8\pi^2c^2n\epsilon_0}\left(\frac{1}{m_e} + \frac{1}{m_h}\right)}_{\beta_{\text{pl}}} N = \beta_{\text{pl}}N \tag{4.8}$$

where m_e and m_h denote the effective masses of the injected electrons and holes, respectively, and n is the refractive index of the semiconductor. Note that β_{pl} is negative so that the refractive index and the wavelength both decrease by using the plasma effect for tuning. In addition to the real part, also the imaginary part of the refractive index changes by $\Delta n''$, yielding the additional optical loss

$$\alpha_{\text{pl}} = -2k_0\Delta n'' = \underbrace{\frac{e^3\lambda^2}{4\pi^2 c^3 n\epsilon_0}\left(\frac{1}{m_e^2\mu_e} + \frac{1}{m_h^2\mu_h}\right)}_{k_{\text{pl}}} N = k_{\text{pl}}N \tag{4.9}$$

where μ_e and μ_h are the mobilities of electrons and holes, respectively. In the usual way we determine the phase-amplitude coupling factor of this effect by means of (2.20) as

$$\alpha_{\text{H,pl}} = -\frac{\partial\Delta n'/\partial N}{\partial\Delta n''/\partial N} = -\frac{\Delta n'}{\Delta n''} = 2k_0\frac{\Delta n'}{\alpha_{\text{pl}}} \tag{4.10}$$

Using (4.8) and (4.9) and considering that the mobilities are related to the effective masses by $\mu_{e,h} = e\tau_r/m_{e,h}$, where τ_r is the dielectric relaxation time (typ. 50–100 fs), we may simplify (4.10) as

$$\alpha_{\text{H,pl}} = -\omega\tau_r \tag{4.11}$$

where $\omega = c/k_0$ is the optical angular frequency.

Numerical Example: Taking $\lambda = 1,500$ nm ($\omega = 1.257\cdot10^{15}$ s^{-1}), $n = 3.3$, $m_e = 0.05\,m_0$, $m_h = 0.5\,m_0$, $\mu_e = 2,000$ cm^2/Vs, $\mu_h = 200$ cm^2/Vs (corresponding to $\tau_r = 57$ fs), we get $\beta_{\text{pl}} = -6.7\cdot10^{-21}$ cm^3, $k_{\text{pl}} = 7.8\cdot10^{-18}$ cm^2, and $\alpha_{\text{H,pl}} = -72$. For an ambipolar injection of $N = P = 3\cdot10^{18}$ cm^{-3}, an index change $\Delta n' = -0.02$ and a loss $\alpha_{\text{pl}} = 23$ cm^{-1} are obtained.

In addition to the plasma effect, the injection of an electron-hole plasma changes the spectral shape of the band to band optical absorption via bandgap shrinkage and band filling [21] yielding an index change of the same sign and order as that due to the carrier polarization. Therefore, β_{pl} can be as large as $-1.3\cdot10^{-20}$ cm^3 and maximal refractive index changes up to about -0.04 can be achieved at a 1,550-nm wavelength with $N = P = 3\cdot10^{18}$ cm^{-3} injected into InGaAsP with a bandgap wavelength λ_g of 1,300 nm.

Besides the optical losses that are due to carrier scattering (4.9), the intervalence band absorption (IVBA) [22] by the injected holes causes significant losses, which can be described by

$$\alpha_{\text{IVBA}} = k_{\text{IVBA}}P = k_{\text{IVBA}}N \tag{4.12}$$

where the latter equality holds for carrier injection into an undoped tuning region. In In-GaAsP at a 1,550-nm wavelength, the coefficient k_{IVBA} is of the order $2-4\cdot10^{-17}$ cm^2 [23–25] so that $\alpha_{\text{IVBA}} > \alpha_{\text{pl}}$. Accordingly, the formula for the alpha-factor must be completed by the contribution of the intervalence band absorption. Neglecting the dispersion by the weak wavelength dependence of α_{IVBA}, we may modify (4.11) as

$$\alpha_{\text{H,pl}} = -\frac{\omega\tau_r}{1 + k_{\text{IVBA}}/k_{\text{pl}}} \tag{4.13}$$

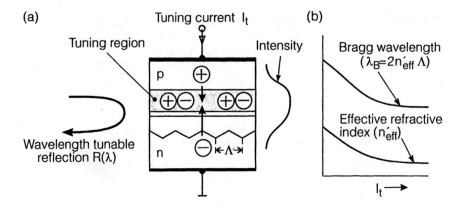

Figure 4.13   Schematic longitudinal view of current tunable Bragg reflector (a) with tuning characteristics (b).

Taking $k_{\mathrm{IVBA}} = 3 \cdot 10^{-17} \, \mathrm{cm}^2$, we obtain for the numerical example above ($N = P = 3 \cdot 10^{18} \, \mathrm{cm}^{-3}$) an optical loss of $\alpha_{\mathrm{IVBA}} = 90 \, \mathrm{cm}^{-1}$ and a reduced alpha-factor of -15, close to the typical values of passive tuning sections around -20 [26].

For illustration, a current-tunable Bragg reflector that exploits the free-carrier plasma effect is shown schematically in Figure 4.13. Here, the tuning region with a lower bandgap energy is embedded in a double-heterostructure with higher bandgap energy confinement layers and is transversely integrated with a Bragg grating. Accordingly, the index reduction Δn_t in the tuning region by the injected carriers reduces the effective refractive index n_{eff} of the transverse mode as

$$\Delta n_{\mathrm{eff}} = \Gamma_t \Delta n_t \tag{4.14}$$

where Γ_t is the transverse confinement factor (2.26) of the tuning region. As the Bragg wavelength change, $\Delta \lambda$, is proportional to the changes of the real part of the effective refractive index (c. f., (3.4))

$$\Delta \lambda = \lambda_B \frac{\Delta n'_{\mathrm{eff}}}{n_{g,\mathrm{eff}}} \tag{4.15}$$

this device represents a wavelength selective reflector with a tunable reflection wavelength (i. e., the Bragg wavelength). As with (4.7) the effective group index appears in the denominator because of the wavelength dependence of n'_{eff}. The relationship between wavelength shift $\Delta \lambda$ and injected carrier density N thus reads

$$\Delta \lambda = \frac{\beta_{\mathrm{pl}} \Gamma_t \lambda_B}{n_{g,\mathrm{eff}}} N \tag{4.16}$$

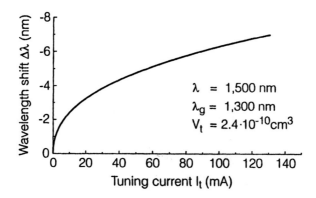

Figure 4.14   Wavelength shift versus tuning current for a λ_g =1,300-nm tunable Bragg reflector operated at a 1,500-nm wavelength comprising an InGaAsP tuning region with $\beta_{pl} = -1.3 \cdot$
10^{-20} cm^3, $L = 400\,\mu$m, $d = 0.3\,\mu$m, $w = 2\,\mu$m, $\Gamma_t = 0.3$, $\tau_s \to \infty$, $B = 10^{-10}$ cm^3/s, and
$C = 3 \cdot 10^{-29}$ cm^6/s.

where the carrier density N is related to the tuning current I_t by way of the stationary
solution of the carrier rate equation (2.55) as

$$I_t = eV_t(N/\tau_s + BN^2 + CN^3) \tag{4.17}$$

where $V_t = dwL$ is the volume of the tuning region. It should be noted that the recombination coefficients in (4.17) are those of the tuning region with bandgap energy higher than
that of the active region to avoid absorption and may thus differ from the recombination
coefficients of the latter. This particularly holds for the Auger recombination coefficient
C that strongly decreases with increasing bandgap energy [27].

   Numerical Example: Consider a tunable Bragg reflector with a λ_g =1,300-
nm InGaAsP tuning region operated at a Bragg wavelength of 1,500 nm with $\beta_{pl} =$
$-1.3 \cdot 10^{-20}$ cm^3, the dimensions $L = 400\,\mu$m, $d = 0.3\,\mu$m, and $w = 2\,\mu$m, a confinement factor $\Gamma_t = 0.3$, an infinite spontaneous recombination time constant, a bime-
locular recombination constant $B = 10^{-10}$ cm^3/s, and an Auger recombination constant
$C = 3 \cdot 10^{-29}$ cm^6/s. We obtain the $\Delta\lambda$ versus tuning current I_t characteristic plotted in
Figure 4.14. Typically the tuning efficiency

$$\eta_t = \left| \frac{d\lambda}{dI_t} \right| \tag{4.18}$$

is large at small tuning currents and significantly decreases with increasing tuning current
according to the square-root-like $N - I_t$ relationship in (4.17).

   Because loss and index changes scale equally with the confinement factor,
the alpha-factor of the structure equals the alpha-factor of the tuning region. As a

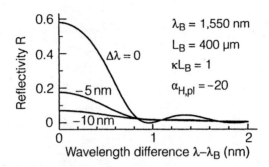

Figure 4.15   Power reflectivity versus wavelength deviation from Bragg wavelength for a typical tunable Bragg reflector at a 1,550-nm wavelength with the Bragg wavelength tuning $\Delta\lambda$ as parameter.

consequence, the wavelength shift that is due to the carrier injection (4.15) and the additional mode loss $\alpha_{\text{eff,pl}} = \Gamma_t \alpha_{\text{pl}}$ can be related to $\Delta\lambda$ by way of the alpha-factor (4.10):

$$\alpha_{\text{eff,pl}} = 2k_0 \frac{\Delta n'_{\text{eff}}}{\alpha_{\text{H,pl}}} = \frac{4\pi n_{g,\text{eff}}}{\lambda_B^2 \alpha_{\text{H,pl}}} \Delta\lambda \tag{4.19}$$

Assuming $\alpha_{\text{H,pl}} = -20$, for instance, a wavelength shift of -1 nm typically corresponds to a mode loss change around $8 \, \text{cm}^{-1}$. Besides the reduced reflectivity, the losses have a major impact on the wavelength selectivity. This is shown for $\alpha_{\text{H,pl}} = -20$ in Figure 4.15, where the power reflectivity is plotted versus the wavelength difference with respect to the center wavelength λ_B for a Bragg wavelength tuning of 0, -5, and -10 nm, respectively. As can clearly be seen, both the reflectivity and the curvature of the $R(\lambda)$ characteristic (which corresponds to the wavelength selectivity) are strongly reduced by the wavelength tuning. The essential parameter that determines the degradation of the reflector performance is $\alpha_{\text{H,pl}}$, which should have a magnitude as large as possible. This represents a measure to compare the suitability of various effects and devices.

Because the injected electron-hole pairs recombine, a sustained current must be applied to the tuning region. This means not only parasitic heat generation, which, among other things, reduces the laser power and efficiency, but also a relatively large time constant (several nanoseconds) that is due to the electron-hole recombination process (c. f., (2.77)).

4.5.2   The Quantum Confined Stark Effect

While the electro-optic effect, including the Franz-Keldysh effect [28], is rather weak in the usual III/V-semiconductors ($-1.68 \cdot 10^{-10}$ cm/V [29]), enhanced refractive index changes may be achieved in multiquantum well (MQW) structures exploiting the QCSE [30]. With the QCSE, a quantum well (QW) structure is placed within a reversely biased pn-junction, so that the applied electric field influences the refractive index. This is illustrated in Figure 4.16 showing the band edges and wavefunctions for electrons and

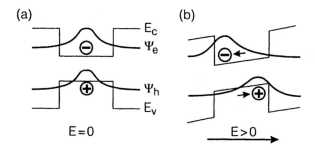

Figure 4.16   The QCSE: By applying an electric field to a QW structure (a), the band edges become inclined and the wavefunctions are displaced with respect to each other and their energy difference (effective bandgap energy) is slightly reduced (b).

holes in a single QW. By the application of the electric field, the band edges become inclined and the electron and hole wavefunctions become displaced relative to each other and the energy difference between the lowest order wavefunctions in the conduction and valence band (effective bandgap energy) becomes reduced. This also reduces the optical matrix element and thus modifies the refractive index. It should be noted that significant effects on the refractive index are achieved only for photon energies near the bandgap energy, where also absorption occurs. So the adjustment of laser wavelength and QW structure is critical, and α_H is usually only of the order -10 [16].

The refractive index changes are typically of the order 10^{-3} to 10^{-2}, depending on how closely the bandgap wavelength of the QW structure used for tuning matches to the laser wavelength [16, 30]. In the case of asymmetric QW structures, refractive index changes above 0.01 have been observed [17, 31].

In addition to the relatively small refractive index changes, the optical confinement achievable in these QWs is distinctly smaller than in the case of the bulk semiconductor structures used for the plasma effect. This is because even in the case of MQW structures, a significant part of the field intensity is distributed within the passive confinement layers between the QWs, which do not contribute to the tuning effect. As a consequence, the largest tuning ranges have been achieved so far with the plasma effect. On the other hand, however, in QCSE devices, essentially no current flows and heat generation does not occur. Further, no carrier lifetime limitation exists that may limit the tuning speed, so that the tuning speed is only limited by parasitic capacitances and inductances.

4.5.3   Thermal Tuning

As the bandgap energy and the Fermi distribution are temperature sensitive, temperature changes may also control the emission wavelength of a laser diode. Thereby both the gain peak wavelength λ_p of the active medium as well as the refractive index show a temperature dependence. In practice, one finds that the emission wavelength of 1,550-nm laser diodes changes by about 0.5 nm/K on average for Fabry–Perot type lasers and by about 0.1 nm/K for DFB and DBR lasers [32]. The principal behavior for the two cases is shown in Figure 4.17. As can be seen, the Fabry–Perot lasers exhibits mode

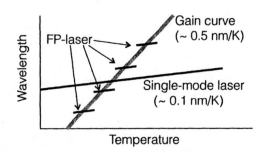

Figure 4.17   Wavelength versus temperature characteristics for 1,500-nm InGaAsP/InP Fabry–Perot (FP) and single-mode lasers, and for the active region gain.

jumps with changing temperature. While the temperature dependence is rather weak for each particular longitudinal mode (0.1 nm/K), the Fabry–Perot lasers on average show the same high temperature dependence around 0.5 nm/K of the wavelength as the gain curve, that is the gain peak wavelength. On the contrary, the wavelength of single-mode lasers increases by only 0.1 nm/K over the entire temperature range. This is because the wavelength of each particular mode of a Fabry–Perot laser (c. f., (2.48)) and the mode of a single-mode laser (c. f., (3.4)) are functions of the refractive index and do not explicitly depend on the gain curve. It is important to notice that the wavelength increases with the temperature. The carrier injection and recombination processes in case of the plasma effect also cause heating of the device so that the plasma effect is inevitably associated with a parasitic thermal tuning. Because the wavelength shifts of these effects exhibit different signs, they compensate each other to a certain degree. As will be shown in Section 4.7, the different dynamic behavior of the two mechanisms may therefore lead to a worsened modulation response, which in certain cases (e. g., current-tuned DFB lasers) may lead to a frequency-dependent sign of $d\lambda/dI_t$.

With a tuning efficiency of 0.1 nm/K and an operating temperature range of about 20 to 80 °C, one may obtain a wavelength tuning by about 6 nm. Placing the tuning region far away from the active region, however, higher temperatures can be accepted without increasing the threshold current and thermal tuning ranges as large as 15 nm can be achieved [33]. Note, however, that in many cases the excess heating cannot be accepted because it either leads to an exceedingly large threshold current or reduced optical power, or it may degrade the laser performance otherwise.

A comparison of the above-described physical effects appears in Table 4.1. Here, we not only consider the basic material parameters but also include the device related issues, such as the optical confinement factor, that essentially influence the suitability of the effects for the various applications.

4.6   INTEGRATION TECHNIQUES

It became obvious in the last section that a current- or voltage-tunable Bragg reflector, such as shown in Figure 4.13, may provide the tunable wavelength selectivity of the cavity gain as required for a single-mode tunable laser (Figure 4.1(b)). In addition, the refractive

Table 4.1

Comparison of the most important physical mechanisms used for tunable laser diodes with respect
to practically achievable performance quoting typical parameter values.

Parameter	Plasma Effect	QCSE	Temperature
Δn	-0.04	-0.01	0.01
Γ	0.5	0.2	1
$\Delta \lambda_{tune}$	$-8\,nm$	$-1\,nm$	$+5\,nm$
f_{3dB}	$100\,MHz$	$>10\,GHz$	$<1\,MHz$
α_H	-20	-10	large
Heat generation	large	negligible	very large
Technology	moderate	demanding	simple

index tuning anywhere within the laser cavity or the mode volume, respectively, serves as
a tunable phase-shifting element (Figure 4.1(a)) that may provide the electronic control
of the optical cavity length $n'_{eff}L$ and, using (2.48), the control of the spectral positions
of the comb modes. So the integration of these two basic components enables the realization of single-mode and wavelength-tunable laser diodes that are tuned continuously,
discontinuously, or quasicontinuously as described in Section 4.1.

The complete tunable laser diode thus consists of an integrated optoelectronic
circuit comprising an active region, a wavelength-selective tunable reflector, and/or tunable phase shifter. Principally, this integration can be performed in any spatial dimension;
however, the lateral integration technique (y-direction) is technologically critical and offers no benefits with respect to the tuning performance. In practice, therefore, the integration is done either in the longitudinal or the transverse direction, respectively, as shown
schematically in Figure 4.18. Referring to Figures 3.13 and 3.16, the longitudinally integrated devices resemble the DBR-type lasers, while the transverse integration yields
DFB-type laser diodes. In the longitudinally integrated lasers, the tuning section 1 allows
the electronic control of the cavity roundtrip gain curve (i. e., the gain peak wavelength
λ_p), while the tuning section 2 enables the phase control (i. e., the shift of the comb-mode
spectrum). So the three tuning techniques described in Sections 4.2 through 4.4 can be
performed.

The continuous tuning is thereby achieved by a proper simultaneous control of
both tuning sections. Because of the nonlinear recombination law (4.17) and the different confinement factors of the two tuning sections, however, this simultaneous control of
the two effective refractive indices reveals extremely complicated [34]. In the case of the
transverse integration, only one tuning region is required even for the continuous tuning
scheme. Moreover, this device structure is inherently continuously tunable since the tuning of the effective refractive index scales the Bragg wavelength and the optical cavity
length equally. So these devices behave like DFB lasers with an electronically tunable
Bragg wavelength, and the single tuning section simultaneously performs the two basic
tuning functions presented in Figure 4.12. The inherent continuous tunability of the transversely integrated devices represents an essential advantage for the practical application
as compared with the longitudinal integration. The reason for this decisive different behavior is that due to their geometrical dimensions ($d \ll L$), laser diodes usually may

(a) Longitudinal integration

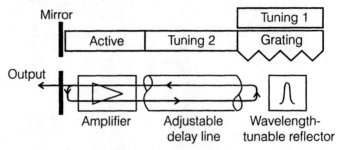

(b) Transverse integration

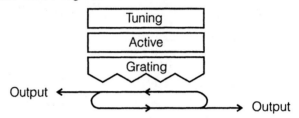

Figure 4.18   Longitudinal (a) and transverse (b) integration of active region and tuning elements in wavelength-tunable laser diodes.

operate only in one guided transverse mode, while operation in many longitudinal modes is possible. As a consequence, transverse mode changes are impossible while, on the contrary, longitudinal mode changes are likely to occur even by a slight change of the longitudinal index distribution. A detailed comparative analysis of the two integration techniques with respect to the tuning performance can be found in [3].

4.7   DYNAMIC BEHAVIOR

In many applications, the speed at which wavelength tuning may be performed is an important parameter. This is not only true for high-speed FM modulation but also, for instance, in the case of a local oscillator in an optical heterodyne receiver, where the wavelength setting and wavelength control by a phase-locked loop (PLL) require a minimal bandwidth. The three physical mechanisms described in Section 4.5 behave quite differently with respect to their tuning speeds. In general, the electro-optical QCSE is the fastest effect with practically no internal time constant, so that the speed limitation is given by parasitic elements, such as contact pads or bonding wires. Up to more than 3-GHz modulation bandwidth has been achieved [35] so far with a QCSE-section integrated vertically with a DFB laser.

On the other hand, the thermal tuning is by far the slowest technique because it requires the heating or cooling of the laser chip. Depending on whether the tuning is done by controlling the heat sink temperature or by placing heating elements near to the active

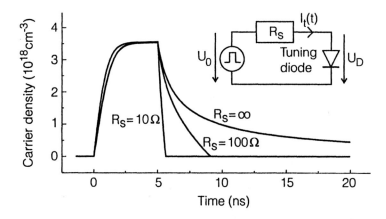

Figure 4.19   Time response of the carrier density of a diode driven by a pulse-voltage source with variable series resistance.

region on top of the laser chip [18, 36], however, strongly different response times are obtained. While the response is in the millisecond regime in the former case, response times in the microsecond range are obtained in the latter case.

An intermediate dynamic behavior is observed for the plasma effect, where the differential carrier lifetime (2.77) plays an important role. As shown in Figure 4.19, the impedance of the bias network has also a significant effect on the tuning speed. This is because the carrier density in the tuning diode, to which the wavelength shift is proportional, is linked to the diode voltage by way of the quasi-Fermi levels. So the control of the (inner) diode voltage would in principle allow an arbitrarily fast modulation of the carrier density and, consequently, the laser wavelength. Because of series resistances of the diodes, however, only a limited improvement can be achieved this way. The improved time response of the low resistive modulation source can be understood by inspecting the rate equation (2.52) and (2.18) for the case of a voltage-controlled injection into an undoped tuning region operated in the LED mode (i. e., no stimulated emission term):

$$\frac{dN}{dt} = \frac{U_0(t) - U_D(t)}{R_s e V_t} - N/\tau_s - BN^2 - CN^3 \qquad (4.20)$$

where the diode current I_t has been substituted by $(U_0 - U_D)/R_s$. Neglecting contact and series resistances in the device, the diode voltage U_D is related to the quasi-Fermi level difference as

$$U_D = (E_{Fc} - E_{Fv})/e \qquad (4.21)$$

where the dependence of E_{Fc} and E_{Fv} on the injected carrier density $N = P$ can be well approximated by Joyce and Dixon's formula [37]:

$$U_D = \frac{k_B T}{e} \left[\ln\left(\frac{N^2}{N_c N_v}\right) + \frac{N}{\sqrt{8}} (1/N_c + 1/N_v) \right] + \frac{E_g}{e} \qquad (4.22)$$

with N_c and N_v denoting the equivalent carrier densities of conduction and valence band, respectively.

Numerical Example: Consider a $\lambda_g = 1{,}300$-nm tuning region at $T = 300$ K with $w = 1\,\mu m$, $d = 0.3\,\mu m$, $L = 400\,\mu m$, $\tau_s = \infty$, $B = 10^{-10}$ cm^3/s, $C = 3 \cdot 10^{-29}$ cm^6/s, $N_c = 4 \cdot 10^{17}$ cm^{-3}, and $N_v = 8 \cdot 10^{19}$ cm^{-3}. This yields for the tuning region volume $V_i = 1.2 \cdot 10^{-10}$cm^3. Calculations of the time response for various series resistances are presented in Figure 4.19, choosing U_0 such for each R_s that the maximal carrier density equals $3 \cdot 10^{18}$ cm^{-3}. Apparently, a drastic improvement of the response is possible by using a low-impedance pulse source instead of the more common current source ($R_s \rightarrow \infty$), particularly with respect to the trailing edge.

The pulse response in the thermal tuning behaves completely differently because the temperature-time relationship cannot be described by a single time constant, as the heat dissipation mechanism resembles more a transmission line rather than a first-order low pass filter. On the other hand, the thermal tuning is a linear process in contrast to the nonlinearity of the plasma effect that is due to the nonlinear recombination law (4.20) [38, 39]. Assuming that the wavelength change by temperature is proportional to the average temperature in the laser waveguide of radius R_0 in the upside-up mounted homogeneous laser chip of thickness H, the response of the wavelength to a pulsed heat source can be calculated (see Appendix D) in a good approximation using the simplified geometry shown in the inset of Figure 4.20 as

$$\frac{T(t)}{T(\infty)} = \frac{1}{\ln \frac{4H}{\pi R_0} + \frac{1}{2}} \left[\frac{2t}{\tau_{therm}} \left[1 - E_2 \left(\frac{\tau_{therm}}{4t} \right) \right] + \sum_{i=1}^{\infty} (-1)^i E_1 \left(\left(\frac{iH}{R_0} \right)^2 \frac{\tau_{therm}}{t} \right) \right] \quad (4.23)$$

where E_n denotes the exponential integral of order n [40], and $\tau_{therm} = R_0^2/k_{therm}$ is the thermal time constant of the waveguide region. The thermal diffusivity k_{therm} is related to the thermal conductivity χ and the volume heat capacity c_v as $k_{therm} = \chi/c_v$. The calculated pulse response $T(t)/T(\infty)$ of the average temperature within the transverse mode cross-section for an infinitely long pulse is displayed in Figure 4.20 where, for convenience, the time axis is logarithmic. The stationary temperature $T(\infty)$ equals the product of dissipated heat power P_{th} and thermal resistance R_{therm}, which may be calculated by using conformal mapping:

$$R_{therm} = \frac{1}{\chi L} \frac{K}{K'} \quad (4.24)$$

where K and K' are the complete elliptic integrals for argument $\exp(-\pi R_0/H)$. For the usual case $R_0 \ll H$, (4.24) asymptotically reduces to

$$R_{therm} = \frac{1}{\pi \chi L} \left[\ln \frac{4H}{\pi R_0} + 0.5 \right] \qquad H \gg R_0 \quad (4.25)$$

as shown in Appendix D. Depending on the substrate thickness H, the $T(t)$-curve shows an almost logarithmic dependence on t, making the definition of a time constant useless. Owing to the genuine thermal time behavior, therefore, the thermal time response may not simply be described by a low-pass transfer function characterized by a single thermal

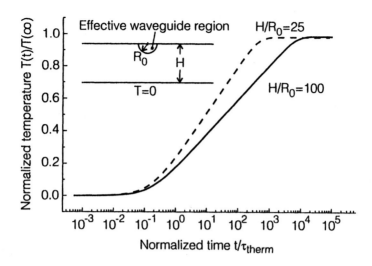

Figure 4.20   Normalized averaged temperature versus normalized time for a thin-wire heat source driven by a steplike heat current source at $t = 0$. Temperature averaging is done within the semicylinder of radius R_0 corresponding to the transverse mode radius.

time constant such as τ_{therm}. As a consequence of the logarithmic time dependence of the average temperature, the temperature strongly increases at the beginning of the pulse but rather slowly approaches the final value.

Numerical Example: Considering an InGaAsP/InP laser structure with $R_0 = 1\,\mu m$, $H = 100\,\mu m$, $k_{\text{therm}} = 0.46\,\text{cm}^2/\text{s}$, $\chi = 0.7\,\text{W/cmK}$ [41], and $L = 400\,\mu m$ we derive $R_{\text{therm}} = 61\,\text{K/W}$ and $\tau_{\text{therm}} = 22\,\text{ns}$. 10%, 50%, and 90% of the final average temperature in the waveguide are approached after 7 ns, 600 ns, and 20 µs, respectively.

Besides the pulse response, the FM response with respect to a small-signal sinusoidal modulation is also an important characteristic for the dynamic behavior. To this end, we perform the Fourier transform on the average temperature $T(t)$ as

$$\tilde{T}(\omega) = \frac{1}{2\pi} \int_{-\infty}^{+\infty} T(t) e^{-j\omega t}\, dt \tag{4.26}$$

$$T(t) = \int_{-\infty}^{+\infty} \tilde{T}(\omega) e^{j\omega t}\, d\omega \tag{4.27}$$

The normalized transfer function $S_{\text{therm}}(\omega) = \tilde{T}(\omega)/\tilde{T}(0)$ for the average temperature in the waveguide as derived in Appendix D reads

$$S_{\text{therm}}(\omega) = \frac{\pi}{\ln\frac{4H}{\pi R_0} + \gamma} \left[\frac{H_1^{(2)}(j\Omega(\omega))}{\Omega(\omega)} + \frac{2j}{\pi\Omega(\omega)^2} - j\sum_{i=1}^{\infty} (-1)^i H_0^{(2)}\left(2i\frac{H}{R_0}j\Omega(\omega)\right) \right] \tag{4.28}$$

where $\Omega(\omega) = \sqrt{j\omega\tau_{\text{therm}}}$, $H_n^{(2)}$ denotes Hankel's function $H^{(2)}$ of order n, and $\gamma = 0.57722\ldots$ is Euler's constant. As with the related problem of the Skin-effect, one may

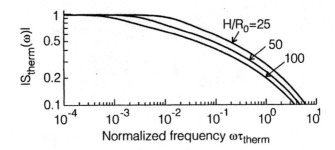

Figure 4.21   Normalized FM response of the average temperature in a waveguide of radius R_0 with various H/R_0 ratios.

replace Hankel's functions for the complex argument $j^{1/2}x$ (x real) by real Kelvin's functions. The absolute value of the normalized FM response for typical H/R_0 ratios is shown in Figure 4.21, assuming the heat source to be an infinitely thin wire located in the waveguide center. As can be seen, the characteristics decay already for angular frequencies far below $1/\tau_{\text{therm}}$. It is important, however, to note that the decay of the FM response above the cutoff frequency is much smaller than for a first-order low-pass filter so that even for relatively large frequencies, the thermal effect may be noticeable and may interfere with the plasma effect.

In the case of the plasma effect, the additional "parasitic" heating reduces the refractive index change. Since the plasma effect has a large cutoff frequency with respect to the thermal tuning and an almost constant phase shift equal to zero at frequencies up to several tens of MHz, the superposition of the two effects in a device yields approximately the total FM response normalized to $\tilde{T}(\infty)$:

$$S_{\text{tot}}(\omega) = \frac{\tilde{T}(\omega)}{\tilde{T}(\infty)} = (1 - K_{\text{therm}}S_{\text{therm}}(\omega)) \tag{4.29}$$

where S_{therm} is the thermal FM response and K_{therm} measures the ratio of thermal tuning and tuning by way of the plasma effect. The resulting composite FM response for various K_{therm} values is shown in Figure 4.22. In the case of a strong and dominating plasma effect K_{therm} is small against unity and only a weak interference is expected. On the other hand, with increasing thermal tuning the FM response is reduced at low frequencies. If the DC thermal tuning is stronger than the plasma effect ($K_{\text{therm}} > 1$), which is usually the case for directly modulated DFB lasers [39, 42], a dip may occur in the FM response in the 10- to 100-kHz frequency range.

As a consequence, the combination of plasma effect and thermal tuning in general deteriorates the tuning performance. A reasonable dynamic behavior may therefore be obtained only if one of the two mechanisms clearly dominates.

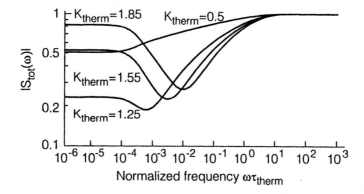

Figure 4.22   Normalized FM response for the combination of plasma effect and thermal tuning. K_{therm} measures the relative magnitude of the thermal effect with respect to the plasma effect.

REFERENCES

[1] Kobayashi, K., and Mito, I., "Single frequency and tunable laser diodes," *IEEE Journal of Lightwave Technology*, Vol. 6, 1988, pp. 1623–1633.

[2] Koch, T. L., and Koren, U., "Semiconductor lasers for coherent optical fiber communications," *IEEE Journal of Lightwave Technology*, Vol. 8, 1990, pp. 274–293.

[3] Amann, M.-C., and Thulke, W., "Continuously tunable laser diodes: Longitudinal versus transverse tuning scheme," *IEEE Journal of Selected Areas in Communications*, Vol. 8, 1990, pp. 1169–1177.

[4] Coldren, L. A., and Corzine, S. W., "Continuously-tunable single-frequency semiconductor lasers," *IEEE Journal of Quantum Electronics*, Vol. 23, 1987, pp. 903–908.

[5] Amann, M.-C., "Broad-band wavelength-tunable twin-guide lasers," *Optoelectronics—Devices and Technologies*, Vol. 10, 1995, pp. 27–38.

[6] Alferness, R. C., "Widely tunable semiconductor lasers (paper TuC5)," *Optical Fiber Conference (OFC '93)*, pp. 11–12, San Jose, CA, 1993.

[7] Favre, F., and Le Guen, D., "82 nm of continuous tunability for an external cavity semiconductor laser," *Electronics Letters*, Vol. 27, 1991, pp. 183–184.

[8] Strzelecki, E. M., Cohen, D. A., and Coldren, L. A., "Investigation of tunable single frequency diode lasers for sensor applications," *IEEE Journal of Lightwave Technology*, Vol. 6, 1988, pp. 1610–1618.

[9] Dieckmann, A., and Amann, M.-C., "FMCW-LIDAR with tunable twin-guide laser diode," *Trends in Optical Fibre Metrology and Standards*, pp. 791–802, Kluwer, 1995.

[10] Nòe, R., Rodler, H., Ebberg, A., Meißner, E., Bodlaj, V., Drögemüller, K., and Wittmann, J., "Fully engineered coherent multichannel transmitters and receivers with low-cost potential," *Electronics Letters*, Vol. 28, 1992, pp. 14–15.

[11] Lau, K. Y., "Broad wavelength tunability in gain-levered quantum well semiconductor lasers," *Applied Physics Letters*, Vol. 57, 1990, pp. 2632–2634.

[12] Westbrook, L. D., "Measurement of dg/dN and dn/dN and their dependence on photon energy in λ=1.5 μm InGaAsP laser diodes," *IEE Proceedings*, Part J, Vol. 133, 1986, pp. 135–142.

[13] Okuda, M., and Onaka, K., "Tunability of distributed Bragg-reflector laser by modulating refractive index in corrugated waveguide," *Japanese Journal of Applied Physics*, Vol. 16, 1977, pp. 1501–1502.

[14]   Bennet, B., Soref, R., and DelAlamo, J., "Carrier-induced change in refractive index of InP, GaAs, and InGaAsP," *IEEE Journal of Quantum Electronics*, Vol. 26, 1990, pp. 113–122.

[15]   Miller, D. A. B., Chemla, D. S., Damen, T. C., Gossard, A. C., Wiegmann, W., Wood, T. H., and Burrus, C. A., "Band edge electroabsorption in quantum well structures: the quantum confined Stark effect," *Physical Review Letters*, Vol. 53, 1984, pp. 2173–2176.

[16]   Zucker, J. E., Bar-Joseph, I., Miller, B. I., Koren, U., and Chemla, D. S., "Quaternary quantum wells for electro-optic intensity and phase modulation at 1.3 and 1.55 μm," *Applied Physics Letters*, Vol. 54, 1988, pp. 10–12.

[17]   Susa, N., and Nakahara, T., "Enhancement of change in the refractive index in an asymmetric quantum well," *Applied Physics Letters*, Vol. 60, 1992, pp. 2457–2459.

[18]   Woodward, S. L., Koren, U., Miller, B. I., Young, M. G., Newkirk, M. A., and Burrus, C. A., "A DBR laser tunable by resistive heating," *IEEE Photonics Technology Letters*, Vol. 4, 1992, pp. 1330–1332.

[19]   Kameda, T., Mori, H., Onuki, S., Kikugawa, T., Takahashi, Y., Tsuchiya, F., and Nagai, H., "A DBR laser employing passive-section heaters, with 10.8 nm tuning range and 1.6 MHz linewidth," *IEEE Photonics Technology Letters*, Vol. 5, 1993, pp. 608–610.

[20]   Soref, R. A., and Lorenzo, J. P., "All-silicon active and passive guided-wave components for $\lambda = 1.3$ and 1.6 μm," *IEEE Journal of Quantum Electronics*, Vol. 22, 1986, pp. 873–879.

[21]   Weber, J.-P., "Optimization of the carrier-induced effective index change in InGaAsP waveguides—application to tunable Bragg filters," *IEEE Journal of Quantum Electronics*, Vol. 30, 1994, pp. 1801–1816.

[22]   Childs, G. N., Brans, S., and Adams, R. A., "Intervalence band absorption in semiconductor laser materials," *Semiconductor Science and Technology*, Vol. 1, 1986, pp. 116–120.

[23]   Asada, M., Kameyama, A., and Suematsu, Y., "Gain and intervalence band absorption in quantum-well lasers," *IEEE Journal of Quantum Electronics*, Vol. 20, 1984, pp. 745–753.

[24]   Casey, H. C., Jr., and Carter, P. L., "Variation of intervalence band absorption with hole concentration in p-type InP," *Applied Physics Letters*, Vol. 44, 1984, pp. 82–83.

[25]   Joindot, I., and Beylat, J. L., "Intervalence band absorption coefficient measurements in bulk layer, strained and unstrained multiquantum well 1.55 μm semiconductor lasers," *Electronics Letters*, Vol. 29, 1993, pp. 604–606.

[26]   Kotaki, Y., and Ishikawa, H., "Spectral characteristics of a three-section wavelength-tunable DBR laser," *IEEE Journal of Quantum Electronics*, Vol. 25, 1989, pp. 1340–1345.

[27]   Bardyszewski, W., and Yevick, D., "Compositional dependence of the Auger coefficient for InGaAsP lattice matched to InP," *Journal of Applied Physics*, Vol. 58, 1985, pp. 2713–2723.

[28]   Chuang, S. L., *Physics of optoelectronic devices*, Chichester, U.K., Wiley, 1995.

[29]   Faist, J., and Reinhart, F.-K., "Phase modulation in GaAs/AlGaAs double heterostructures. II. Experiment," *Journal of Applied Physics*, Vol. 67, 1990, pp. 7006–7012.

[30]   Yamamoto, H., Asada, M., and Suematsu, Y., "Electric-field induced refractive index variation in quantum-well structure," *Electronics Letters*, Vol. 21, 1985, pp. 579–580.

[31]   Susa, N., "Electric-field-induced refractive index changes in InGaAs-InAlAs asymmetric coupled quantum wells," *IEEE Journal of Quantum Electronics*, Vol. 31, 1995, pp. 92–100.

[32]   Chinen, K., Gen-Ei, K., Suhara, H., Tanaka, A., Matsuyama, T., Konno, K., and Muto, Y., "Low-threshold 1.55 μm InGaAsP/InP buried heterostructure distributed feedback lasers," *Applied Physics Letters*, Vol. 51, 1987, pp. 273–275.

[33] Öberg, M., Nilsson, S., Klinga, T., and Ojala, P., "A three-electrode distributed Bragg reflector laser with 22 nm wavelength tuning range," *IEEE Photonics Technology Letters*, Vol. PTL-3, 1991, pp. 299–301.

[34] Kuindersma, P. I., "Continuous tunability of DBR lasers," *International Conference on Integrated Optics and Optical Fiber Communication*, pp. 19A2–1, Kobe, Japan, 1989.

[35] Wolf, T., Drögemüller, K., Borchert, B., Westermeier, H., Veuhoff, E., and Baumeister, H., "Tunable twin-guide lasers with flat frequency modulation response by quantum confined Stark effect," *Applied Physics Letters*, Vol. 60, 1992, pp. 2472–2474.

[36] Sakano, S., Tsuchiya, T., Suzuki, M., Kitajima, S., and Chinone, N., "Tunable DFB laser with a striped thin-film heater," *IEEE Photonics Technology Letters*, Vol. 4, 1992, pp. 321–323.

[37] Joyce, W. B., and Dixon, R. W., "Analytic approximation for the Fermi energy of an ideal Fermi gas," *Applied Physics Letters*, Vol. 31, 1977, pp. 354–356.

[38] Pandian, G. S., and Dilwali, S., "On the thermal FM response of a semiconductor laser diode," *IEEE Photonics Technology Letters*, Vol. 4, 1992, pp. 130–133.

[39] Correc, P., Girard, O., and De Faria, I., Jr., "On the thermal contribution to the FM response of DFB lasers: theory and experiment," *IEEE Journal of Quantum Electronics*, Vol. 30, 1994, pp. 2485–2490.

[40] Abramowitz, M., and Stegun, I. A., *Handbook of mathematical functions*, New York, NY, Dover Publications, 1964.

[41] Madelung, O., Schulz, M., and Weiss, H. (eds.), *Landolt–Börnstein: Numerical data and functional relationships in science and technology*, Vol. 17 d (Semiconductors), Berlin, Germany, Springer, 1992.

[42] Kitamura, M., Yamazaki, H., Ono, T., Sasaki, T., Hamao, H., and Mito, I., "High power and narrow spectral linewidth 1.5 μm MQW-DFB-LD's with low FM dip frequency," *IEEE Photonics Technology Letters*, Vol. 2, 1990, pp. 778–780.

Chapter 5

Wavelength-Tunable Single-Mode Laser Diodes

In Chapter 5, we investigate the integration of the tuning function into a single-mode laser diode in order to achieve wavelength-tunable single-mode laser diodes. Referring to Section 4.6, this comprises the detailed investigation and comparison of the longitudinal and the transverse integration techniques with respect to the device parameters relevant for the wavelength tuning, such as tuning range, emission spectrum, wavelength control, and tuning speed. Depending on the device structure, continuous, discontinuous, or quasicontinuous tuning schemes or a combination of these may be accomplished. Since the generally preferred continuous tuning scheme exhibits the smallest maximal tuning range, we also investigate the physical limitations of the continuous tuning in transversely and longitudinally integrated InGaAsP/InP laser diodes in the 1,550-nm wavelength range. The last section of Chapter 5 covers the FM-modulation behavior of the various devices.

5.1 LONGITUDINALLY INTEGRATED STRUCTURES

The longitudinal integration technique for wavelength-tunable laser diodes has been shown schematically in Figure 4.18. As illustrated in this figure, tuning may be performed in these devices by controlling the refractive index of two different regions (tuning 1 and tuning 2) either to tune the gain peak wavelength λ_p of the cavity gain characteristic (tuning 1) or the comb-mode spectrum (tuning 2) or by tuning both regions simultaneously. Accordingly, the laser development has resulted in two- and three-section DBR laser diodes, depending on whether only one or both of the tuning regions are used. While the former devices offer the simpler handling by only two control currents, one for the gain region and one for the tuning region, the latter enable the continuous tuning over much larger wavelength ranges. The multisection tunable DFB laser respresents a special case, which may not be understood immediately by the concepts presented in Chapter 4. In contrast to the relatively simple device technology, which only requires the splitting of the top p-contact of a DFB laser, however, the device handling is rather complicated because all control currents affect all laser parameters at the same time, and no clear functional separation exists.

In all these structures, the tuning of the cavity gain peak wavelength λ_p is essentially done by an electronic control of the Bragg wavelength λ_B. In fact, because of the

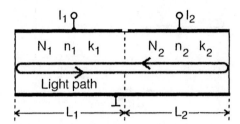

Figure 5.1   Simplified longitudinal view of two-section Fabry–Perot laser with inhomogeneous biasing and longitudinally inhomogeneous optical parameters.

broad material gain characteristic, the cavity gain peak wavelength may be well approximated by the Bragg wavelength $\lambda_p \approx \lambda_B$. On the other hand, the electronic tuning of the comb-mode spectrum by changing the refractive index in the active sections is less simple in practical laser structures. This is because additional loss or gain is introduced by changing the real part of the refractive index as determined by the corresponding α_H factor. The gain-clamping mechanism requires that all gain or loss changes are exactly compensated by complementary gain changes in the active region. As a consequence of a nonvanishing α_H factor in the active region, these gain changes are accompanied by changes of the real part of the refractive index in the active region, which finally lead to a further shift of the comb-mode spectrum. This interaction between tuning regions and active region is important in tunable laser diodes since it may increase the wavelength tuning by up to about 50 %.

To investigate the comb-mode spectrum shift $\Delta\lambda_c$ in multisection laser diodes, we will first study the simple case of an inhomogeneously biased two-section Fabry–Perot laser as shown in Figure 5.1. In this laser, we assume that small deviations of the carrier densities and the optical constants from homogeneity may be achieved by an inhomogeneous electric biasing. Extending the oscillation condition of the homogeneous one-section Fabry–Perot laser (2.42) to the case of the two-section Fabry–Perot laser, we find by neglecting the weak reflections at the boundary of the two regions:

$$2j(\beta_1 L_1 + \beta_2 L_2) + \alpha_m(L_1 + L_2) = 2j\pi N \tag{5.1}$$

where β_1 and β_2 are the propagation constants in regions 1 and 2, respectively, and N is the longitudinal mode number. Assuming a wavelength-independent end loss α_m, the changes of β_1 and β_2 are related as

$$\Delta\beta_1 L_1 + \Delta\beta_2 L_2 = 0 \tag{5.2}$$

since N is fixed. With $\lambda_N = \lambda_{N,0} + \Delta\lambda_c$, $\beta_1 = k_0 n_1$ and $\beta_2 = k_0 n_2$, (5.2) reads

$$\frac{2\pi\left(n_1(\lambda_{N,0} + \Delta\lambda_c)L_1 + n_2(\lambda_{N,0} + \Delta\lambda_c)L_2\right)}{\lambda_{N,0} + \Delta\lambda_c} - \frac{2\pi\left(n_1(\lambda_{N,0})L_1 + n_2(\lambda_{N,0})L_2\right)}{\lambda_{N,0}} = 0 \tag{5.3}$$

Taking

$$n_1(\lambda_{N,0} + \Delta\lambda_c) = n_1(\lambda_{N,0}) + \Delta n_1^{tot} \quad \text{with} \quad |\Delta n_1^{tot}| \ll n_1 \tag{5.4}$$

$$n_2(\lambda_{N,0} + \Delta\lambda_c) = n_2(\lambda_{N,0}) + \Delta n_2^{tot} \quad \text{with} \quad |\Delta n_2^{tot}| \ll n_2 \tag{5.5}$$

and assuming small relative wavelength changes ($|\Delta\lambda_c| \ll \lambda_{N,0}$) and small imaginary parts of the indices ($|n_1''| \ll n_1'$ and $|n_2''| \ll n_2'$), we find in a good approximation

$$\frac{\Delta\lambda_c}{\lambda_0} = \frac{\Delta n_1^{tot}L_1 + \Delta n_2^{tot}L_2}{n_1'(\lambda_0)L_1 + n_2'(\lambda_0)L_2} \tag{5.6}$$

where we substituted the mode wavelength $\lambda_{N,0}$ by the center wavelength of the laser spectrum, λ_0, because the wavelength differences between laser modes are usually very small with respect to the wavelength. In the derivation of (5.6), we neglected the higher order terms (i. e., products of the small quantities).

The index changes Δn_1^{tot} and Δn_2^{tot} each consist of two parts, one for the induced index change by way of tuning, Δn_1 and Δn_2, and one due to dispersion:

$$\Delta n_1^{tot} = \Delta n_1 + \Delta\lambda_c \left.\frac{dn_1'}{d\lambda}\right|_{\lambda=\lambda_0} \tag{5.7}$$

$$\Delta n_2^{tot} = \Delta n_2 + \Delta\lambda_c \left.\frac{dn_2'}{d\lambda}\right|_{\lambda=\lambda_0} \tag{5.8}$$

where the dispersion of the imaginary part of the refractive indices (or the gain, respectively) has been neglected. Evaluating the real part of (5.6), we may now write for the relative wavelength change

$$\frac{\Delta\lambda_c}{\lambda_0} = \frac{\Delta n_1'}{\bar{n}_g}\Gamma_1^{long} + \frac{\Delta n_2'}{\bar{n}_g}\Gamma_2^{long} \tag{5.9}$$

where we introduced the longitudinal confinement factors of regions 1 and 2, respectively:

$$\Gamma_1^{long} = \frac{L_1}{L_1 + L_2} \tag{5.10}$$

$$\Gamma_2^{long} = \frac{L_2}{L_1 + L_2} \tag{5.11}$$

and the average group index of the cavity:

$$\bar{n}_g = n_{g,1}\Gamma_1^{long} + n_{g,2}\Gamma_2^{long} \tag{5.12}$$

Here, $n_{g,1}$ and $n_{g,2}$ are the group indices of the respective region (c. f., (2.50)). From the imaginary part of (5.6) we have

$$\Delta n_1''L_1 + \Delta n_2''L_2 = 0 \tag{5.13}$$

Noting that Δn_1 and Δn_2 are caused by carrier density changes, their real and imaginary parts are related by the corresponding α_H factor (c. f., (2.20)) as $\Delta n_1'' = -\Delta n_1'/\alpha_{H,1}$ and $\Delta n_2'' = -\Delta n_2'/\alpha_{H,2}$, where $\alpha_{H,1}$ and $\alpha_{H,2}$ denote the α_H factor in regions 1 and 2, respectively. Thus we may rewrite (5.13) as

$$\frac{\Delta n_1'}{\alpha_{H,1}} L_1 + \frac{\Delta n_2'}{\alpha_{H,2}} L_2 = 0 \tag{5.14}$$

Using this relation to substitute $\Delta n_1'$ in (5.9), we obtain for the relative wavelength shift caused by a change of the real part of n_2:

$$\frac{\Delta \lambda_c}{\lambda_0} = \frac{\Delta n_2'}{\bar{n}_g} \Gamma_2^{\text{long}} \left(1 - \frac{\alpha_{H,1}}{\alpha_{H,2}} \right) \tag{5.15}$$

Noting that in laser diodes with their composite transverse and lateral layer structure, it is the effective refractive index of the relevant lateral mode, which is relevant, we have to replace Δn_2 by $\Delta n_{\text{eff},2}$ and $\bar{n}_g$ by the average effective group index $\bar{n}_{g,\text{eff}}$. $\Delta n_{\text{eff},2}$ is caused by a refractive index change in a tuning region (phase shift region), which we may denote as Δn_2, as

$$\Delta n_{\text{eff},2} = \Gamma_2 \Delta n_2 \tag{5.16}$$

where Γ_2 is the two-dimensional (lateral and transverse) optical confinement factor of the corresponding tuning region according to (2.34). Defining the three-dimensional optical confinement factor

$$\Gamma_2^{\text{3d}} = \Gamma_2 \Gamma_2^{\text{long}} \tag{5.17}$$

finally yields

$$\frac{\Delta \lambda_c}{\lambda_0} = \frac{\Delta n_2'}{\bar{n}_{g,\text{eff}}} \Gamma_2^{\text{3d}} \left(1 - \frac{\alpha_{H,1}}{\alpha_{H,2}} \right) \tag{5.18}$$

Numerical Example: Given a two-section Fabry–Perot laser at a wavelength λ_0 of 1,550 nm with a tuning section length of 300 μm, a total length of 600 μm, α_H factor in the tuning region (subscript 2) of -10, α_H factor in the gain region (subscript 1) of 5, an average effective group index of 4, a (two-dimensional) confinement factor of the tuning region of 0.4, and a maximal refractive index change in the tuning region of -0.03, we calculate $\Gamma_2^{\text{3d}} = 0.2$ and a tuning range of $\Delta \lambda_c \approx -3.5$ nm.

The result of this investigation clearly shows that wavelength tuning of longitudinally intersected laser diodes by inhomogeneous biasing is possible only if the two sections have different α_H factors. Accordingly, a usual Fabry–Perot laser with longitudinally invariant α_H factor would not be tunable by an inhomogeneous pumping. As a consequence, the comb-mode spectrum of the two-section DBR laser studied in the next section is not tunable, hence only discontinuous tuning using variations of the Bragg wavelength is possible. On the other hand, the three-section DBR lasers presented in Section 5.1.2 enable the continuous wavelength tuning because besides the tunable Bragg

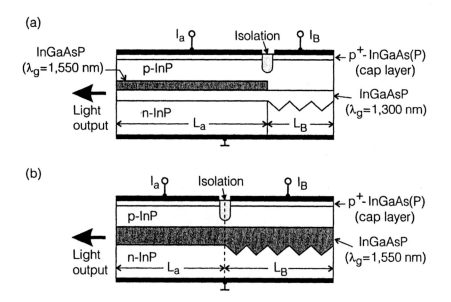

Figure 5.2   Schematic longitudinal views of wavelength-tunable two-section DBR lasers: (a) with passive (active-passive structure) Bragg region and (b) with amplifying (active-active structure) Bragg region. Structure (b) may also be viewed as a DFB laser with a partial grating.

region, the laser cavity is longitudinally intersected with two regions of different composition and, consequently, different α_H factors. Wavelength tuning of multisection DFB lasers as presented in Section 5.1.3 is possible in the continuous and discontinuous tuning scheme because the complex field distribution in DFB lasers leads to longitudinally varying effective α_H factors [1], that must be used instead of the material α_H factor for the evaluation of (5.15). Even though the material α_H factors may be equal in all regions, therefore, the effective α_H factors may differ so that nonvanishing wavelength tuning can be achieved also with multisection DFB lasers. A nonuniform α_H factor may also be possible in an asymmetric biased QW device.

5.1.1   Two-Section DBR Laser

Integrating longitudinally an amplifying section with a tunable Bragg reflector yields the two-section tunable DBR laser. Depending on whether the DBR region exhibits optical gain (i.e., an active waveguide layer), or is purely passive, we may distinguish the two different structures shown in Figure 5.2. In both devices, the top p-electrode is separated into two parts while the n-electrode and the n-substrate are common to both sections. Current I_a into the active (gain) section of length L_a mainly controls the optical gain and the optical power, while current I_B into the Bragg section of length L_B controls the Bragg wavelength, which in turn determines the emission wavelength. While the devices with the passive Bragg region (active-passive structure) [2, 3] correspond to what was

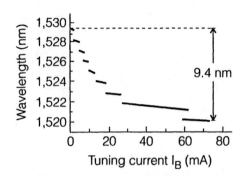

Figure 5.3   Wavelength versus Bragg tuning current of tunable two-section DBR laser with passive tuning section (c. f., Figure 5.2(a)). Active section length L_a is 298 μm and Bragg section length L_B is 250 μm. (Reprinted with permission from *Applied Physics Letters*, Vol. 53, pp. 1036–1038, ©1988 American Institute of Physics.)

logically derived as a tunable laser in Chapter 4, the lasers with an amplifying Bragg section (active-active structure) [4, 5] have also been investigated because of their simpler fabrication process. In particular, the latter devices require no overgrowth and matching of the two waveguide cross-sections, which improves the light coupling and reduces parasitic reflectances. As a matter of fact, the first proposal for a tunable laser diode over the electronic refractive index control was based on the active-active structure [6].

Referring to the discussion in Section 4.2, the two-section DBR lasers enable the electronic control of the spectral shape of the cavity gain by the tuning of the Bragg wavelenth over current I_B. Because of the lacking option for comb-mode spectrum tuning, these lasers are suited only for the discontinuous wavelength tuning comprising mode jumps from one longitudinal mode to the next.

A representative tuning characteristic is plotted in Figure 5.3 for a laser with an MQW active region, an active section length $L_a = 298\,\mu$m, a Bragg section length $L_B = 250\,\mu$m, and a coupling coefficient $\kappa = 140\,\text{cm}^{-1}$ [3]. Owing to the large κL-product of about 3.5, the reflection at the end facet of the DBR section can be neglected, hence the random phase problem of the end facet reflection plays no role and the application of an antireflection coating is not required. Varying the tuning current from 0 to 75 mA results in a wavelength tuning of 9.4 nm in nine different longitudinal modes. Referring to Figure 4.14, the different and increasingly large current regions for operation in the corresponding longitudinal modes are due to the nonlinear recombination law in the tuning region, which yields a smaller slope of the refractive index and carrier density versus current characteristics at higher tuning currents. Note the negative slope of the wavelength versus I_B characteristic for each longitudinal mode, which is due to the refractive index reduction in the Bragg section shifting the entire comb-mode spectrum to shorter wavelengths. While most of the published two-section DBR lasers exploit the free-carrier plasma effect, a discontinuous tuning range of 2.5 nm with wavelength-switching times in the sub-nanosecond range was reported applying the Franz-Keldysh effect in a reversely biased optimized tuning diode [7].

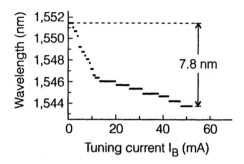

Figure 5.4   Laser wavelength versus Bragg tuning current for a tunable two-section DBR laser with active tuning section (c. f., Figure 5.2(b)). Active and Bragg section lengths are 600 μm and 300 μm, respectively, and the current into the active section is kept constant at 60 mA. (Reprinted with permission from *Applied Physics Letters*, Vol. 52, pp. 1285–1287, ©1988 American Institute of Physics.)

   Comparably large tuning ranges may also be achieved with the active-active structure in Figure 5.2(b). The laser wavelength versus the Bragg tuning current for a typical device with $L_a = 600\,\mu$m and $L_B = 300\,\mu$m is shown in Figure 5.4 with current I_a being kept constant at 60 mA ($P \approx 0.5 - 1.5$ mW) [5]. As can be seen, a tuning range of the order 8 nm is obtained with lasing in about 20 longitudinal modes. Unfortunately, the tuning characteristic is more irregular than for the active-passive structure (c. f., Figure 5.3) and several longitudinal modes are not addressable, resulting in larger wavelengths steps of different size. A jump over three longitudinal modes occurs; for instance, at $I_B \approx 4$ mA yielding a wavelength jump by about 1 nm ($\Delta\lambda_m \approx 0.3$ nm) from 1,550.2 nm down to 1549.1 nm.

5.1.2   Three-Section DBR Laser

Because of the limitations of the two-section DBR laser with respect to continuous tuning, more advanced longitudinally integrated devices have been developed. This particularly concerns the additional longitudinal integration of a tunable phase shifter (Figure 4.12(a)) as an adjustable delay line as shown in Figure 4.18(a) to perform the comb-mode spectrum shift. In this way, we obtain the most important longitudinally integrated tunable laser, the three-section DBR laser, as shown schematically in Figure 5.5. This laser consists of an active section providing the optical gain for the laser operation, and passive phase shift and Bragg reflector sections. In this way, the three-section DBR laser most closely resembles the ideal longitudinally integrated wavelength-tunable laser as displayed in Figure 4.18(a). With its three p-electrodes, this device allows the almost independent control of optical gain and optical power via I_a, of the location of the comb-mode spectrum via I_p and of the cavity gain peak wavelength, which in a good approximation equals the Bragg wavelength, via I_B. Therefore, the appropriate mutual adjustment of the comb-modes and the cavity gain peak wavelength by the phase and Bragg currents I_p and I_B, respectively, yields the continuous wavelength tuning as described in Chapter 4. It is

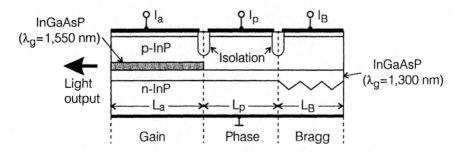

Figure 5.5   Schematic longitudinal section of three-section DBR laser consisting of a gain region and passive phase shift and Bragg reflector regions.

obvious that the tuning range in the discontinuous tuning scheme is determined by the maximal change of the Bragg wavelength as in the case of the two-section DBR laser. With (4.15), the latter can be related to the maximal effective refractive index change achievable by the carrier injection as

$$\frac{\Delta \lambda_B}{\lambda_0} = \frac{\Delta n'_{\text{eff},B}}{n_{g,\text{eff},B}} \tag{5.19}$$

where the index B indicates the Bragg section and λ_0 is the initial Bragg wavelength without tuning.

The continuous tuning range, on the other hand, is usually limited by the maximal phase shift in the phase-shift section. This can easily be understood by assuming that throughout the entire tuning range the device lases at the (variable) Bragg wavelength so that no phase change occurs at the Bragg reflector. Then (5.15) applies, yielding

$$\frac{\Delta \lambda_c}{\lambda_0} = \frac{\Delta n'_{\text{eff},p}}{\bar{n}_{g,\text{eff}}} \Gamma_p^{\text{long}} \left(1 - \frac{\alpha_{H,a}}{\alpha_{H,p}} \right) \tag{5.20}$$

where the index p stands for the phase section, and the continuous tuning requires the adjustment of I_B and I_p such that $\Delta \lambda_c = \Delta \lambda_B$. In contrast to (5.19) for the Bragg section, the product $\Gamma_p^{\text{long}} \left(1 - \alpha_{H,a}/\alpha_{H,p} \right)$ appears in (5.20), which is usually less than unity since $\Gamma_p^{\text{long}} \approx 0.3 - 0.5$ and $1 - \alpha_{H,a}/\alpha_{H,p} \leq 1.5$. Assuming similar group indices, (5.20) further reveals that $|\Delta n'_{\text{eff},p}|$ must usually be larger than $|\Delta n'_{\text{eff},B}|$, which means that the maximal achievable effective refractive index change in the phase region limits the continuous tuning range.

As mentioned above, the continuous tuning requires the simultaneous control of I_p and I_B to shift the comb-mode spectrum and the cavity gain peak wavelength at the same rate. Again the nonlinear recombination law in Bragg and phase section complicates this relationship because for a given wavelength shift, the injection into the phase section must be higher than into the Bragg section. As a consequence of the nonlinear recombination, therefore, the ratio I_p/I_B changes during tuning, so that a simple splitting network for the

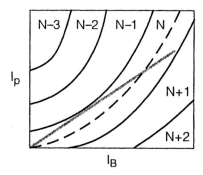

Figure 5.6   Regimes in the $I_B - I_p$-plane for laser operation of particular longitudinal modes. The solid curves indicate the mode boundaries at which mode and wavelength jumps occur. Continuous single-mode tuning in mode N is possible, for instance, along the gray line or the broken curve.

two control currents would not be adequate. This is illustrated schematically in Figure 5.6 indicating the regimes in the $I_B - I_p$-plane for lasing in various longitudinal modes. The gray line shows what may be achieved with an optimized splitting of the two control currents (e. g., by means of a resistance network [8]). Obviously, the margins are rather small, and a safer continuous tuning may be accomplished by using nonlinear curves adapted to the mode boundaries as indicated by the broken curve.

It should be stressed that due to heating an additional wavelength change also occurs during I_a changes. Thus, the emission wavelength of the tunable three-section DBR laser in fact is a function of all three control currents.

This is demonstrated experimentally in Figure 5.7 [9], showing the laser wavelength as function of each of the control currents while keeping the other two control currents fixed. As can be seen, the wavelength critically depends on all currents, and wavelength jumps limit the continuous tuning range for one-current tuning to below about

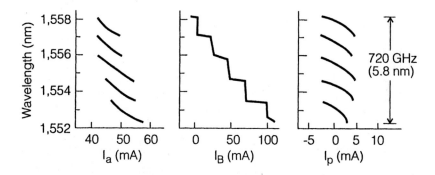

Figure 5.7   Influence of all three control currents on the laser wavelength of an experimental three-section DBR laser. (Reprinted with permission from *Electronics Letters*, Vol. 23, pp. 403–405, ©1987 IEE.)

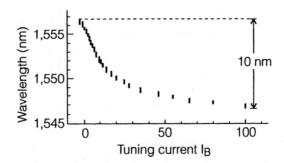

Figure 5.8   Quasicontinuous tuning over 10 nm with a three-section DBR laser. The wavelength variation within each longitudinal mode at constant I_B is accomplished by changing the phase current I_p. (Reprinted with permission from *Electronics Letters*, Vol. 24, pp. 577–579, ©1988 IEE.)

1 nm. By adjusting I_p and I_B, the continuous tuning of this laser can be extended to about 3 nm. In the discontinuous tuning scheme, on the other hand, a 5.8-nm total tuning range is achieved as indicated in the figure.

Extensive theoretical [10, 11] and experimental [12–16] research has been performed to optimize the tuning range of the three-section DBR lasers in the 1,550-nm wavelength range. According to the theoretical analysis, the maximal continuous tuning ranges of these devices are of the order 4 nm, while the discontinuous tuning may be extended to typically 10 nm [12, 14, 17]. A record discontinuous tuning range of 17 nm has been achieved with the three-section DBR lasers [18].

Because the tuning range of the comb-mode spectrum by way of the phase section usually extends over several longitudinal mode spacings, the three-section DBR lasers are well suited for the quasicontinuous tuning scheme [14, 15, 17] as described in Section 4.4. In this way, therefore, all wavelengths within the entire discontinuous tuning range may be addressable by proper $I_p - I_B$ combinations. A representative plot of a quasicontinuously tuned device with a 10-nm tuning range is shown in Figure 5.8. As can clearly be seen, the wavelength control in this tuning scheme is extremely critical so that the practical application requires extensive device characterization and the use of a computer control and a data base. Because ageing may shift the tuning characteristics, the long-term reliability of this tuning method is a challenge.

The thermal tuning was also applied successfully to three-section DBR lasers [19–21]. As the remote location of the Bragg section with respect to the gain region allows a significant heating of the Bragg section without affecting the gain mechanism, extended tuning ranges may be expected with thermal tuning of the Bragg section. This tuning may either be performed by driving a reverse bias through the Bragg section diode [19], or by placing a resistive heater on top of the device [20, 21]. In the former case, one can additionally exploit the plasma effect under forward bias. Correspondingly, the ambipolar biasing yields optimized tuning ranges up to 22 nm [19] as shown in Figure 5.9. Because of the different physical mechanisms employed, the tuning behavior (tuning speed and efficiency) is different for positive and negative tuning currents.

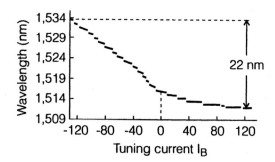

Figure 5.9   Wavelength tuning over 22 nm by using ambipolar current injection into the Bragg section. This yields heat generation and thermal tuning for negative I_B values. (Reprinted with permission from *IEEE Photonics Technology Letters*, Vol. 3, pp. 299–301, ©1991 IEEE.)

        The principal device structure of a resistive-heated tunable three-section DBR laser is shown in Figure 5.10 [21]. Here, the heating does not affect the tuning diodes and is galvanically isolated from the active section, so that the device degradation may be small and the device handling simpler. On the other hand, the plasma effect may not be used, so that the total tuning range is limited to about 10 nm. As with the other three-section DBR lasers, the tuning over this wavelength range may be accomplished using the

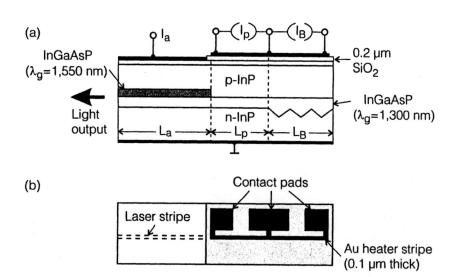

Figure 5.10   Schematic longitudinal (a) and top (b) view of three-section DBR laser with thermal control of Bragg wavelength and phase shift using gold-stripe heaters on top of the device. (Reprinted with permission from *IEEE Photonics Technology Letters*, Vol. 5, pp. 608–610, ©1993 IEEE.)

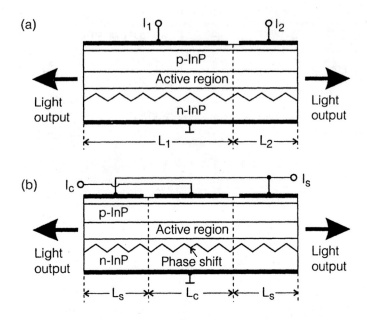

Figure 5.11   Schematic longitudinal views of two-section (a) and three-section (b) DFB lasers. While the two-section DFB lasers usually exhibit different section lengths, the three-section devices are symmetrical with respect to the cavity center and commonly comprise a phase-shifted grating.

discontinuous or the quasicontinuous tuning scheme. While the thermal tuning is slower than the electronic tuning using the plasma effect, it exhibits the important advantage that the spectral linewidth remains small during tuning. A linewidth below 1.6 Mhz was reported for the 10-nm tuning range [21], adjusting the laser wavelength each in the center of the corresponding mode boundaries.

5.1.3   Multisection DFB Laser

Besides the multisection DBR lasers, also multisection DFB lasers play an important role among the longitudinally integrated tunable lasers. In fact, these devices were among the first tunable laser diodes [22, 23], since their fabrication technology is almost identical to that of the conventional DFB lasers. By simply dividing the top p-contact of a DFB laser in two or more parts as shown schematically in Figure 5.11, a tunable multisection DFB laser is realized. In contrast to their relatively simple technology, the operation principle of the multisection DFB lasers is complicated [24, 25] and the handling and wavelength control is difficult [22].

As mentioned above, wavelength tuning in a DFB laser is possible only if the effective α_H factor, $\alpha_{H,\text{eff}}$ [1], varies longitudinally. The effective α_H factor depends on the material α_H factor, which might be longitudinally homogeneous, as well as on the

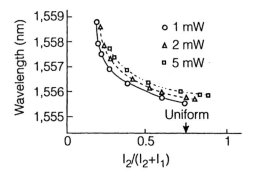

Figure 5.12   Wavelength versus current ratio $I_2/(I_2 + I_1)$ at various optical power levels for a two-section DFB laser with different section lengths (after [29]). Uniform longitudinal biasing occurs at $I_2/(I_2 + I_1) = L_2/L = 0.7$.

longitudinal field distribution, which can be rather complicated in DFB lasers. In contrast to the Fabry–Perot laser, therefore, the effective α_H factor of DFB lasers depends on the longitudinal coordinate so that an appropriate inhomogeneous pumping can lead to $\alpha_{H,\text{eff},1} \neq \alpha_{H,\text{eff},2}$ and to nonvanishing wavelength changes. Further, the material α_H factor generally depends on the carrier density so that additional differences occur in case of strongly inhomogeneous pumping, particularly in the case of QW lasers. In contrast to the multisection DBR lasers, however, the continuous tuning ranges of multisection DFB lasers are usually rather small [26] unless thermal tuning effects become important [27].

Numerous two-section [23, 28, 29] and three- or more-section [30–34] DFB lasers have been presented so far. According to theoretical calculations [26], tuning ranges of the order of the longitudinal mode spacing are usually obtained. In the case of the two-section DFB lasers, both a red and a blue shift of the laser wavelength can be achieved by increasing one of the control currents and keeping the other constant [23]. Keeping the total current $I_1 + I_2$ constant but varying the ratio I_1/I_2 also leads to a wavelength tuning, by which a continuous tuning up to 1 nm was demonstrated [28]. The largest continuous tuning ranges were achieved with the two-section devices by employing sections of different lengths. Tuning characteristics of an 800-μm-long as-cleaved ($R_1 = R_2 \approx 0.35$) two-section DFB laser with $\kappa L = 4$ ($L = L_1 + L_2$) and $L_1/L_2 = 1/3$ are plotted in Figure 5.12 with the optical power as a parameter. As can be seen, continuous tuning of up to 3.3 nm is obtained at a constant optical power of 1 mW.

The tuning behavior of the symmetrical three-section DFB lasers with a phase-shifted grating and antireflection-coated end facets, on the other hand, may be more predictable and regular than for the two-section devices. This is because the single-longitudinal-mode operation is securely provided by the phase shift, and no ambiguities occur because of the random mirror-grating phase as discussed in Chapter 3. One commonly uses the symmetrical three-section device as shown in Figure 5.11(b) with the $\lambda/4$ phase shift in the center and the side electrodes connected to each other. Experimental results [30] for a 1,200-μm-long laser with $L_s = 300\,\mu$m and $L_c = 600\,\mu$m, $\kappa L \approx 2 - 3$ ($L = 2L_s + L_c$), and an SiN antireflection coating on each facet are displayed

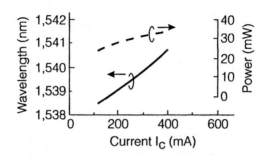

Figure 5.13   Wavelength and optical power versus center current I_c of a three-section DFB laser with side current I_s being fixed at 180 mA. (Reprinted with permission from *Electronics Letters*, Vol. 25, pp. 990–992, ©1989 IEE.)

in Figure 5.13. Here, the side current I_s is kept constant at 180 mA. As is obvious, the wavelength tuning is rather regular and a continuous tuning range of 2.2 nm was demonstrated with rather large optical power of around 30 mW. The largest continuous tuning range around 7 nm with a narrow linewidth around 1 MHz was claimed for a 1,200-μm-long strained-layer three-section tunable DFB laser by exploiting the additional effect of thermal heating by a strong variation of the control currents [35]. The application of three-section DFB lasers with a chirped Bragg-grating (i. e., a grating with longitudinally varying period length), has also been successfully demonstrated [36]. A continuous tuning over 2 nm with an *SSR* over 40 dB was reported for these devices.

5.2   TRANSVERSELY INTEGRATED STRUCTURES

The transverse integration technique for tunable laser diodes was briefly introduced in Section 4.6, mentioning the potential for an inherent continuous tunability. Accordingly, these devices play an important role for applications where continuous tuning is indispensable. Their operation principle deserves a more detailed investigation.

The wavelength tuning mechanism of the transversely integrated laser diodes can most easily be understood by considering a hypothetical single-mode DFB laser, the length of which can be smoothly stretched or compressed. Referring to Chapter 3, the single-mode operation of this DFB laser may be provided, for instance, by a quarter-wavelength shifted grating, an antireflection/high-reflection (AR/HR) coating on the end facets, or favorable mirror to grating phases of an as-cleaved device, and we assume that lasing occurs at the Bragg wavelength. The wavelength tuning is illustrated schematically in Figure 5.14, where the DFB laser with initial length L_1 and grating period Λ_1 is expanded to length L_2 and grating period Λ_2. Obviously, the stretching factor is equal for both the laser length and the grating period. This can be expressed mathematically as

$$\frac{L_2}{L_1} = \frac{\Lambda_2}{\Lambda_1} \tag{5.21}$$

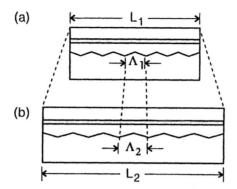

Figure 5.14   Schematic illustration of tuning mechanism in transversely integrated structures. The equal relative longitudinal stretching of the optical cavity length and grating pitch yields an inherent continuous tuning of the Bragg and laser wavelength, respectively.

While the laser wavelength (i. e., the Bragg wavelength) is proportional to the grating period and increases by the stretching, the number of half-wavelengths fitting longitudinally into the laser (or, in other words, the mode number N) remains constant during the stretching. Consequently, laser operation in the same longitudinal mode is obtained by the stretching even though the wavelength increases. This means that no mode jumps appear during tuning and that the tuning behavior is continuous, provided that the stretching is longitudinally homogeneous. This hypothetical laser essentially represents a DFB laser with a mechanically tunable Bragg wavelength.

A semiconductor cannot be stretched significantly, however, so the tuning method of Figure 5.14 cannot immediately be applied. Nevertheless, we may exploit this tuning principle by noting that it is not the stretching of the geometrical laser length, but of the optical laser length (i. e., the product of laser length and effective refractive index) that is important. The latter, however, can be varied electronically over refractive index changes as with the longitudinally integrated tunable lasers presented in the previous section. With respect to Figure 4.18, this may be accomplished by placing a tuning region in parallel to the active region of the DFB laser as shown in Figure 5.15, so that the effective refractive index of the relevant transverse laser mode can be modulated or, alternatively, by omitting the tuning region but heating the entire DFB laserchip, which increases the effective refractive index of the complete transverse structure.

We study the wavelength tuning by changing the optical laser length, assuming laser operation at the Bragg wavelength λ_B:

$$\lambda = \lambda_B = 2\Lambda n'_{\text{eff}} \tag{5.22}$$

The total roundtrip phase ϕ for the laser light:

$$\phi = 2\beta L = \frac{4\pi n'_{\text{eff}}}{\lambda} L \tag{5.23}$$

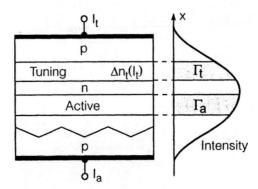

Figure 5.15   Schematic longitudinal view of a transversely integrated tunable laser diode. Depending on the confinement factor of the tuning region Γ_t, the electronically induced refractive index changes in the tuning region cause changes of the laser wavelength. Active region and tuning region are biased via I_a and I_t, respectively, and the common ground electrode is placed laterally beneath to the laser stripe.

can be expressed by means of (5.22) as

$$\phi = 2\pi\frac{L}{\Lambda} \tag{5.24}$$

This clearly shows that the total roundtrip phase, and, consequently, the longitudinal mode number $N = \phi/2\pi = L/\Lambda$ remains unchanged by the longitudinally *homogeneous* n'_{eff} changes as induced to change the laser wavelength corresponding to (5.22). As a consequence, this kind of wavelength tuning yields an *inherently* continuous tuning without mode jumps and the corresponding singularities of the laser characteristics.

To investigate the tuning range of the transversely tunable laser diodes, we consider the combined effect of the direct electronic tuning, usually by the free-carrier plasma effect, and the thermal tuning due to an applied heater or by the heat generation associated to the tuning function by the nonradiative recombination in the tuning region and the ohmic losses in the series and contact resistances of the tuning diode. Further, as already discussed in Section 5.1.3, the interaction between active and tuning region by way of the gain-loss coupling has to be taken into account. As a consequence of the homogeneous longitudinal refractive index change (c. f., (5.21)), the wavelength changes for the gain peak wavelength (i. e., the Bragg wavelength) and the comb-mode spectrum are exactly equal:

$$\Delta\lambda = \Delta\lambda_B = \Delta\lambda_c \tag{5.25}$$

The total wavelength change caused by the tuning using I_t may be split into the electronic and the thermal contribution:

$$\Delta\lambda = \Delta\lambda_{\mathrm{el}} + \Delta\lambda_{\mathrm{therm}} \tag{5.26}$$

where $\Delta\lambda_{el}$ and $\Delta\lambda_{therm}$ denote the purely electronic and thermal contributions to the total tuning. The latter arises from the temperature change ΔT:

$$\Delta\lambda_{therm} = \xi\Delta T \tag{5.27}$$

with $\xi \approx 0.1$ nm/K (c. f., Section 4.5.3), while the purely electronic wavelength shift may be derived using the Bragg condition (3.4):

$$\frac{\Delta\lambda_{el}}{\lambda_0} = \frac{\Delta n'_{eff}}{n_{g,eff}} \tag{5.28}$$

where λ_0 is the initial laser wavelength, $n_{g,eff}$ is the effective group index, which takes into account the disperion of n_{eff}, and $\Delta n'_{eff}$ is the induced change of n_{eff} as caused by the tuning current. As in the case of the longitudinally integrated structures, the change of n_{eff} due to refractive index changes in the active (index a) and tuning region (index t) can be written as

$$\Delta n_{eff} = \Delta n_{eff,a} + \Delta n_{eff,t} \tag{5.29}$$

where

$$\Delta n_{eff,a} = \left(1 - i/\alpha_{H,a}\right)\Delta n'_{eff,a} \tag{5.30}$$

and

$$\Delta n_{eff,t} = \left(1 - i/\alpha_{H,t}\right)\Delta n'_{eff,t} \tag{5.31}$$

with $\alpha_{H,a}$ and $\alpha_{H,t}$ denoting the linewidth enhancement factors in the active and the tuning region, respectively.

In the lasing regime, the total gain/loss changes are canceled by the active region; that is, the mode gain always equals the total loss because of the "gain-clamping mechanism" (c. f., Section 2.5), so that the imaginary part of Δn_{eff} equals zero. With the imaginary part of (5.29) this yields:

$$\frac{\Delta n'_{eff,a}}{\alpha_{H,a}} + \frac{\Delta n'_{eff,t}}{\alpha_{H,t}} = 0 \tag{5.32}$$

Substituting this into the real part of (5.29), we obtain for the real part of Δn_{eff}

$$\Delta n'_{eff} = \Delta n'_{eff,t}\left(1 - \frac{\alpha_{H,a}}{\alpha_{H,t}}\right) \tag{5.33}$$

With (5.28), the electronic wavelength change caused by the refractive index change (real part) $\Delta n'_t$ in the tuning region reads

$$\frac{\Delta\lambda_{el}}{\lambda_0} = \frac{\Delta n'_{eff,t}}{n_{g,eff}}\left(1 - \frac{\alpha_{H,a}}{\alpha_{H,t}}\right) = \frac{\Delta n'_t}{n_{g,eff}}\Gamma_t\left(1 - \frac{\alpha_{H,a}}{\alpha_{H,t}}\right) \tag{5.34}$$

where Γ_t is the two-dimensional confinement factor of the tuning region (2.34).

The comparison with the longitudinally integrated structures (5.15) shows an almost complete equivalence, the only difference being the appearance of the longitudinal confinement factor of the tuning region in the longitudinally integrated structures. Because of the longitudinal homogeneous structure, the longitudinal confinement factor of the transversely integrated lasers is exactly unity. Using the three-dimensional confinement factor of the tuning region (5.17), we find that $\Gamma_t^{3d} = \Gamma_t$ so that the wavelength tuning for longitudinally and transversely integrated structures may be described by exactly the same formula:

$$\frac{\Delta\lambda_{el}}{\lambda_0} = \frac{\Delta n_t'}{n_{g,\text{eff}}}\Gamma_t^{3d}\left(1 - \frac{\alpha_{H,a}}{\alpha_{H,t}}\right) \tag{5.35}$$

which corresponds to (5.18). Noting that the longitudinal confinement factor of the longitudinally integrated structures is smaller than unity, with typical values of 0.3 to 0.5, the three-dimensional confinement factor of the transversely integrated lasers is usually larger, resulting in larger continuous tuning ranges.

Numerical Example: Consider a transversely integrated laser at a 1,550-nm wavelength with $\alpha_{H,a} = 5$, $\alpha_{H,t} = -10$, $n_{g,\text{eff}} = 4$, $\Gamma_t = 0.4$, and a maximum refractive index change in the tuning region of -0.03. We obtain a wavelength tuning of about -7 nm. The comparison with the related numerical example for the longitudinally integrated structure in Section 5.1 ($\Delta\lambda_c \approx -3.5$ nm) clearly illustrates the significantly larger continuous tuning capability of the transverse integration.

Technologically, a remarkable difference between the longitudinally and transversely integrated devices is the more effective usage of the wafer area by the latter and the homogeneous longitudinal structure, which avoids coupling losses and reflections at the interfaces between active and passive sections. On the other hand, the separate contacting of active and tuning sections is rather challenging with the transverse integration technique.

5.2.1   Tunable Twin-Guide DFB Laser

The tunable twin-guide (TTG) DFB laser was developed in 1989 [37] and represents the practical realization of a transversely-integrated tunable laser diode according to Figure 4.18(b) and Figure 5.15. Electronically, the TTG DFB laser consists of a *pnp*-heterostructure with two decoupled *pn*-heterojunction diodes. Unlike the heterojunction bipolar transistor, the carrier injection does not occur into the base *n*-InP region; instead the high bandgap energy *n*-InP layer in the center plays the role of the *n*-confinement layer supplying electrons into the active and tuning regions of lower bandgap energy. As the electron flow into both regions is controlled by the corresponding hole currents I_t and I_a, respectively, the diodes are effectively separated by the center *n*-InP layer and can independently be biased. It should be noted that the *n*-contact supplying the electron sum current $I_t + I_a$ is placed laterally beneath the laser and thus cannot be shown in the longitudinal view.

Optically, on the other hand, both regions are strongly coupled as described by large confinement factors Γ_t and Γ_a for the tuning and active region, respectively. Con-

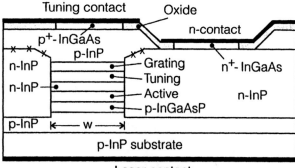

Figure 5.16   Schematic cross-section of MOVPE-compatible TTG laser in InGaAsP/InP for a 1,550-nm wavelength. The crosses indicate a forward-biased InP *pn*-homojunction placed in parallel to the tuning diode.

sequently, both the optical gain in the active region, as controlled by I_a, and the refractive index of the tuning region, as controlled by I_t, strongly influence the lasing transverse mode. As with the multisection DBR lasers, the tuning region exhibits a larger bandgap energy than the active region. Because the photon energy is thus smaller than the bandgap energy of the tuning region the injected carriers undergo no band-to-band stimulated recombination by the laser light. This decouples the carriers in the tuning region from the gain-clamping mechanism and makes their dynamics independent of the light power. Further, the desired homogeneous longitudinal carrier distribution and index change are achieved in the tuning region because no hole-burning effects occur. Typically, the bandgap wavelength of the tuning region is chosen between 1,200 and 1,400 nm for TTG DFB lasers in the 1,550-nm wavelength region.

The analysis of the TTG DFB laser transverse structure [38] shows that a tradeoff exists between threshold current and tuning range, because Γ_a and Γ_t cannot be maximized simultaneously. This is the analogous situation to the longitudinally integrated three-section DBR laser, where the longitudinal confinement factors of active and phase shifter region sum up to unity, so that an independent optimization is excluded. However, the analysis reveals that continuous tuning ranges around 8 nm and threshold currents below 100 mA should be achievable with properly designed 600-μm-long TTG DFB lasers at a 1,550-nm wavelength using bulk active regions.

TTG DFB lasers have been fabricated using the RW [39] as well as the BH [40] lateral laser structure. While the RW TTG DFB lasers suffer from lateral carrier diffusion out of the active and tuning region, the leakage currents outside the stripe region are important for the BH TTG DFB lasers. Experimentally, therefore, the RW TTG DFB lasers achieve the larger optical powers, whereas the BH TTG DFB lasers provide by far the largest tuning ranges. The fabrication process for the more usual BH TTG DFB laser has been described in detail in [41].

The lateral supply of the electrons from the common *n*-contact via the burying *n*-InP confinement layers in a BH TTG DFB laser [40] is shown in the schematic cross-sectional view of Figure 5.16. In this structure, the grating layer is placed above the tuning region. As is evident from this figure, a *pnp*-structure with the less usual *p*-type substrate is chosen to get an *n*-doped center region with low resistance; consequently, the voltage drop between the active stripe region and the 10-to-20-μm-spaced *n*-contact can be kept small, avoiding excess heating. As with all BH-type lasers, the suppression of leakage currents outside the stripe region is an important issue [42]. In the particular structure of Figure 5.16 no blocking *pn*-junctions are provided outside the stripe; instead, forward-biased InP *pn*-junctions with large areas exist beneath the active and tuning region. As a result, the leakage currents can be kept small only by using large bandgap energy differences between active and tuning region on the one hand and the burying InP layers on the other hand. In the case of the InGaAsP/InP BH TTG DFB laser with bandgap energy differences of 0.55 eV (active InGaAsP region to InP), and 0.4 eV (tuning region to InP), the lateral current confinement performs reasonably well, particularly by using an optimized doping profile in the *p*-InP regions [43].

Scanning electron micrographs of typical BH TTG DFB laser cross- and longitudinal sections together with the schematic device structure are shown in Figure 5.17, with the grating placed below the active region. All relevant regions of the laser can clearly be distinguished by comparison with the schematic structure.

The threshold currents of the TTG lasers with as-cleaved end facets range between 5 mA and 15 mA for laser lengths between 200 and 600 μm; and the optical power per facet at 100 mA current into the laser active region is typically between 3 mW ($L = 600 \mu$m) and 10 mW ($L = 200 \mu$m). From the viewpoint of optical power and threshold current margin, long laser cavities are advantageous. On the other hand, however, the *SSR* decreases with increasing laser length. Optimal device performance has been achieved for laser length around 400 μm where the *SSR* is typically larger than 40 dB. According to the theoretical investigations, the TTG DFB lasers easily achieve continuous tuning ranges of the order 7 nm. Experimental laser spectra for a 400-μm-long BH TTG DFB laser driven with a constant laser current I_a of 150 mA and tuning currents between 0 and 75 mA are plotted in Figure 5.18. As can be seen, a convenient continuous tuning without mode jumps is achieved by simply changing one control current (I_t), and the *SSR* of this laser exceeds 30 dB over the entire tuning range. The limitation of the tuning range to about 7.1 nm is not due to a limitation of the refractive index change in the tuning region; instead, the decreasing laser optical power from the optical losses in the tuning region is the limiting process in this particular structure.

To investigate the tuning range of the TTG laser realistically, we have to consider the combined effects of the direct electronic tuning, usually using the free-carrier plasma effect, and the thermal tuning due to the associated heat generation by the tuning function. The latter arises from the nonradiative recombination in the tuning region and the ohmic losses in the series and contact resistances of the tuning diode.

With (5.35) and (4.8), the electronic wavelength tuning may be written for the case of carrier injection N_t into the tuning region (plasma effect)

$$\frac{\Delta\lambda_{el}}{\lambda_0} = \frac{\beta_{pl}N_t}{n_{g,eff}}\Gamma_t^{3d}\left(1 - \frac{\alpha_{H,a}}{\alpha_{H,t}}\right) \tag{5.36}$$

where β_{pl} is typically around -10^{-20} cm^3 (c. f., Section 4.5.1). The electronic tuning yields negative wavelength changes ($\Delta\lambda_{el} < 0$), which will therefore be partly compen-

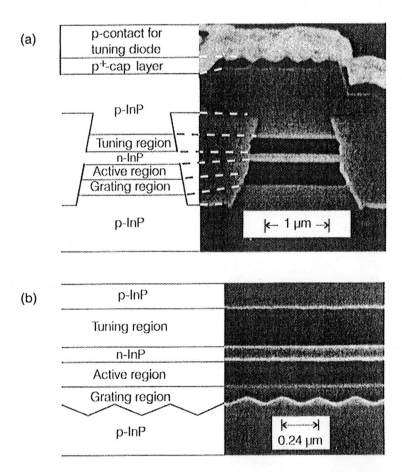

Figure 5.17   Scanning electron micrograph and schematic structure of an InGaAsP/InP BH TTG DFB laser for a 1,550-nm wavelength. The various regions can clearly be distinguished in the cross- (a) and longitudinal (b) sections.

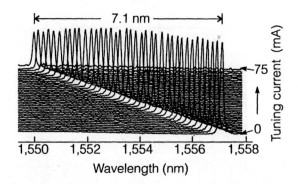

Figure 5.18   Emission spectra of a 400-μm-long InGaAsP/InP BH TTG DFB laser for the 1,550-nm
wavelength range. Laser current I_a and heat-sink temperature are kept at 150 mA and 25 °C,
respectively. The optical power changes by about a factor of three over the 7.1-nm tuning
range.

sated by the positive thermal tuning $\Delta\lambda_{\text{therm}}$ obtained from (5.27) with the temperature
change:

$$\Delta T = R_{\text{therm}}U_t(I_t)I_t \qquad (5.37)$$

where R_{therm} and U_t stand for the thermal resistance of the laser and the tuning diode
voltage, respectively. A large tuning range by the electronic tuning mechanism (plasma
effect) may be achieved by reducing the thermal contribution using low series resistance
of the tuning diode and low thermal resistance.

On the other hand, thermal tuning may be used to increase the total continuous
tuning range by allowing the reverse biasing of the tuning diode [44]. Exceeding the
breakthrough voltage of the tuning diode, a reverse current flows that leads to a heating
of the laser without injecting carriers into the tuning region. Under reverse bias, therefore, pure thermal tuning may be accomplished, yielding a positive wavelength shift for
increasing reverse bias current. The tuning diode voltage $U_t(I_t)$ of the ambipolar-driven
TTG DFB laser can be approximated by

$$U_t = \begin{cases} U_f + R_sI_t & I_t > 0 \\ U_b & I_t < 0 \end{cases} \qquad (5.38)$$

where R_s stands for the tuning diode series resistance, and U_f (typ. 1V for λ_g =1,300-nm
InGaAsP tuning region) and U_b (< 0) denote the forward and backward (inner) diode
voltage, respectively.

To enable the thermal tuning by heating the laser with reverse tuning diode bias
without damaging the tuning region, a low-breakthrough voltage InP homojunction is
placed in parallel to the tuning diode as indicated by the crosses in Figure 5.16. This can
be established by a high p-doping of $1.5 \cdot 10^{18}$ cm^{-3} of the upper p-InP confinement layer.
Together with a high n-doping (e. g., $N_D = 2 - 3 \cdot 10^{18}$ cm^{-3}) of the burying n-InP region,
a breakthrough voltage U_b near -3 V can be obtained [44], which is markedly lower than

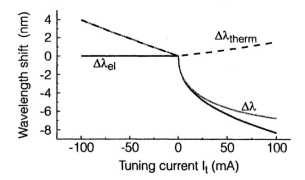

Figure 5.19   Calculated electronic ($\Delta\lambda_{el}$), thermal ($\Delta\lambda_{therm}$), and total ($\Delta\lambda$) wavelength shift in a representative bipolar tunable 400-μm-long InGaAsP/InP BH TTG DFB laser assuming a breakthrough voltage of the tuning diode of –3 V, a series resistance of 3 Ω, and a thermal resistance of 120 K/W.

that of the tuning region pn-junction (estimated ≈ -10 V) but larger than the forward voltage ($\simeq 1$ V) of the tuning diode. Accordingly, under reverse bias, the current flows over this shunt path to the tuning diode, yielding a strong heating effect without degrading the tuning region.

   Numerical Example: Calculated tuning characteristics for a bipolar-tunable BH TTG DFB laser are presented in Figure 5.19 using the following device parameters: $L = 400\,\mu$m, $w = 1\,\mu$m, tuning region thickness $d_t = 0.3\,\mu$m, $\Gamma_t = 0.4$, $\Lambda = 238$ nm, $R_{therm} = 120$ K/W, tuning region bimolecular recombination coefficient $B_t = 10^{-10}$ cm^3/s, tuning region Auger recombination coefficient $C_t = 3 \cdot 10^{-29}$ cm^6/s, $R_s = 3\,\Omega$, $U_b = -3$ V, $U_f = 1$ V, $\alpha_{H,a} = 5$, $\alpha_{H,t} = -20$, $\xi = 0.1$ nm/K, and $\beta_t = -7.5 \cdot 10^{-21}$cm^3. Tuning current and wavelength shifts are obtained through (4.17), (5.27), (5.36), and (5.37). As can be seen, the thermal tuning for negative tuning currents (reverse bias) increases up to 4 nm at $I_t = -100$ mA, while under forward bias at 100 mA, the –8-nm electronic tuning is reduced by about 1.6 nm because of the thermal tuning. So a total tuning range of about 11 nm (4 nm under reverse bias and 7 nm under forward bias) can be expected with this type of BH TTG DFB laser.

   Representative experimental tuning and optical power characteristics of a bipolar biased 400-μm-long BH TTG DFB laser designed according to the numerical example above is displayed in Figure 5.20. Using tuning currents between –100 and +100 mA, a strictly continuous tuning range of 13 nm or 1.6 THz is obtained, keeping the current into the laser active region constant at 100 mA [44]. No degradation of the tuning diode by the reverse biasing and heating has been found. As with the multisection DBR lasers, the largest tuning efficiency $|d\lambda/dI_t|$ is achieved at small (forward) tuning currents. With an increasing forward tuning current, the tuning efficiency decreases monotonically, while the almost constant breakthrough voltage yields an approximately constant tuning efficiency of 0.04 nm/mA under reverse bias. As predicted by the analysis, the thermal tuning under reverse bias contributes about 4 nm to the tuning range at $I_t = 100$ mA, corresponding to a temperature rise of 40 °K and a thermal resistance around 120 to 130 K/W.

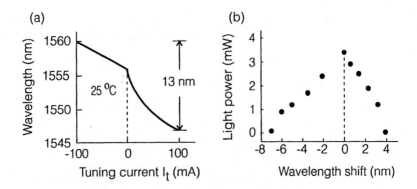

Figure 5.20   Wavelength versus tuning current (a) and light power versus wavelength shift (b) at constant laser current of 100 mA for a 400-μm-long ambipolar-tunable BH TTG DFB laser.

The optical power at one end facet measured with a numerical aperture of 0.5 at an active region current of 100 mA is shown in Figure 5.20(b) versus the wavelength shift. Starting with 3.5-mW optical power at zero tuning region bias, the optical power drops almost linearly with an increasing wavelength shift at both forward and backward bias. An optical power above 1 mW can be maintained over a tuning range of about 9 nm, keeping the active region current constant at 100 mA. The *SSR* over the 9-nm tuning range remains above 40 dB. The optical power depends strongly on the wavelength shift in this device and the tuning range of 13 nm is determined by the extinction of the laser operation at large tuning currents and not by the limitations on the effective refractive index change.

Various attempts have been made to increase the tuning range of the TTG DFB laser further. Neither the use of sophisticated QW tuning regions [45] nor the improvement of the current-injection structure [46] resulted in larger tuning ranges. However, higher optical powers and smaller spectral linewidth were achieved at moderate tuning ranges of 2 to 5 nm [43, 46, 47].

RW TTG DFB lasers were also presented that exploit the QCSE (c. f., Section 4.5.2) for tuning [48]. Although these devices achieved only small tuning ranges of a few tenths of a nanometer, the wavelength switching can be fast and the frequency modulation speed can be in the GHz range, making these devices promising candidates for high-speed FM light sources.

5.2.2   Striped Heater DFB Laser

In the preceding section, thermal tuning has been realized in the TTG DFB laser by an electronic heating of the tuning region. Thermal tuning may also be accomplished by simply heating the total laser. This may be done, for instance, by heating the laser submount (heat sink). While the thermal tuning by way of the electronic heating of the tuning region occurs near to the active stripe and therefore yields a relatively fast response in the μs regime (c. f., Section 4.7), the thermal tuning by heating the submount is slow with re-

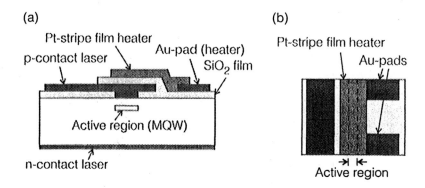

Figure 5.21   Schematic cross-section (a) and top view (b) of a thermally tunable DFB laser with a striped platinum thin-film heater.

sponse times at around 0.1 sec. On the other hand, the technological effort is significantly smaller for the latter approach.

A successful combination of a short response time and a relatively simple fabrication technology can be achieved by means of the so-called *striped heater DFB lasers* [49]. The schematic cross-section and top view of such a device are shown in Figure 5.21. This laser is made by completing a DFB laser on top with a thin resistive stripe isolated by a thin oxide film. Heater stripe and DFB laser are electrically completely decoupled, while the heat generated in the stripe immediately heats up the waveguide region and thus causes the wavelength tuning. To achieve larger temperature changes with a certain heat power, the thermal resistance was increased [49] by using 200-μm-thick laser chips, which are about twice as thick as conventional lasers.

A similar device structure is the striped heater three-section DBR laser [21] as described in Figure 5.10 allowing a discontinuous or quasicontinuous tuning over 10.8 nm. In the case of the striped heater DFB laser, continuous tuning can easily be achieved from the transverse integration technique, and maximal tuning ranges around 4 nm were achieved. The smaller tuning range compared with the striped heater DBR laser is due to the heating of the active region, which reduces the optical gain and optical power of the laser and thus limits the maximal operation temperature. Owing to the spacing of Bragg grating and active region in the three-section DBR laser, the Bragg region can be heated much more without affecting the active region. The tuning range of the striped heater DFB laser is also smaller than that of the TTG DFB laser, which is 13 nm, because no additional electronic tuning effects are used.

The tuning characteristics of a striped heater DFB laser with 800-μm cavity length are shown in Figure 5.22 as a function of the heater current. The optical power was kept constant at 20 mW by adjusting the laser current. With a heater resistance around 17 Ω the maximum heating power is about 1 W at 250 mA, yielding a wavelength shift of 4 nm. Since this wavelength shift corresponds to a temperature raise of about 40 °K, we estimate the thermal resistance to about 40 K/W. The wavelength versus heater current characteristic shows a parabola-like shape because the heating power is proportional to the heater

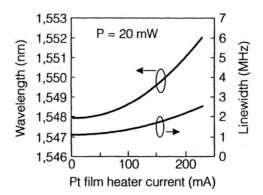

Figure 5.22   Wavelength and spectral linewidth versus platinum film heater current for the laser structure of Figure 5.21. (Reprinted with permission from *IEEE Photonics Technology Letters*, Vol. 4, pp. 321–323, ©1992 IEEE.)

current squared. The spectral linewidth is also shown versus the heating current, indicating an increase from 1 to 2.5 MHz.

5.3   PHYSICAL LIMITATIONS ON THE CONTINUOUS TUNING RANGE

In this section, we briefly investigate and compare the physical limitations on the continuous tuning range of the longitudinally and the transversely integrated tunable laser diodes exploiting the free-carrier plasma effect. The reader interested in more details of the calculations is referred to [50].

Inducing the continuous tuning in the three-section DBR laser requires the simultaneous application of the phase and Bragg section currents so that the shifts of the comb-mode spectrum and the Bragg wavelength are equal:

$$\Delta\lambda = \Delta\lambda_c = \Delta\lambda_B \tag{5.39}$$

Owing to the finite α_H factors in the Bragg and phase section, optical losses occur that must be compensated by an increasing active region gain, which in turn manifests itself in an increasing active region carrier density. Accordingly, the carrier injection into the tuning region of the TTG laser causes optical losses in the practical case of a finite α_H factor, so that again the active region gain automatically compensates the losses by increasing the carrier density.

The continuous tuning in the three-section DBR laser is done by increasing the Bragg section current I_B. This reduces the effective refractive index of the Bragg section, yielding a corresponding shift of the Bragg wavelength. The selectivity of the Bragg reflector is assumed large enough so that the Bragg wavelength determines the peak wavelength of the cavity gain and we assume that through the entire tuning range the longitudinal mode order of the lasing mode is kept constant while the laser wavelength exactly equals the Bragg wavelength. For this purpose the phase section current I_p is increased such that the phase condition of the lasing mode is met for each I_B-value. Consequently, no phase change occurs for the reflection at the boundary between phase and Bragg section (c. f., Figure 5.5). This boundary plane may therefore be considered as a reflecting mirror, the power reflectivity $R_1 = R_B$ of which decreases during tuning because of the additional optical losses introduced by the carrier injection into the Bragg section. Accordingly, R_B can be considered a function of the wavelength tuning $R_B = R_B(\Delta\lambda)$.

On the other hand, the reflectivity R_2 at the left end of the laser cavity, which is due to the Fresnel reflection between the high-refractive laser cavity and free space, is independent of the wavelength tuning. The end loss change due to the tuning is therefore given as

$$\Delta\alpha_m(\Delta\lambda) = \frac{1}{2(L_a + L_p)} \ln\left(\frac{R_B(0)}{R_B(\Delta\lambda)}\right) \tag{5.40}$$

$R_B(\Delta\lambda)$ is calculated with (3.29) and (3.25), allowing a complex or imaginary $\Delta\beta = \Delta\beta' + j\Delta\beta''$ to include the losses $\alpha_B(\Delta\lambda)$ in the Bragg section. Since lasing is assumed at the Bragg wavelength, the real part of $\Delta\beta$ vanishes, while the imaginary part is proportional to the losses:

$$\Delta\beta'' = -\alpha_B/2 \tag{5.41}$$

where the factor of two is due to the fact that the losses refer to intensity, while β refers to field. With (5.19), and using the α_H factor, we may express α_B in terms of the wavelength tuning as

$$\alpha_B(\Delta\lambda) = \frac{4\pi n_{g,\text{eff}}\Delta\lambda}{\lambda_0^2 \alpha_{H,B}} + \alpha_i \tag{5.42}$$

where α_i is the tuning-independent internal loss. For the power reflectivity of the Bragg section, we obtain

$$R_B(\Delta\lambda) = \left\{\sqrt{1 + \left(\frac{\Delta\beta''}{\kappa}\right)^2} \coth\left(\kappa L_B \sqrt{1 + \left(\frac{\Delta\beta''}{\kappa}\right)^2}\right) - \frac{\Delta\beta''}{\kappa}\right\}^{-2} \tag{5.43}$$

Considering the end loss change in the oscillation condition (5.1), the relation for the imaginary parts of the refractive indices of the active and tuning region is obtained by using (5.13) as

$$2k_0(\Delta n_a''\Gamma_a^{3d} + \Delta n_p''\Gamma_p^{3d}) = \Delta\alpha_m(\Delta\lambda) \tag{5.44}$$

while the relation for the real parts of the refractive indices yields with (5.9)

$$\frac{\Delta\lambda}{\lambda_0} = \frac{\Delta n_a'}{\bar{n}_g}\Gamma_a^{3d} + \frac{\Delta n_p'}{\bar{n}_g}\Gamma_p^{3d} \tag{5.45}$$

With the α_H factor we may express the imaginary part of Δn_p by its real part. Using (4.8) and approximating the active region gain by (2.9), we obtain two linear equations for the carrier density in the phase shift region, N_p, and the carrier density change in the active region, $\Delta N_a = N_a - N_{a0}$:

$$\frac{\alpha_{H,a}a\lambda_0}{4\pi\bar{n}_g}\Gamma_a^{3d}\Delta N_a - \frac{\beta_{pl,p}}{\bar{n}_g}\Gamma_p^{3d}N_p = -\frac{\Delta\lambda}{\lambda_0} \qquad (5.46)$$

$$\frac{a\lambda_0}{4\pi}\Gamma_a^{3d}\Delta N_a - \frac{\beta_{pl,p}}{\alpha_{H,p}}\Gamma_p^{3d}N_p = \frac{\lambda_0}{4\pi}\Delta\alpha_m(\Delta\lambda) \qquad (5.47)$$

where N_{a0} is the carrier density in the active region without tuning, which is required to provide a gain equal to the sum of the internal losses in active and tuning section and the mirror losses at $\Delta\lambda = 0$.

From the carrier densities, the recombination constants, the geometrical parameters, and using the recombination law (2.18), we calculate the currents and current densities into the active section (I_a and J_a) and into the phase section (I_p and J_p), respectively.

The current density J_B and current I_B into the Bragg section are also obtained as functions of the wavelength shift $\Delta\lambda$ using (4.16), the geometrical parameters of the Bragg section and its recombination constants.

With these calculations, we thus may relate the current densities into all laser sections with the wavelength tuning and may determine the largest one for each $\Delta\lambda$. Assuming reasonable maximal bias current densities, particularly with respect to thermal heating, the largest the $\Delta\lambda$ achievable determines the continuous *electronic* tuning range of the particular three-section DBR laser structure.

Analogous calculations are also performed for the transversely integrated TTG laser. The results for the tuning region carrier density N_t and the active region carrier density change ΔN_a are

$$N_t(\Delta\lambda) = \frac{n_{g,\text{eff}}}{\beta_{pl,t}\Gamma_t\left(1 - \alpha_{H,a}/\alpha_{H,t}\right)}\frac{\Delta\lambda}{\lambda_0} \qquad (5.48)$$

$$\Delta N_a = N_t\frac{2k_0\beta_{pl,t}}{\alpha_{H,t}a}\frac{\Gamma_t}{\Gamma_a} \qquad (5.49)$$

where $\beta_{pl,t}$ is the derivative of the real part of the refractive index versus the carrier density (4.8) for the tuning region. Again, with the corresponding geometrical parameters, the recombination constants, and α_H factors of active and tuning region we may calculate the current densities J_a and J_t into the active and tuning region, respectively.

For the calculation of the maximal continuous tuning ranges and the comparison of the two integration techniques, we next consider both a well-designed three-section DBR and a TTG laser diode. The relevant device parameters are compiled in Table 5.1.

The various carrier densities are shown schematically in Figure 5.23, versus the wavelength shift in the continuous tuning scheme. As can be seen, in the case of the three-section DBR laser, the phase section carrier density is the most critical one that usually limits the continuous tuning range, because carrier densities in excess of about $4 \cdot 10^{18}$ cm^{-3} may not be achieved in InGaAsP. This figure therefore clearly illustrates why continuous tuning in the three-section DBR is at most about 3 to 4 nm. In the case of the TTG laser it depends on the layer thicknesses or the optical confinement factors of active and tuning region, respectively, whether the carrier density in the tuning or in the

Table 5.1

Typical device parameters of three-section DBR and TTG laser used for the calculations. The indices a, t, p, and B each refer to the active, tuning, phase, and Bragg region.

Parameter	Dimension	3S-DBR	TTG
d_a	μm	0.15	
d_t, d_p	μm	0.3	
L_a	μm	250	400
L_p	μm	150	-
L_B	μm	500	-
n_g	-	4	
α_i	cm^{-1}	20	
κ	cm^{-1}	50	
Γ_a	-	0.28	0.29
Γ_p, Γ_B	-	0.42	-
Γ_t	-	-	0.3
$\alpha_{H,a}$	-	5	
$\alpha_{H,t}, \alpha_{H,p}, \alpha_{H,B}$	-	-10	
N_{tr}	cm^{-3}	$1.2 \cdot 10^{18}$	
a	cm^2	$3 \cdot 10^{-16}$	
B_a	cm^{3}s^{-1}	$7 \cdot 10^{-11}$	
B_t, B_p, B_B	cm^{3}s^{-1}	10^{-10}	
C_a	cm^{6}s^{-1}	$9 \cdot 10^{-29}$	
C_t, C_p, C_B	cm^{6}s^{-1}	$3 \cdot 10^{-29}$	
$\beta_{pl,t}, \beta_{pl,p}$	cm^3	-10^{-20}	
R	-	0.35	

active region is crucial. In the present device it is the tuning region carrier density that first reaches the limit of $4 \cdot 10^{18}$ cm^{-3}, yielding a continuous tuning range of this device around 4 nm.

Investigating the current densities in the active, phase shift, and tuning section, respectively, for two different α_H factors in the passive sections leads to the plots in Figure 5.24. As expected, in the case of larger losses (i. e., smaller α_H factor in the passive sections), shown in Figure 5.24(a), the active section currents are larger than for the case of larger α_H factor in the passive sections. In both cases, however, the threshold current densities are smaller than the current densities into the tuning regions. So the maximal tuning ranges are determined by the maximal allowable current density into the tuning sections. Putting, for instance, $J_p, J_t < 10$ kA/cm^2, we obtain a maximal tuning range of the order 5 and 3.5 nm for the TTG and the three-section DBR laser, respectively. Accordingly, this calculation again shows the superior continuous tuning performance of the transversely integrated laser structures. By allowing a maximum tuning current density of 20 kA/cm^2, we find a maximal electronic tuning range of optimized TTG lasers of the order 6 to 8 nm, which closely corresponds to the experimentally achieved performance. Larger continuous tuning, therefore, requires the additional exploitation of the thermal tuning, which for a maximal temperature rise of 50 °K yields an additional 5 nm. The total continuous tuning range for the InGaAsP laser diodes at a 1,550-nm wavelength,

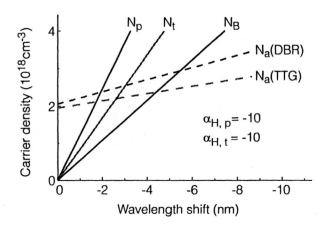

Figure 5.23   Carrier densities in the various regions of continuously tuned three-section DBR and TTG lasers versus wavelength shift. The laser parameters are listed in Table 5.1

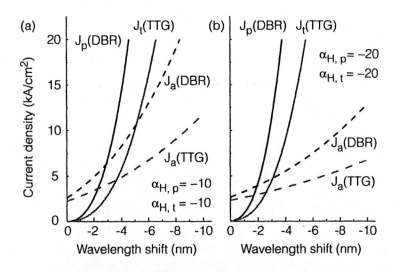

Figure 5.24   Current density in active (J_a), phase shift (J_p) and tuning (J_t) region, respectively, of continuously tuned three-section DBR and TTG lasers for α_H factors of -10 (a) and -20 (b) in the phase shift section and tuning region, respectively.

Table 5.2
Comparison of important DC device parameters and technological aspects of longitudinally- and transversely-integrated tunable laser diodes.

	Longitudinal integration (DFB, DBR)	Transverse integration (TTG)
Max. continuous tuning range	7 nm	13 nm
Typ. continuous tuning range	2–3 nm	3–5 nm
Device area	large	small
Number of control currents	3	2
Handling	complicated	simple
Integratability	good	moderate
Substrate conduction type	n or p	p
Design flexibility	large	small

therefore, seems to be restricted to at most about 13 to 15 nm (i. e., approximately 1 % of the wavelength).

The results of the continuous tuning range calculations, typical experimental performance, and related device characteristics for the longitudinally and transversely integrated devices are displayed in Table 5.2.

5.4   TUNING DYNAMICS AND MODULATION

In this section, we investigate the dynamic characteristics of the wavelength tuning for the various devices presented so far. These characteristics are of interest in applications where the time required for switching among different wavelengths is important or for the case in which tunable lasers are used as frequency-modulated optical sources. Particularly in the latter application, the occurrence of simultaneous amplitude modulation deteriorates the laser performance. So besides the dynamic behavior, the AM/FM ratio also represents an important device parameter that strongly depends on the device structure and the operation conditions.

The principal FM modulation behavior for lasers exploiting the plasma effect and thermal tuning was discussed already in Section 4.7. There, we stressed the important role of the differential carrier lifetime in the case of the plasma effect in a passive tuning region. While this applies to the tunable DBR- and TTG-type lasers, the lifetime shortening by stimulated emission reduces the differential carrier lifetime in wavelength-tunable multisection DFB lasers. At the same time, on the other hand, the modulation efficiency decreases. So among the devices exploiting the free-carrier plasma effect, the largest FM modulation bandwidths can be expected for the multisection DFB lasers.

In fact, theoretical and experimental investigations of multisection DFB lasers revealed their potential for FM modulation in the GHz-regime [51, 52]. The experimental FM response of a symmetric 900-μm-long three-section DFB laser with a $\lambda/4$ phase shift in the center is plotted in Figure 5.25 [52]. As can be seen, strikingly different modulation behavior is achieved depending on whether the side or the center current is modulated.

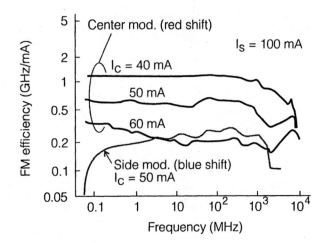

Figure 5.25   FM modulation efficiency versus frequency of a 900-μm-long three-section DFB laser with a $\lambda/4$ phase shift in the center. Modulation of the center and side currents is shown with the center current bias as parameter. (Reprinted with permission from *IEEE Journal of Selected Topics in Quantum Electronics*, Vol. 1, pp. 416–426, ©1995 IEEE.)

This is because the wavelength shift by increasing the side or the center current is toward the blue or the red, respectively. The tuning and modulation by the center current is in phase with the thermal contribution (which yields a red shift), yielding a larger modulation efficiency and no dip at low modulation frequencies, as discussed in Section 4.7. The modulation bandwidth increases with the center current bias and approaches about 10 GHz at $I_c = 60$ mA. On the other hand, the modulation efficiency drops significantly from 1 GHz/mA to 0.3 GHz/mA when I_c increases from 40 to 60 mA.

Much smaller FM modulation bandwidth has been obtained with multisection DBR and TTG lasers using the free-carrier plasma effect. As the essential difference between these two devices, namely the integration technique, has no principal effect on their FM modulation characteristic, we may consider exclusively one of the two device types. The FM response in a logarithmic scale of a TTG laser with an *n*-doped tuning region is shown in Figure 5.26 [53]. The *n*-doping level of $2 \cdot 10^{18}$ cm^{-3} was chosen to reduce the differential carrier lifetime and to increase the modulation bandwidth. Even though the electronic and thermal tuning in the multisection DBR and TTG lasers are of opposite signs, no dip occurs in these characteristics. This is due to the large electronic tuning efficiency of the order 10 GHz/mA, which is about an order of magnitude larger than in the multisection DFB laser investigated above. So the thermal tuning can practically be neglected with respect to the large electronic tuning and no noticeable dips appear in the modulation characteristics. Differing from the multisection DFB lasers, however, the modulation bandwidth is now only of the order of several hundred megahertz (i. e., about two orders of magnitude smaller). Note that because of the reduced differential carrier lifetime, the bandwidth increases (on cost of the efficiency) with increasing tuning current bias. As a consequence of the passive tuning region, the tuning characteristics are flat and regular below the cutoff frequency and show a 3-dB decay per octave above cutoff.

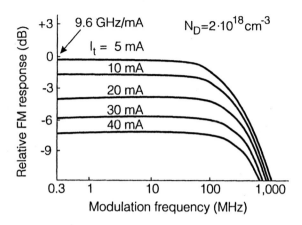

Figure 5.26   FM response versus frequency of a TTG laser with an n-doped tuning region with the tuning current bias as parameter (after [53]).

The effect of the tuning current bias on the tuning efficiency and on the FM bandwidth is studied in Figure 5.27 [53]. Here, the solid and broken curves represent the cases of $N_D = 2 \cdot 10^{18}$ cm^{-3} n-doped and undoped tuning region. As can be clearly seen, doping and tuning current bias both decrease the tuning efficiency but improve the FM bandwidth. While for an undoped tuning region, the FM bandwidth is below 100 MHz at small tuning current bias, FM bandwidths of the order 500 MHz can be achieved at the most at large tuning current bias and/or high doping levels. As a consequence, the TTG and multisection DBR lasers that exploit the free-carrier plasma effect in a passive tuning region are not suited for high-speed FM modulation exceeding several hundred

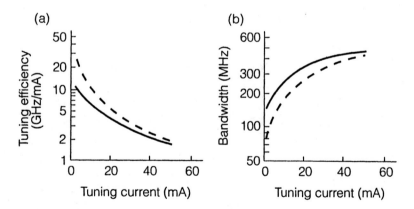

Figure 5.27   Tuning efficiency (a) and 3-dB FM modulation bandwidth (b) versus tuning current bias of a TTG laser with $N_D = 2 \cdot 10^{18}$ cm^{-3} n-doped (solid curves) and undoped (broken curves) tuning region (after [53]).

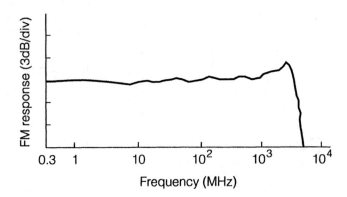

Figure 5.28   Relative FM modulation response versus frequency of a TTG laser with an MQW tuning region exploiting the QCSE. (Reprinted with permission from *Applied Physics Letters*, Vol. 60, pp. 2472–2474, ©1992 American Institute of Physics.).

megahertz but are sufficiently fast for most wavelength-switching applications, such as used in sensing or optical heterodyne receivers.

Using the QCSE (c. f., Section 4.5.2) in the tuning region, carrier lifetime limitations are no longer present, and large FM modulation bandwidth may be accomplished. This was demonstrated for the case of the TTG laser, where the use of the QCSE resulted in a marked bandwidth improvement of up to about 3 to 4 GHz, as shown in Figure 5.28 [48]. On the other hand, however, in these devices the tuning range was reduced to below 1 nm. The dip at about 3 GHz is attributed to the relaxation frequency of the laser active region, which is coupled to the tuning region by way of the gain-loss coupling. The bandwidth limitation to about 4 GHz in this device is mainly due to parasitic capacitances of the tuning region bonding pads.

While the dynamics of the parasitic thermal tuning and its interference with the purely electronic tuning by the plasma effect can be neglected in well-designed TTG lasers, owing to the strong dominance of the electronic tuning effect, the relationship between electronic and thermal tuning is less advantageous in the case of the multisection DBR lasers. Usually, therefore, one has to take into account the combined effects of both tuning mechanisms with different signs and different time constants. The numerical results of a theoretical investigation are plotted in Figure 5.29 [54]. This figure shows the temporal evolution of the wavelength change following three different phase section step currents that all lead to an electronic wavelength shift of –0.48 nm. The left part of this figure displays the time response within the first 5 ns, where the thermal response plays a negligible role, while the right part shows the response over the entire settling time including the thermal effect. It should be noted that unlike our treatment in Section 4.7, the dynamics of the thermal tuning are approached here by assuming a first-order low pass characteristic with a time constant of 0.5 μs. As expected, the fastest electronic switching times are obtained for the large phase section currents, yielding switching times down to 2 ns for the current step from 40 to 60 mA, while a 9-ns switching time occurs for the current step from 6 to 10 mA. However, the slower thermal contribution is much stronger for the former case, as shown in the right part of the figure, showing an almost complete

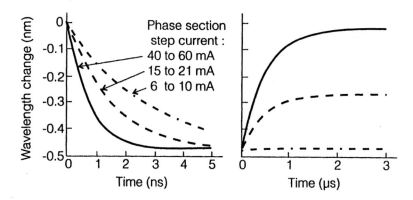

Figure 5.29   Calculated time dependence of the wavelength change for a step change of the phase current in a three-section DBR laser. (Reprinted with permission from *IEEE Photonics Technology Letters*, Vol. 6, pp. 694–696, ©1994 IEEE.)

compensation of the electronic tuning after about 1 μs. In the case of the small current step from 6 to 10 mA, on the other hand, the thermal contribution can be neglected and no compensation occurs. This investigation thus clearly shows that the interaction between thermal and electronic tuning must usually be taken into account.

The possibility to perform a red or a blue shifted tuning or FM modulation, respectively, by modulating the center or the side electrodes of a multisection DFB laser, may be used to perform either a pure FM or a pure AM modulation by a proper distribution of the modulation current. The time-dependent RF current and frequency shift for a three-section DFB laser modulated with a 100-MHz sinusoidal signal is plotted in Figure 5.30 [55]. An obviously opposite and almost equally large frequency shift is obtained

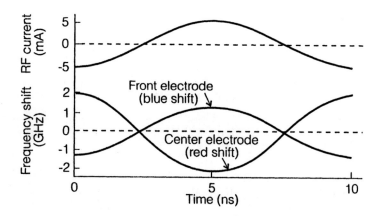

Figure 5.30   Temporal lasing frequency deviation during 100-MHz sinusoidal modulation of the center and front electrode of a three-section DFB laser. (Reprinted with permission from *IEEE Journal of Lightwave Technology*, Vol. 5, pp. 516–522, ©1987 IEEE.)

modulating the front or the center electrodes. So by a combined modulation, both a pure FM modulation as well as a pure AM modulation has been presented [55]. Because the tuning efficiencies strongly depend on the bias conditions and may vary from device to device, however, the practical use of this technique is rather limited. Nevertheless, it represents the principle of a possible approach for high-performance direct laser modulation, either AM modulation without chirping or FM modulation without AM contribution.

REFERENCES

[1] Amann, M.-C., "Linewidth enhancement in distributed-feedback semiconductor lasers," *Electronics Letters*, Vol. 26, 1990, pp. 569–571.

[2] Tohmori, Y., Komori, K., Arai, S., Suematsu, Y., and Oohashi, H., "Wavelength tunable 1.5 μm GaInAsP/InP bundle-integrated-guide distributed Bragg reflector (BIG-DBR) lasers," *The Transactions of the IECE of Japan*, Vol. E 68, 1985, pp. 788–790.

[3] Koch, T. L., Koren, U., and Miller, B. I., "High performance tunable 1.5 μm InGaAs/InGaAsP multiple quantum well distributed feedback Bragg reflector lasers," *Applied Physics Letters*, Vol. 53, 1988, pp. 1036–1038.

[4] Westbrook, L. D., Nelson, A. W., Fiddyment, P. J., and Collins, J. V., "Monolithic 1.5 μm hybrid DFB/DBR lasers with 5 nm tuning range," *Electronics Letters*, Vol. 20, 1984, pp. 957–959.

[5] Broberg, B., and Nilsson, S., "Widely tunable active Bragg reflector integrated lasers in InGaAsP-InP," *Applied Physics Letters*, Vol. 52, 1988, pp. 1285–1287.

[6] Okuda, M., and Onaka, K., "Tunability of distributed Bragg-reflector laser by modulating refractive index in corrugated waveguide," *Japanese Journal of Applied Physics*, Vol. 16, 1977, pp. 1501–1502.

[7] Delorme, F., Slempkes, S., Ramdane, A., Rose, B., and Nakjima, H., "Subnanosecond tunable distributed Bragg reflector lasers with an electrooptical Bragg section," *IEEE Journal of Selected Topics in Quantum Electronics*, Vol. 1, 1995, pp. 396–400.

[8] Ishida, O., Tada, Y., and Ishii, H., "Tuning-current splitting network for three-section DBR lasers," *Electronics Letters*, Vol. 30, 1994, pp. 241–242.

[9] Murata, S., Mito, I., and Kobayashi, K., "Over 720 GHz (5.8 nm) frequency tuning by a 1.5 μm DBR laser with phase and Bragg wavelength control regions," *Electronics Letters*, Vol. 23, 1987, pp. 403–405.

[10] Pan, X., Olesen, H., and Tromborg, B., "A theoretical model of multielectrode DBR lasers," *IEEE Journal of Quantum Electronics*, Vol. 24, 1988, pp. 2423–2432.

[11] Caponio, N. P., Goano, M., Maio, I., Meliga, M., Bava, G. P., Destefanis, G., and Montrosset, I., "Analysis and design criteria of three-section DBR tunable lasers," *IEEE Journal of Selected Areas in Communications*, Vol. 8, 1990, pp. 1203–1213.

[12] Stoltz, B., Dasler, M., and Sahlen, O., "Low threshold-current, wide tuning-range, butt-joint DBR laser grown with four MOVPE steps," *Electronics Letters*, Vol. 29, 1993, pp. 700–702.

[13] Reid, T. J., Park, C. A., Williams, P. J., Wood, A. K., and Buus, J., "3.8 nm continuous tuning range of a low threshold distributed Bragg reflector laser," *12th IEEE International Semiconductor Laser Conference*, pp. 242–243, Davos, Switzerland, 1990.

[14] Koch, T. L., Koren, U., Gnall, R. P., Burrus, C. A., and Miller, B. I., "Continuously tunable 1.5 μm multiple-quantum-well GaInAs/GaInAsP distributed-Bragg-reflector lasers," *Electronics Letters*, Vol. 24, 1988, pp. 1431–1433.

[15] Kotaki, Y., Matsuda, M., Ishikawa, H., and Imai, H., "Tunable DBR laser with wide tuning range," *Electronics Letters*, Vol. 24, 1988, pp. 503–505.

[16] Kuindersma, P. I., "Continuous tunability of DBR lasers," *International Conference on Integrated Optics and Optical Fiber Communication*, pp. 19A2–1, Kobe, Japan, 1989.

[17] Murata, S., Mito, I., and Kobayashi, K., "Tuning ranges for 1.5 μm wavelength tunable DBR lasers," *Electronics Letters*, Vol. 24, 1988, pp. 577–579.

[18] Delorme, F., Grosmaire, S., Gloukhian, A., and Ougazzaden, A., "High power operation of widely tunable 1.55 μm distributed Bragg reflector laser," *Electronics Letters*, Vol. 33, 1997, pp. 210–211.

[19] Öberg, M., Nilsson, S., Klinga, T., and Ojala, P., "A three-electrode distributed Bragg reflector laser with 22 nm wavelength tuning range," *IEEE Photonics Technology Letters*, Vol. PTL-3, 1991, pp. 299–301.

[20] Woodward, S. L., Koren, U., Miller, B. I., Young, M. G., Newkirk, M. A., and Burrus, C. A., "A DBR laser tunable by resistive heating," *IEEE Photonics Technology Letters*, Vol. 4, 1992, pp. 1330–1332.

[21] Kameda, T., Mori, H., Onuki, S., Kikugawa, T., Takahashi, Y., Tsuchiya, F., and Nagai, H., "A DBR laser employing passive-section heaters, with 10.8 nm tuning range and 1.6 MHz linewidth," *IEEE Photonics Technology Letters*, Vol. 5, 1993, pp. 608–610.

[22] Kobayashi, K., and Mito, I., "Single frequency and tunable laser diodes," *IEEE Journal of Lightwave Technology*, Vol. 6, 1988, pp. 1623–1633.

[23] Dutta, N. K., Piccirilli, A. B., Cella, T., and Brown, R. L., "Electronically tunable distributed feedback lasers," *Applied Physics Letters*, Vol. 48, 1986, pp. 1501–1503.

[24] Correc, P., "Tunability of multisection DFB lasers," *IEEE Journal of Quantum Electronics*, Vol. 32, 1996, pp. 972–980.

[25] Tohyama, M., Onomura, M., Funemizu, M., and Suzuki, N., "Wavelength tuning mechanism in three-electrode DFB lasers," *IEEE Photonics Technology Letters*, Vol. 5, 1993, pp. 616–618.

[26] Kusnetzow, M., "Theory of wavelength tuning in two-segment distributed feedback lasers," *IEEE Journal of Quantum Electronics*, Vol. 24, 1988, pp. 1837–1844.

[27] Paschos, V., Sphicopoulos, T., Syvridis, D., and Caroubalos, C., "Influence of thermal effects on the tunability of three-electrode DFB lasers," *IEEE Journal of Quantum Electronics*, Vol. 30, 1994, pp. 660–667.

[28] Amann, M.-C., Baumann, G., Borchert, B., Lang, H., and Unzeitig, H., "Wavelength tunable single-mode metal-clad ridge-waveguide lasers for 1.55 μm wavelength region," *Archiv für Elektronik und Übertragungstechnik—Electronics and Communications*, Vol. 43, 1989, pp. 390–393.

[29] Okai, M., Sakano, S., and Chinone, N., "Wide-range continuous tunable double-sectioned distributed feedback lasers," *15th European Conference on Optical Communications (ECOC '89)*, pp. 122–125, Gothenburg, Sweden, 1989.

[30] Kotaki, Y., Ogita, S., Matsuda, M., Kuwahara, Y., and Ishikawa, H., "Tunable narrow-linewidth and high-power $\lambda/4$-shifted DFB laser," *Electronics Letters*, Vol. 25, 1989, pp. 990–992.

[31] Numai, T., Murata, S., and Mito, I., "1.5 μm wavelength tunable phase-shift controlled distributed feedback laser diode with constant spectral linewidth in tuning operation," *Electronics Letters*, Vol. 24, 1988, pp. 1526–1528.

[32] Okai, M., and Tsuchiya, T., "Tunable DFB lasers with ultra-narrow spectral linewidth," *Electronics Letters*, Vol. 29, 1993, pp. 349–351.

[33] Horita, M., Tsurusawa, M., Utaka, K., and Matsushima, Y., "Wavelength-tunable InGaAsP-InP multiple-$\lambda/4$-shifted distributed feedback laser," *IEEE Journal of Quantum Electronics*, Vol. 29, 1993, pp. 1810–1816.

[34] Leclerc, D., Jacquet, J., Sigogne, D., Labourie, C., Louis, Y., Artigue, C., and Benoit, J., "Three-electrode DFB wavelength tunable FSK transmitter at 1.53 μm," *Electronics Letters*, Vol. 25, 1989, pp. 45–47.

[35] Kuindersma, P. I., Scheepers, W., Cnoops, J. M. H., Thijs, P. J. A., Van der Hofstad, G. L. A., Van Dongen, T., and Binsma, J. J. M., "Tunable three-section, strained MQW, PA-DFB's with large single mode tuning range (72 Å) and narrow linewidth (around 1 MHz)," *12th IEEE Semiconductor Laser Conference*, pp. 248–249, Davos, Switzerland, 1990.

[36] Hillmer, H., Grabmaier, A., Zhu, H.-L., Hansmann, S., and Burkhard, H., "Continuously chirped DFB gratings by specially bent waveguides for tunable lasers," *IEEE Journal of Lightwave Technology*, Vol. 13, 1995, pp. 1905–1912.

[37] Amann, M.-C., Illek, S., Schanen, C., and Thulke, W., "Tunable twin-guide laser: A novel laser diode with improved tuning performance," *Applied Physics Letters*, Vol. 54, 1989, pp. 2532–2533.

[38] Amann, M.-C., Illek, S., Schanen, C., and Thulke, W., "Tuning range and threshold current of the tunable twin-guide (TTG) laser," *IEEE Photonics Technology Letters*, Vol. 1, 1989, pp. 253–254.

[39] Wolf, T., Westermeier, H., and Amann, M.-C., "Continuously tunable metal-clad ridge-waveguide distributed feedback laser diode," *Electronics Letters*, Vol. 26, 1990, pp. 1845–1846.

[40] Wolf, T., Illek, S., Rieger, J., Borchert, B., and Amann, M.-C., "Tunable twin-guide (TTG) distributed feedback (DFB) laser with over 10 nm continuous tuning range," *Electronics Letters*, Vol. 29, 1993, pp. 2124–2125.

[41] Schanen, C. F. J., Illek, S., Lang, H., Thulke, W., and Amann, M.-C., "Fabrication and lasing characteristics of $\lambda = 1.56$ μm tunable twin-guide (TTG) DFB lasers," *IEE Proceedings*, Part J, Vol. 137, 1990, pp. 69–73.

[42] Amann, M.-C., and Thulke, W., "Current confinement and leakage currents in planar buried-ridge-structure laser diodes on n-substrate," *IEEE Journal of Quantum Electronics*, Vol. 25, 1989, pp. 1595–1602.

[43] Illek, S., Wolf, T., Borchert, B., Veuhoff, E., and Rieger, J., "Leakage current reduction in buried heterostructure tunable twin-guide laser diodes," *Japanese Journal of Applied Physics*, Vol. 31, 1992, pp. L689–L691.

[44] Wolf, T., Illek, S., Rieger, J., Borchert, B., and Amann, M.-C., "Extended continuous tuning range (over 10 nm) of tunable twin-guide lasers," *Conference on Lasers and Electro-Optics (CLEO '94)*, p. CWB 1, Anaheim, CA, 1994.

[45] Sakata, Y., Yamaguchi, M., Takano, S., Shim, J.-I., Sasaki, T., Kitamura, M., and Mito, I., "Novel tunable twin-guide lasers with a carrier-control tuning layer," *Optical Fiber Conference (OFC '93)*, pp. 9–10, San Jose, CA, 1993.

[46] Yamamoto, E., Hamada, M., Suda, K., Nogiwa, S., and Oki, T., "Wavelength tuning characteristics of tunable twin-guide lasers with improved current-injection structures," *Applied Physics Letters*, Vol. 60, 1992, pp. 805–806.

[47] Yamamoto, E., Suda, K., Hamada, M., Nogiwa, S., and Oki, T., "Tunable laser diode having a complementary twin-active-guide (CTAG) structure," *Japanese Journal of Applied Physics*, Vol. 30, 1991, pp. L1884–L1886.

[48] Wolf, T., Drögemüller, K., Borchert, B., Westermeier, H., Veuhoff, E., and Baumeister, H., "Tunable twin-guide lasers with flat frequency modulation response by quantum confined Stark effect," *Applied Physics Letters*, Vol. 60, 1992, pp. 2472–2474.

[49] Sakano, S., Tsuchiya, T., Suzuki, M., Kitajima, S., and Chinone, N., "Tunable DFB laser with a striped thin-film heater," *IEEE Photonics Technology Letters*, Vol. 4, 1992, pp. 321–323.

[50] Amann, M.-C., and Thulke, W., "Continuously tunable laser diodes: Longitudinal versus transverse tuning scheme," *IEEE Journal of Selected Areas in Communications*, Vol. 8, 1990, pp. 1169–1177.

[51] Kuznetsov, M., Willner, A. E., and Kaminow, I. P., "Frequency modulation response of tunable two-segment distributed feedback lasers," *Applied Physics Letters*, Vol. 55, 1989, pp. 1826–1828.

[52] Tohyama, M., Funemizu, M., Onomura, M., Takakuwa, C., and Suzuki, N., "Mechanism of wavelength tuning and frequenzy modulation in three-electrode DFB lasers," *IEEE Journal of Selected Topics in Quantum Electronics*, Vol. 1, 1995, pp. 416–426.

[53] Drögemüller, K., and Illek, S., "Frequency modulation characteristics of tunable twin-guide (TTG) DFB lasers," *16th European Conference on Optical Communications (ECOC '90)*, pp. 181–184, Amsterdam, The Netherlands, 1990.

[54] Braagaard, C., Mikkelsen, B., Durhuus, T., and Stubkjaer, K. E., "Modelling the dynamics of wavelength tuning in DBR-lasers," *IEEE Photonics Technology Letters*, Vol. 6, 1994, pp. 694–696.

[55] Yoshikuni, Y., and Motosugi, G., "Multielectrode distributed feedback laser for pure frequency modulation and chirping suppressed amplitude modulation," *IEEE Journal of Lightwave Technology*, Vol. 5, 1987, pp. 516–522.

Chapter 6

Linewidth Broadening

In many applications, the spectral linewidth is an important parameter of single-mode laser diodes. In particular, optical heterodyning [1], as used, for example, in optical spectrum analysis and coherent optical communications [2], reflectometry [3] and ranging [4] are very sensitive to linewidth broadening mechanisms. Also, spectroscopic and sensing applications usually require a certain spectral purity [5]. We will see that the electronic wavelength tuning may have genuine effects on the spectral linewidth of laser diodes. While the deterioriation of the optical spectrum and the linewidth of a discontinuously tuned laser diode is obvious, also the spectral linewidth of continuously tunable laser diodes may be worsened by the tuning. Besides the linewidth broadening by the additional losses introduced by the tuning function, shot noise of the injected carriers becomes significant in the most important case where the plasma effect is applied.

Since the thermal tuning has a negligible influence on the spectral linewidth [6], our investigations in Chapter 6 cover in particular the spectral linewidth characteristics of lasers tuned by the free-carrier plasma effect. This also includes the influences of electronic noise sources in the bias circuit. Because of the variable *SSR* of the discontinuously and quasicontinuously tunable laser diodes, their spectral linewidth shows strong variations during tuning, including singularities at the mode boundaries where wavelength jumps occur [7]. Accordingly, the spectral linewidth is not well defined for this type of lasers and has not yet attracted particular attention. On the other hand, the continuously tunable laser diodes have been studied extensively with respect to their spectral linewidth, and their spectral performance is well understood. We thus restrict the investigations in this chapter on the spectral linewidth of the continuously tunable laser diodes.

Strong linewidth broadening has been observed for most types of continuously tunable lasers that use the free-carrier plasma effect [8, 9]. In particular, it has been found that the spectral linewidth shows a distinct broadening upon applying the tuning current, whereby the devices with a larger tuning range exhibit the larger broadening. As a representative example Figure 6.1 shows the total spectral linewidth versus tuning current of a widely tunable 400-μm-long TTG DFB laser with a tuning range of 7 nm. As can clearly be seen, the linewidth increases from 5 MHz at a zero tuning current to about 50 MHz at a tuning current of about 6 mA (i. e., an increase by an order of magnitude). Increasing the tuning current above 6 mA leads to a slight decreasing spectral linewidth. Such a striking linewidth variation with a peak at small tuning currents has also been

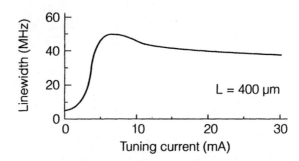

Figure 6.1   Spectral linewidth of a widely tunable (7-nm) 400-μm-long TTG laser versus tuning current.

observed for other types of tunable laser diodes [8], however, the peak may not be clearly visible in weakly tunable devices [10]. This spectral behavior cannot be explained by the additional optical losses introduced by the injected carriers because the latter increase monotonically with the tuning current. Instead, it has been shown that the shot noise of the carriers injected into the tuning region determines the linewidth broadening [11]. The corresponding injection-recombination shot noise (IRSN) theory is derived in Section 6.1, and the effects of the various device parameters are investigated. The effects of the impedance and thermal noise of the bias source on the IRSN are discussed in Section 6.2. The local noise currents and carrier density fluctuations along the tuning diode may be electronically correlated over the *p*- and *n*-contacts. Correspondingly, the effect of the correlation on the linewidth broadening is studied in Section 6.3. In addition, $1/f$ electronic noise can occur, for example, by surface recombination at the laser facets, and may strongly affect the spectral performance. Experimental and theoretical work on the effect of electronic $1/f$ noise on the spectral linewidth of tunable laser diodes and techniques to reduce it are compiled in Section 6.4. Finally, the contribution of bias source fluctuations is outlined in Section 6.5

6.1 INJECTION-RECOMBINATION SHOT NOISE IN THE TUNING REGION

The physical origin for the distinct linewidth broadening of current-tuned laser diodes exploiting the plasma effect is the carrier density fluctuation in the tuning regions caused by the shot noise effect of the carrier injection and recombination. This electronic noise mechanism, referred to as IRSN, leads to corresponding refractive index and loss fluctuations that, in turn, produce fluctuations of the instantaneous laser frequency that finally leads to a broadened spectral line. Since the IRSN is statistically independent from the spontaneous recombination in the active region, its contribution $\Delta\nu_t$ to the total laser linewidth $\Delta\nu_{tot}$ may be added to the Schawlow-Townes-Henry (STH) natural linewidth component $\Delta\nu_{STH}$ (3.82) provided both phase noise sources are Gaussian.

A simplified laser model for IRSN is outlined in Figure 6.2. As illustrated in Figure 6.2(a), the fluctuating carrier density in the tuning region, which is placed within the laser cavity, may affect the light propagating along the laser axis. The relevant effects of the carrier density fluctuations on laser characteristics are shown in the schematic dia-

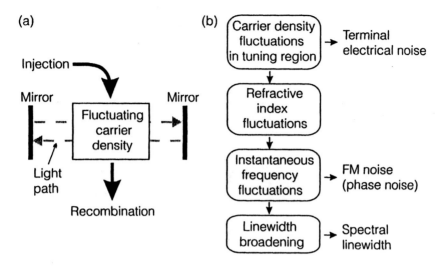

Figure 6.2   Linewidth broadening by IRSN in the tuning region: (a) simplified laser model and (b) effects of IRSN on various device parameters.

gram of Figure 6.2(b), indicating also the measurable electronic and optical parameters. In fact, IRSN occurs in the active region of any laser diode; however, the gain-clamping mechanism suppresses carrier density fluctuations so that the effect of IRSN in the active region on the spectral linewidth can usually be neglected.

We now investigate the effect of the IRSN in the tuning diode on the terminal electric noise, the FM-noise, and the spectral linewidth, applying the FM noise treatment of Henry [12]. For the sake of convenience, we first consider the TTG laser because it requires only one tuning region for continuous tuning. Noting that the carrier density fluctuations are relatively small with respect to the stationary value, the calculation of the IRSN in the tuning region starts with the small-signal approximation for the rate equations as derived in Section 2.6. The carrier density fluctuations in the tuning region are obtained by adding the Langevin noise force $F_t(t)$ to the rate equation. Since stimulated emission does not occur in the tuning region, the rate equation (corresponding to (2.52)) for the carrier density in the tuning region reads

$$\frac{dN_t}{dt} = \frac{I_t}{eV_t} - R_t(N_t) + F_t(t) \tag{6.1}$$

where the index t stands for the tuning region. We decompose the carrier density into a stationary and a (small) time-dependent part:

$$N_t(t) = N_{t0} + \Delta N_t(t) \tag{6.2}$$

and use the concept of the differential carrier lifetime (2.77) to approximate the recombination rate as

$$R_t(N_t) = R_t(N_{t0}) + \frac{\Delta N_t}{\tau_d} \tag{6.3}$$

Noting that $dN_{t0}/dt = 0$ we can split (6.1) into two equations, one for the stationary terms

$$R_t(N_{t0}) = \frac{I_{t0}}{eV_t} \tag{6.4}$$

where $I_{t0} = <I_t>$, with $< \dots >$ denoting ensemble averaging, and one for the fluctuating terms

$$\frac{d\Delta N_t}{dt} = -\frac{\Delta N_t}{\tau_d} + F_t \tag{6.5}$$

The Langevin force F_t has a mean value of zero:

$$< F_t(t) >= 0 \tag{6.6}$$

and is assumed to be Markoffian; that is, it has no memory and its autocorrelation function is [13]

$$\rho_F(\tau) = <F_t(t)F_t(t+\tau)> = \frac{2R_t(N_{t0})}{V_t} \delta(\tau) = \frac{2I_{t0}}{eV_t^2} \delta(\tau) \tag{6.7}$$

where $\delta(\tau)$ is Dirac's delta function.

Because of the linearization by the small-signal approximation, the rate equation (6.5) can be solved by applying Fourier transformation (4.26) expressing $\Delta N_t(t)$ and $F_t(t)$ in the time domain as $\Delta \tilde{N}_t(\omega)$ and $\tilde{F}_t(\omega)$ in the frequency domain. (6.5) then becomes

$$j\omega \Delta \tilde{N}_t = -\frac{\Delta \tilde{N}_t}{\tau_d} + \tilde{F}_t \tag{6.8}$$

and (6.6) and (6.7) can be transformed into

$$< \tilde{F}_t(\omega) >= 0 \tag{6.9}$$

and

$$< \tilde{F}_t(\omega)\tilde{F}_t^*(\omega + \Delta\omega) >= \frac{I_{t0}}{\pi eV_t^2} \delta(\Delta\omega) \tag{6.10}$$

Using (4.27), (6.8), and (6.10), the autocorrelation function of ΔN_t is obtained as

$$\rho_{\Delta N}(\tau) = <\Delta N_t(t)\Delta N_t(t+\tau)> = \frac{I_{t0}\tau_d}{eV_t^2} e^{-|\tau/\tau_d|} \tag{6.11}$$

The autocorrelation function of the tuning diode terminal voltage fluctuation ΔU_D is

$$\rho_D(\tau) = \left(\frac{dU_D}{d\Delta N_t}\right)^2 \rho_{\Delta N}(\tau) \qquad (6.12)$$

where $dU_D/d\Delta N_t$ can be developed as

$$\frac{dU_D}{d\Delta N_t} = \underbrace{\frac{dU_D}{dI_t}}_{R_d} \underbrace{\frac{dI_t}{dR_t}}_{eV_t} \underbrace{\frac{dR_t}{d\Delta N_t}}_{1/\tau_d} \qquad (6.13)$$

with R_d denoting the differential tuning diode electrical resistance. According to the Wiener–Khintchine theorem [14], the spectral noise spectral power density $W_D(f)$ of U_D and the autocorrelation function $\rho_D(\tau)$ (6.12) form a Fourier transform pair

$$W_D(f) = 4 \int_0^\infty \rho_D(\tau) \cos(2\pi f \tau) \, d\tau \qquad (6.14)$$

$$\rho_D(\tau) = \int_0^\infty W_D(f) \cos(2\pi f \tau) \, df \qquad (6.15)$$

With (6.11), (6.12), and (6.14), we thus obtain

$$W_D(f) = \frac{4eI_{t0}R_d^2}{1 + (2\pi f \tau_d)^2} \qquad (6.16)$$

For an ideal diode, the current voltage characteristic reads $I_t(U_D) \propto e^{eU_D/k_BT}$, yielding $R_d = k_BT/eI_{t0}$. Inserting this into (6.16) shows that for low frequencies ($f \ll 1/2\pi\tau_d$), the double-heterostructure shows a noise-power spectral density identical to that of the thermal noise of an ideal resistor with resistance R_d (i. e., $W_D(f) = 4k_BTR_d$). $W_D(f)$ can be measured at the tuning diode terminals, so that deviations from ideality can easily be distinguished. A detailed theoretical investigation of the noise processes in pn-junction light emitters and the associated voltage fluctuations can be found in [15].

The contribution of the IRSN in the tuning region to the spectral spectral power density $W_{FM}(f)$ of the laser FM noise is calculated as

$$W_{FM,t}(f) = \left(\frac{df}{dU_D}\right)^2 W_D(f) = 4e\frac{c^2}{\lambda^4}\left(\frac{d\lambda}{dI_t}\right)^2 \frac{I_{t0}}{1 + (2\pi f \tau_d)^2} \qquad (6.17)$$

where df/dU_D has been expanded as

$$\frac{df}{dU_D} = \underbrace{\frac{df}{d\lambda}}_{-c/\lambda^2} \underbrace{\frac{d\lambda}{dI_t}}_{} \underbrace{\frac{dI_t}{dU_D}}_{1/R_d} \qquad (6.18)$$

The autocorrelation function of the frequency deviation from the IRSN, which is the Fourier transform of $W_{FM,t}(f)$, reads

$$\rho_{\Delta f}(\tau) \; = \; < \Delta f(t) \Delta f(t+\tau) > = \left(\frac{df}{d \Delta N_t} \right)^2 \rho_{\Delta N}(\tau) \tag{6.19}$$

$$= \; \frac{e I_{t0} c^2}{\tau_d \lambda^4} \left(\frac{d\lambda}{dI_t} \right)^2 e^{-|\tau/\tau_d|} \tag{6.20}$$

The linewidth broadening $\Delta \nu_t$ due to this FM noise is calculated analogous to (3.78) and (3.79) as

$$\Delta \nu_t = \lim_{t \to \infty} \frac{< \Delta \phi_t^2 >}{2 \pi t} \tag{6.21}$$

where $\Delta \phi_t$ is the optical phase change due to the fluctuations, the variance of which is

$$< \Delta \phi_t^2 > = \int_0^t \int_0^t < \Delta \dot\phi_t(\xi) \Delta \dot\phi_t(\xi') > d\xi' \, d\xi \tag{6.22}$$

Noting that $\Delta \dot\phi_t = 2\pi \Delta f$ and putting $\xi' = \xi + \tau$, we rewrite (6.22) as

$$< \Delta \phi_t^2 > = (2\pi)^2 \int_0^t \int_{-\xi}^{t-\xi} \rho_{\Delta f}(\tau) \, d\tau \, d\xi \tag{6.23}$$

Evaluating (6.23) with (6.20) and inserting the result into (6.21) finally yields for the linewidth broadening by IRSN in the tuning region

$$\Delta \nu_t = 4\pi e \frac{c^2}{\lambda^4} \left(\frac{d\lambda}{dI_t} \right)^2 I_t \tag{6.24}$$

Numerical Example: Taking the TTG laser from Figure 5.20 with $\lambda = 1{,}550 \, \text{nm}$, $d\lambda/dI_t = 0.4 \, \text{nm/mA}$ at $I_{t0} = 5 \, \text{mA}$ yields $\Delta \nu_t = 12.5 \, \text{MHz}$, which well compares with the linewidth broadening of typical TTG lasers.

The case of the continuously tuned three-section DBR laser is more complicated because both the phase section and Bragg section produce IRSN. Denoting the Bragg section and phase section currents as I_B and I_p, respectively, the composite linewidth broadening was calculated as [11]

$$\Delta \nu_t = 4\pi e \frac{c^2}{\lambda^4} \left\{ \left(\frac{\partial \lambda}{\partial I_p} \right)^2_{I_B = \text{const.}} I_p + \kappa L_B \left(\frac{\partial \lambda}{\partial I_B} \right)^2_{I_p = \text{const.}} I_B \right\} \tag{6.25}$$

where L_B is the length of the Bragg section and κ is the coupling coefficient of the Bragg grating. As can be seen, the linewidth broadening is each proportional to the tuning efficiencies $d\lambda/dI_t$, $\partial \lambda/\partial I_p$, and $\partial \lambda/\partial I_B$ squared.

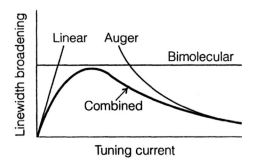

Figure 6.3   Effect of the various recombination processes on the IRSN linewidth broadening versus tuning current.

Numerical Example: Considering the 1,550-nm three-section DBR laser from Figure 5.7 with $I_B = 20$ mA, $\partial\lambda/\partial I_B \approx 0.15$ nm/mA, $I_p = 3$ mA, and $\partial\lambda/\partial I_p \approx 0.3$ nm/mA and assuming $\kappa L_B = 3$ yields $\Delta\nu_t \approx 22$ MHz.

A detailed theory of the more general case of a tunable multisection DFB laser [16] also showed the proportionality between linewidth broadening and tuning efficiency squared. However, in the case of the DFB laser, the tuning efficiency is much smaller than for the TTG and most three-section DBR lasers. Accordingly, the IRSN linewidth broadening is less important and the natural linewidth usually determines the total DFB laser linewidth.

Decomposing the tuning efficiency in (6.24) as

$$\frac{d\lambda}{dI_t} = \frac{d\lambda}{dn_{eff}}\frac{dn_{eff}}{dN_t}\frac{dN_t}{dI_t} = \frac{\lambda}{n_{eff}}\beta_{pl,t}\Gamma_t\frac{dN_t}{dI_t} \tag{6.26}$$

reveals that $\Delta\nu_t$ is proportional to $I_t(dN_t/dI_t)^2$. Here, $\beta_t = dn'_t/dN_t$ (c. f., (4.8)) measures the tuning region refractive index change (real part) by carrier density changes into the tuning region, and Γ_t is the tuning region confinement factor. Inspection of the stationary rate equation (2.17) and the recombination law (2.18) shows that in the cases of purely linear recombination ($B = C = 0$) $\Delta\nu_t \propto I_{t0}$, purely bimolecular recombination ($1/\tau_s = C = 0$) $\Delta\nu_t =$ const., and pure Auger recombination ($1/\tau_s = B = 0$) $\Delta\nu_t \propto I_{t0}^{-1/3}$. This is illustrated schematically in Figure 6.3, showing also the broadening for the most practical case where all recombination processes occur simultaneously. Obviously the broadening in the case of combined recombination well resembles the experimentally observed linewidth broadening plotted in Figure 6.1. Moreover, (6.24) also predicts, that the linewidth broadening is proportional to the continuous tuning range squared. Consequently, a wide continuous tuning range inevitably causes a large additional linewidth. This statement is also fairly well confirmed by the compilation of published linewidth data of various continuously tunable laser diodes in Figure 6.4. It should be noted that this diagram shows the total spectral linewidth, including the natural linewidth caused by spontaneous emission (Schawlow-Townes-Henry linewidth). Accordingly, the IRSN linewidth broadening dominates at large tuning range, while the data for small tuning ranges may consist mainly of the natural linewidth.

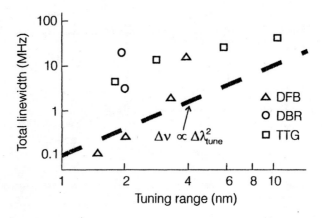

Figure 6.4   Maximal spectral linewidth data versus tuning range for various electronically tunable laser diodes taken from literature. The gray line indicates the proportionality to the tuning range squared.

Numerical Example: Considering purely bimolecular recombination in the tuning region of a TTG laser

$$\frac{I_{t0}}{eV_t} = B_t N_t^2 \tag{6.27}$$

we develop $d\lambda/dI_t$ as

$$\frac{d\lambda}{dI_t} = \frac{d\lambda}{dN_t}\frac{dN_t}{dI_t} \tag{6.28}$$

where $d\lambda/dN_t$ is assumed to be independent of N_t, and dN_t/dI_t is obtained by differentiating (6.27) as

$$\frac{dI_t}{dN_t} = 2eV_t B_t N_t \tag{6.29}$$

The linewidth broading by the IRSN is then calculated from (6.24) as

$$\Delta \nu_t = \frac{\pi}{V_t B_t}\frac{c^2}{\lambda^4}\left(\frac{d\lambda}{dN_t}\right)^2 \tag{6.30}$$

The tuning range $\Delta\lambda_{\text{tune}}$ is approached at the maximal possible injection $N_{t,\text{max}}$, obtained at the tuning current $I_{t,\text{max}}$:

$$\Delta\lambda_{\text{tune}} = \frac{d\lambda}{dN_t}N_{t,\text{max}} \tag{6.31}$$

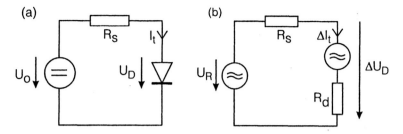

Figure 6.5   Bias circuit (a) and equivalent bias circuit (b) for tuning diode, including the effect of finite bias-source resistance R_s.

yielding with (6.30)

$$\Delta\nu_t = \pi e \frac{c^2}{\lambda^4} \frac{\Delta\lambda^2_{\text{tune}}}{I_{t,\text{max}}} \qquad (6.32)$$

For 1,550-nm lasers, this can also be written as

$$\Delta\nu_t \text{ [in MHz]} = 8 \frac{\Delta\lambda^2_{\text{tune}} \text{ [in nm}^2]}{I_{t,\text{max}} \text{ [in mA]}} \qquad (6.33)$$

For a tuning range of 8 nm at a tuning current of 50 mA, we thus obtain an IRSN broadening around 10 MHz.

6.2   IMPEDANCE AND THERMAL NOISE OF BIAS SOURCE

Up to now, we have investigated the current-controlled operation of the tuning diode, which means that the bias source resistance is assumed infinite and that the diode voltage has no effect on the current. This type of operation is most usual in practice. However, the application of a low-impedance bias source to operate the tuning diode in the voltage-controlled mode may reduce the IRSN linewidth broadening significantly. The influence of the bias-source impedance is studied by using the bias circuit shown in Figure 6.5. Besides the bias source internal resistance, R_s also contains the series and contact resistances of the tuning diode. Depending on R_s, this network allows the investigation of both, the current ($R_s \rightarrow \infty$) and voltage ($R_s \rightarrow 0$) controlled tuning schemes. The diode series and contact resistances usually put a lower limit to R_s of typically a few ohms. Consequently a complete voltage control is impossible in practice.

The reduction of the IRSN linewidth broadening by a low-impedance bias network can immediately be understood by considering that the carrier density fluctuations in the tuning diode are correlated with terminal voltage fluctuations via the splitting of the quasi-Fermi levels (4.21). Consequently, a reduction of the terminal voltage fluctuations by a low-resistive bias network would reduce the fluctuations of the quasi-Fermi level splitting, which in turn yields a reduction of the carrier density fluctuations. Because the time constant for the carrier relaxation is of the order 0.1 ps, we may assume that the carrier densities instantaneously follow any changes of the quasi-Fermi level split-ting or the diode voltage, respectively. On the other hand, thermal noise is introduced by R_s as indicated by the noise voltage source U_R in the figure. The reduction of the IRSN linewidth broadening by a *low-impedance* bias network seems to contradict the shot noise suppression of light-emitting diodes and laser diodes driven by a *high-impedance* bias source [17, 18]. This disagreement is resolved by considering that the linewidth broad-ening by phase noise is caused by carrier density fluctuations and not directly by current fluctuations, while the noise of the emitted light power is due to fluctuations of the carrier recombination rate and not directly due to carrier density fluctuations. Accordingly, in the case of a high-impedance bias, we get vanishing fluctuations of the tuning current but large fluctuations of the injected carrier density, while a low-impedance bias yields large current noise but suppresses the carrier density fluctuations.

The effect of the finite bias source resistance is taken into account by again sepa-rating the tuning current I_t into a stationary and fluctuating part:

$$I_t = I_{t0} + \Delta I_t \tag{6.34}$$

where $< \Delta I_t >= 0$. Both terms can be calculated by means of Figure 6.5 as

$$I_{t0} = \frac{U_0 - U_{D0}}{R_s} \qquad \text{and} \qquad \Delta I_t = \frac{U_R - \Delta U_D}{R_s} \tag{6.35}$$

U_R is the thermal noise voltage of the series resistance R_s with spectral spectral power density

$$W_R(f) = 4k_B T R_s \tag{6.36}$$

and autocorrelation function

$$\rho_R(\tau) = 2k_B T R_s \delta(\tau) \tag{6.37}$$

The fluctuating part of I_t is added to the small-signal rate equation for ΔN_t (6.5):

$$\frac{d\Delta N_t}{dt} = -\frac{\Delta N_t}{\tau_d} + F_t + \frac{\Delta I_t}{eV_t} \tag{6.38}$$

$$= -\frac{\Delta N_t}{\tau_d} + F_t + \frac{U_R - \Delta U_D}{eV_t R_s} \tag{6.39}$$

A damping feedback occurs via ΔU_D, because positive ΔN_t yields positive ΔU_D leading to negative $d\Delta N_t/dt$ using (6.39), which finally reduces ΔN_t. Using (6.37) and (6.13), we substitute $\Delta U_D = \Delta N_t dU_D/d\Delta N_t$, yielding a simple rate equation:

$$\frac{d\Delta N_t}{dt} = -\frac{\Delta N_t}{\tau_{\text{eff}}} + F_{\text{eff}} \tag{6.40}$$

with an effective time constant:

$$\tau_{\text{eff}} = \frac{\tau_d}{1 + R_d/R_s} \tag{6.41}$$

and an effective Langevin force F_{eff}. F_{eff} includes the contributions of the IRSN, F_l, and of the thermal noise in the series resistance, so that its autocorrelation function is obtained by combining (6.7) and (6.37) as

$$\rho_{F,\text{eff}}(\tau) = \frac{2I_{t0}}{eV_t^2}\left(1 + \frac{k_B T}{eI_{t0}R_s}\right)\delta(\tau) \tag{6.42}$$

The linewidth calculation follows the same method as in the preceding section and yields

$$\Delta\nu_t = 4\pi e \frac{c^2}{\lambda^4}\left(\frac{d\lambda}{dI_t}\right)^2 I_{t0} \underbrace{\frac{1 + k_B T/eR_s I_{t0}}{(1 + R_d/R_s)^2}}_{\zeta} \tag{6.43}$$

where the effect of the finite bias source impedance is put into the factor ζ. In case of an idealized tuning diode where $R_d = k_B T/eI_{t0}$, ζ reduces to

$$\zeta = \left(1 + \frac{k_B T}{eR_s I_{t0}}\right)^{-1} \tag{6.44}$$

According to the results from the preceding section, we see that in the current controlled tuning scheme ($R_s \to \infty$) one gets $\tau_{\text{eff}} \to \tau_d$ and $\zeta = 1$, while in the case of an ideal voltage control ($R_s \to 0$) the IRSN linewidth broadening vanishes completely since ζ approaches zero. Obviously ζ strongly depends on the tuning current. Starting with $\zeta = 0$ at $I_{t0} = 0$, ζ asymptotically approaches unity for $I_{t0} \to \infty$. It can be concluded from (6.43) and (6.44) that the regime of I_{t0}-values for which ζ and, consequently, the linewidth broadening remain small is approximately inversely proportional to R_s. Therefore the effect of the bias source resistance on the linewidth broadening is most dominant at small tuning currents (i. e., large R_d). As can be seen from the experimental data, also the strongest broadening occurs at relatively small tuning currents, so that the use of a low-resistive bias network will be effective in reducing the maximal IRSN linewidth broadening.

An experimental demonstration of the influence of the bias-source impedance on the spectral linewidth of a TTG laser is shown in Figure 6.6. In agreement with theory, the bias-source resistance has a strong effect on the linewidth, particularly for a small wavelength shift and, hence, small tuning current. It should finally be noted, that it is not necessary in practice to prepare a particular bias source with small impedance. In most cases it is sufficient to connect a capacitor of a capacity of a few microfarads in parallel to the tuning diode, yielding an effective low-impedance bias source for the AC voltage fluctuations, but not for the DC bias current.

6.3   CORRELATION OF NOISE SOURCES

In the previous sections, we neglected the longitudinal distribution of the current density injected into the tuning diode by implicitly assuming uncorrelated longitudinal current density. However, the inspection of a more detailed tuning diode equivalent circuit shown in Figure 6.7 indicates that the voltage fluctuations at any longitudinal location

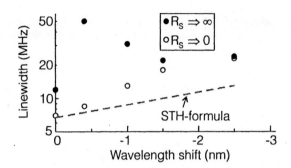

Figure 6.6 Experimentally observed effect of bias-source series resistance on spectral linewidth of a 400-μm-long TTG laser with a 7-nm tuning range. The broken curve represents the natural linewidth according to the Schawlow-Townes-Henry (STH) formula. (Reprinted with permission from *Electronics Letters*, Vol. 27, pp. 531–532, ©1991 IEE.)

changes the voltage between the *p*- and *n*-contact and thus may lead to a change of the current density along the entire laser axis. Here the series resistances within the diode (R_c) because of resistive (*p*-)confinement layers and contact resistance are considered as a parallel circuit of admittances χ_c, and the differential tuning diode resistance R_d is separated into admittances χ_d. Each admittance comes with an associated thermal noise current density j_c and j_d, respectively. Obviously, the noise current sources each influence the current density into the diode at any location and are correlated. This correlation of the internal noise sources is negligible in the case of large internal series resistance R_c, including the contact resistance. In the more common case, however, R_c is of the order of the differential tuning diode resistance R_d, so that the correlation becomes important. The effect of the relevant laser parameters on the correlation of the noise sources and the linewidth broadening was studied in detail [19], revealing that in case of low internal re-

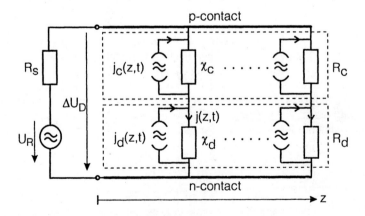

Figure 6.7 Small-signal equivalent circuit of a tuning diode with longitudinally distributed noise sources and conductances.

sistances and low tuning currents (large R_d) correlation usually occurs. Since a complete correlation reduces the IRSN linewidth broadening by a factor of 2, the experimental linewidth broadening becomes less pronounced at small tuning currents but remains almost unaffected at large currents. So the most important effect of the spatial correlation in well-designed tuning diodes is to reduce the peak linewidth broadening and making the spectral linewidth less dependent on the tuning current.

6.4   1/f NOISE

Even though the IRSN theory described in the previous sections may explain the major part of the tuning-induced linewidth broadening of the current tuned laser diodes, one usually still observes an even larger broadening. Again, this deviation is most pronounced for the widely continuously tunable devices. It was demonstrated [20] that this additional linewidth broadening stems from the nonideality of the tuning diode; namely, the occurrence of $1/f$ noise. This was experimentally verified by measuring the power spectra of the mean square terminal voltage noise as shown in Figure 6.8(a). As can be seen, $1/f$ noise is dominant for frequencies below about 1 MHz, showing an increase of the noise level of up to 30 dB at 1 kHz.

Also the power spectra of the angular frequency fluctuations (i. e., FM noise), clearly reveal this $1/f$ noise component as shown in Figure 6.8(b). Because the spectral linewidth is mainly determined by the low-frequency phase noise components, a marked linewidth broadening far above the contribution of the IRSN occurs. Significant $1/f$ FM noise was also reported for tunable DBR laser diodes [6]. Extending the linewidth analysis by including the $1/f$ noise, an excellent agreement is found with respect to the experimental findings [20]. It should be noted that the strong correlation between the terminal electrical noise and the FM noise may be used for noise reduction using an electrical feedback scheme [21].

As with other III-V semiconductor devices [22] and in agreement with noise measurements on InGaAsP MQW lasers [23], surface recombination at the laser facets was identified as relevant physical origin for the $1/f$ noise. Besides the production of $1/f$ noise, the surface recombination also modifies the current-voltage characteristics of the diodes [24]. This noise source also exists in the active region of the laser diodes; however, the gain-clamping mechanism cancels the associated carrier density fluctuations. Accordingly, the facet passivation with sulfur [25] yields a significant reduction of the $1/f$ noise with the corresponding reduced phase noise and smaller linewidth broadening [26]. As a consequence, TTG DFB lasers were developed with buried facets (BF TTG DFB laser) as shown in Figure 6.9(a) [27], in which the tuning and the active region are entirely embedded within a semiconductor material with a higher bandgap energy. The spectral linewidth measurements, which are plotted in Figure 6.9 together with data of common TTG DFB lasers, clearly prove the improved spectral performance of the BF TTG DFB lasers and confirm the impact of the $1/f$ recombination noise at the laser facets on the laser linewidth.

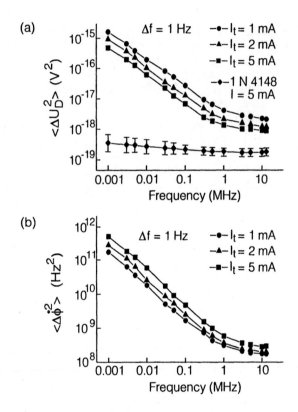

Figure 6.8   Spectra of mean square noise voltage at the tuning diode (a) and mean square angular frequency deviation (b) for a 400-μm-long TTG laser. For comparison measurements of the 1 N 4148 silicon pn-diode is added. (Reprinted with permission from *Applied Physics Letters*, Vol. 70, pp. 1512–1514, ©1997 American Institute of Physics.)

6.5   FLUCTUATIONS OF BIAS SOURCE

Considering that maximal tuning efficiencies of the order 1 nm/mA (i. e., about 125 GHz/mA at a 1,550-nm wavelength) may be achieved at $I_t = 1$ mA, clearly shows that fluctuations of the tuning current may strongly deteriorate the laser spectrum. If we assume a laser linewidth of 35 MHz, then, according to (6.24), a current change by about 0.35 μA leads to a wavelength shift comparable to the spectral linewidth. To exclude the deterioration of the spectrum by source current noise, a careful filtering is required and the current noise in this example should be kept below about 0.1 μA, corresponding to a voltage noise of only about 5 μV for a 50 Ω bias impedance. This also includes the suppression of induced currents due to antenna effects in the bias circuit so that one usually applies an effective low-pass filter near the tuning diode terminals. For accurate measurements of linewidth and in demanding applications, a stable power supply must be used (e. g., a battery).

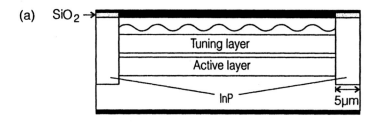

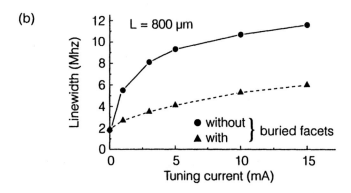

Figure 6.9   Longitudinal section of buried facets (BF) TTG laser (a) and spectral linewidth versus tuning current for equivalent TTG lasers with and without the buried facets (b). (Reprinted with permission from *Electronics Letters*, Vol. 33, pp. 1389–1390, ©1997 IEE.)

REFERENCES

[1] Shapiro, J. H., "Quantum noise and excess noise in optical homodyne and heterodyne receivers," *IEEE Journal of Quantum Electronics*, Vol. 21, 1985, pp. 237–250.

[2] Kazovsky, L. G., "Impact of laser phase noise on optical heterodyne communication systems," *Journal of Optical Communications*, Vol. 7, 1986, pp. 66–78.

[3] Uttam, D., and Culshaw, B., "Precision time domain reflectometry in optical fiber systems using a frequency modulated continuous wave ranging technique," *IEEE Journal of Lightwave Technology*, Vol. 3, 1985, pp. 971–977.

[4] Strzelecki, E. M., Cohen, D. A., and Coldren, L. A., "Investigation of tunable single frequency diode lasers for sensor applications," *IEEE Journal of Lightwave Technology*, Vol. 6, 1988, pp. 1610–1618.

[5] Sonnenfroh, D. M., and Allen, M. G., "Observation of CO and CO_2 absorption near 1.57 μm with an external-cavity diode laser," *Applied Optics*, Vol. 36, 1997, pp. 3298–3300.

[6] Ishii, H., Kano, F., Tohmori, Y., Kondo, Y., Tamamura, T., and Yoshikuni, Y., "Narrow spectral linewidth under wavelength tuning in thermally tunable super-structure-grating (SSG) DBR lasers," *IEEE Journal of Selected Topics in Quantum Electronics*, Vol. 1, 1995, pp. 401–407.

[7] Koch, T. L., Koren, U., Gnall, R. P., Burrus, C. A., and Miller, B. I., "Continuously tunable 1.5 μm multiple-quantum-well GaInAs/GaInAsP distributed-Bragg-reflector lasers," *Electronics Letters*, Vol. 24, 1988, pp. 1431–1433.

[8] Kotaki, Y., and Ishikawa, H., "Spectral characteristics of a three-section wavelength-tunable DBR laser," *IEEE Journal of Quantum Electronics*, Vol. 25, 1989, pp. 1340–1345.

[9]   Amann, M.-C., and Borchert, B., "Spectral linewidth of tunable twin-guide laser diodes," *Archiv für Elektronik und Übertragungstechnik—Electronics and Communications*, Vol. 46, 1992, pp. 63–72.

[10] Okai, M., and Tsuchiya, T., "Tunable DFB lasers with ultra-narrow spectral linewidth," *Electronics Letters*, Vol. 29, 1993, pp. 349–351.

[11] Amann, M.-C., and Schimpe, R., "Excess linewidth broadening in wavelength-tunable laser diodes," *Electronics Letters*, Vol. 26, 1990, pp. 279–280.

[12] Henry, C. H., "Theory of the phase noise and power spectrum of a single mode injection laser," *IEEE Journal of Quantum Electronics*, Vol. 19, 1983, pp. 1391–1397.

[13] Henry, C. H., "Phase noise in semiconductor lasers," *IEEE Journal of Lightwave Technology*, Vol. 4, 1986, pp. 298–311.

[14] Priestley, M. B., *Spectral analysis and time series*, London, U.K., Academic Press, 1981.

[15] Kim, J., and Yamamoto, Y., "Theory of noise in p-n junction light emitters," *Physical Review B*, Vol. 55, 1997, pp. 9949–9959.

[16] Tromborg, B., Olesen, H., and Pan, X., "Theory of linewidth for multielectrode laser diodes with spatially distributed noise sources," *IEEE Journal of Quantum Electronics*, Vol. 27, 1991, pp. 178–192.

[17] Yamamoto, Y., and Machida, S., "High-impedance suppression of pump fluctuation and amplitude squeezing in semiconductor lasers," *Physical Review A*, Vol. 35, 1987, pp. 5114–5130.

[18] Edwards, P. J., "Reduction of optical shot noise from light-emitting diodes," *IEEE Journal of Quantum Electronics*, Vol. 29, 1993, pp. 2302–2305.

[19] Amann, M.-C., "The effect of spatial correlation on the linewidth broadening in tunable laser diodes," *IEEE Journal of Quantum Electronics*, Vol. 29, 1993, pp. 1799–1804.

[20] Amann, M.-C., Hakimi, R., Borchert, B., and Illek, S., "Linewidth broadening by 1/f noise in wavelength-tunable laser diodes," *Applied Physics Letters*, Vol. 70, 1997, pp. 1512–1514.

[21] Goobar, E., Karlsson, A., and Machida, S., "Measurements and theory of correlation between terminal electrical noise and optical noise in a two-section semiconductor laser," *IEEE Journal of Quantum Electronics*, Vol. 29, 1993, pp. 386–395.

[22] Su, Y. K., Liaw, U. H., Sun, T.-P., and Chen, G.-S., "Origin of 1/f noise in indium antimonide photodiodes," *Journal of Applied Physics*, Vol. 81, 1997, pp. 739–743.

[23] Fukuda, M., Hirono, T., Kurosaki, T., and Kano, F., "1/f noise behaviour in semiconductor laser degradation," *IEEE Photonics Technology Letters*, Vol. 5, 1993, pp. 1165–1167.

[24] Henry, C. H., Logan, R. A., and Merritt, F. R., "Origin of n$\simeq$2 injection current in $Al_xGa_{1-x}As$ heterojunctions," *Applied Physics Letters*, Vol. 31, 1977, pp. 454–456.

[25] Rajesh, K., Huang, L. J., Lau, . M., Bruce, R., Ingrey, S., and Landheer, D., "Oxidation and sulfur passivation of GaInAsP(100)," *Journal of Applied Physics*, Vol. 81, 1997, pp. 3304–3310.

[26] Hakimi, R., and Amann, M.-C., "Reduction of 1/f carrier noise in InGaAsP/InP heterostructures by sulphur passivation of facets," *Semiconductor Science and Technology*, Vol. 12, 1997, pp. 778–780.

[27] Schmidt, B., Hakimi, R., Illek, S., and Amann, M.-C., "Tunable twin-guide (DFB) laser with buried facets for reduced spectral linewidth broadening," *Electronics Letters*, Vol. 33, 1997, pp. 1389–1390.

Chapter 7

Widely Tunable Laser Diodes

We have seen in Chapters 4 and 5 that the continuous tuning range $\Delta\lambda$ is limited by $\Delta\lambda/\lambda \approx \Delta n/n_g$, where Δn is the index change and n_g the group index of the tuning section. Under normal circumstances, this will limit the tuning range to about 15 nm. A higher tuning range is possible under extreme temperature tuning; 22 nm has been reported [1]. (Note that in this case, the tuning is discontinuous.) The tuning range should be compared with the spectral width of the gain curve, which can exceed 100 nm, and, for applications in optical communications, also with the width of the gain curve for Erbium doped fiber amplifiers, which is about 30 to 40 nm. (We note that the width of the gain band for fiber amplifiers may be increased in the future [2].)

In this Chapter, we consider methods for extending the tuning range beyond the $\Delta\lambda/\lambda \approx \Delta n/n_g$ limit. Such extensions make it possible to exploit the large width of the gain curve of semiconductor lasers and the full gain width of optical amplifiers. It is characteristic of the various schemes for extended tuning that the resulting wavelength is no longer a relatively simple monotonous function of a single control parameter. Instead, it is necessary to use two or more controls (quasicontinuous tuning). One important issue is therefore wavelength coverage (i.e., access to any wavelength within the tuning range).

In general, the principle behind the various schemes for wide tuning is that a refractive index *difference* (rather than the refractive index itself) is changed, and that the relative changes in this difference, which are proportional to the relative wavelength changes, can be quite large.

7.1 THE VERNIER EFFECT

Readers will probably be familiar with the Vernier effect, which is used in high-resolution distance measurements. The principle of a Vernier is shown in Figure 7.1. If we realize a laser structure where each end has a comb-like reflection characteristic, but where the two comb pitches are different, we can exploit the Vernier effect to expand the tuning range. This principle is illustrated in Figure 7.2. By shifting the position of one reflectivity curve by the pitch difference $\delta\lambda$, the wavelength of coincidence shifts by $\Delta\lambda$. Note that $\Delta\lambda$ is equal to the wavelength pitch for the other reflector. As an example

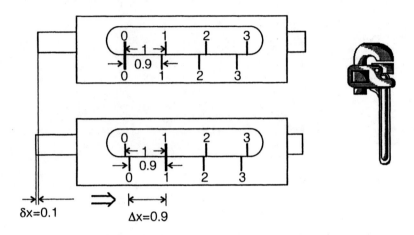

Figure 7.1   A Vernier using two scales with a 10% pitch difference. A shift of one scale by δx leads to a shift of the point where the scales coincide by $\Delta x = 9\delta x$.

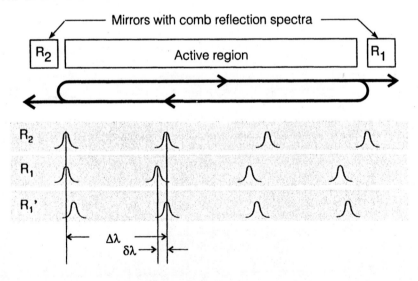

Figure 7.2   Laser structure where each end reflectivity has a comb characteristic. Sufficient cavity gain for lasing is only available where the reflection peaks coincide.

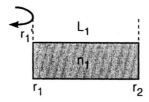

Figure 7.3   Cavity used as reflector.

of a reflector with a comb characteristic, we consider a laser where one facet has been replaced by a cavity with field reflection coefficients r_1 and r_2, refractive index n_1, no gain or loss, and length L_1, as shown in Figure 7.3. Using transfer matrix analysis (see Appendix C) it is easy to show that the field reflection coefficient for the cavity is given by

$$r_1' = r_1 + \frac{(1 - r_1^2)r_2'}{1 + r_1 r_2'} \tag{7.1}$$

where

$$r_2' = r_2 \exp\left(-j\frac{4\pi}{\lambda}n_1 L_1\right) \tag{7.2}$$

The phase term in (7.2) gives constructive or destructive interference and leads to a wavelength dependence of the magnitude of r_1', with maxima spaced by

$$\Delta\lambda_1 = \frac{\lambda^2}{2n_{g,1}L_1} \tag{7.3}$$

where $n_{g,1}$ is the group index for the cavity. This is exactly the same as the expression for the mode spacing derived in Chapter 2.

   If the other facet is also replaced by a cavity, the field reflection at that end behaves in a similar way, with the maxima spacing determined by the parameters of the cavity.

   Numerical Example: For $\lambda = 1,550$ nm, $n_1 = n_{g,1} = 3.5$, $L_1 = 160\,\mu$m we have $\Delta\lambda_1 = 2.15$ nm. For the same refractive index, but a length of $L_2 = 200\,\mu$m, the spacing is 1.72 nm. In Figure 7.4 the reflection curves are shown for these two cases, using a value of 0.1 for all the individual field reflection coefficients.

   When both end reflectivities have a comb characteristic, the product of the reflectivities will have a beat pattern. (This assumes that the refractive index of the center cavity has been adjusted appropriately.) If the refractive indices are identical, the beat period is given by

$$\Delta\lambda' = \frac{\lambda^2}{2n_g(L_2 - L_1)} \tag{7.4}$$

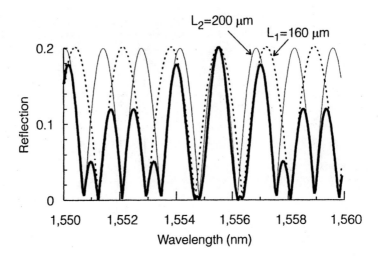

Figure 7.4   Magnitude of cavity reflections as functions of the wavelength for the values in the numerical example; the (normalized) product of the two reflectivities is shown in bold.

This follows from

$$N\Delta\lambda_1 = (N+1)\Delta\lambda_2 \tag{7.5}$$

with

$$N = \frac{L_1}{L_2 - L_1} \tag{7.6}$$

An example is shown in Figure 7.4.

If we increase the refractive index of the "long" cavity in Figure 7.4, the wavelengths corresponding to reflection maxima will increase, and the wavelength of coincidence will jump from 1,555.5 nm to 1,557.2 nm. A tuning of the long cavity by $\delta\lambda = \Delta\lambda_2/N = \Delta\lambda_1/(N+1)$, where $N = L_1/(L_2 - L_1)$, leads to an increase in the wavelength where the reflection maxima coincide by $\Delta\lambda_1$. Assuming that the round trip phase condition is satisfied, this means that the wavelength change is larger than the change in the cavity reflection peak position $\delta\lambda$ by a "tuning enhancement factor" of $N+1$. Note that if the refractive index of the "short" cavity is increased, the coincidence will move to shorter wavelengths, and the enhancement factor will be N.

There are some practical limitations on the use of this effect in tunable lasers:

- Either the coincidence spacing must exceed the width of the gain spectrum or modes at neighbor coincidences must be suppressed by some other method.

- The difference in the reflection periods should be comparable with the width of the individual reflection maxima.

- The cavity gain difference must be sufficient to suppress other modes.

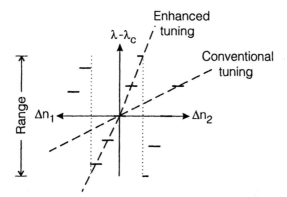

Figure 7.5   Tuning using the Vernier effect. The figure is based on the parameter values used in Figure 7.4 and shows the wavelength relative to the wavelength of coincidence in Figure 7.4, λ_c. Only one of the refractive indices is changed at a time. Lasing is assumed to be limited to a range symmetrical around λ_c. The line marked "conventional tuning" indicates the wavelength change expected under continuous tuning. The line marked "enhanced tuning" shows wavelength jumps due to the Vernier effect.

- The phase condition must be satisfied, meaning that there must be a way of ensuring that the round trip phase for the desired mode is a multiple of 2π.

In Figure 7.5, we show a schematic representation of the tuning behavior for the structure considered in Figure 7.4. It is clear that the tuning characteristic is not continuous; instead, the wavelength will jump between discrete values. This limitation can be overcome by changing both refractive indices simultaneously. In this manner the wavelength of coincidence can be moved continuously, and if the range that can be covered in this way exceeds the wavelength jumps, it will be possible to get access to all wavelengths in the tuning range by quasicontinuous tuning, as described in Section 4.4. For the case considered here, the total tuning range is given by the beat period (7.4).

7.2   GENERAL THEORY FOR DISTRIBUTED REFLECTORS

In practice it is not possible to implement high-reflectivity discrete reflectors, and we have to consider more general reflectors. We first consider the case of discrete reflectors. Referring to Figure 7.6, we can write the following expression for the total field reflection at the position z_0:

$$r_1 = \frac{r_0 + r' \exp\left(-2j\beta\Delta z\right)}{1 + r_0 r' \exp\left(-2j\beta\Delta z\right)} \tag{7.7}$$

where β is the propagation constant. By identifying

$$\tanh\left(a\right) = r_1 \tag{7.8}$$

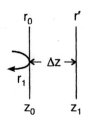

Figure 7.6   Reflection from two discrete reflectors spaced by a distance Δz.

$$\tanh(b) = r_0 \tag{7.9}$$

$$\tanh(c) = r' \exp(-2j\beta\Delta z) \tag{7.10}$$

we see that the reflectivities in (7.7) add up like the tanh function

$$\tanh(a) = \tanh(b+c) = \frac{\tanh(b) + \tanh(c)}{1 + \tanh(b)\tanh(c)} \tag{7.11}$$

For small values of r' we have to first order

$$r_1 = r_0 + r' \exp(-2j\beta\Delta z)(1 - r_0^2) \tag{7.12}$$

In this expression, the first two terms are a simple addition, and the last bracket can be interpreted as a term accounting for the depletion of the input beam. The result in (7.12) can also be found directly by neglecting all but the first two terms in a series of multiple reflections, as shown in Figure 7.7. The change in reflectivity from the presence of the second reflector is

$$\Delta r = r_1 - r_0 = r' \exp(-2j\beta\Delta z)(1 - r_0^2) \tag{7.13}$$

We consider the case where the reflection is caused by a grating. At the Bragg wavelength, the reflections are in phase, and the phase term in (7.13) can be neglected.

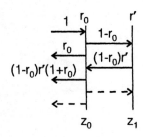

Figure 7.7   Multiple reflection terms for a two-reflector system.

We also recall from Chapter 3 that the reflection per unit length is given by the coupling coefficient κ. Using

$$r' = \kappa \Delta z \tag{7.14}$$

we get from (7.13)

$$\frac{\Delta r}{\Delta z} = \kappa(1 - r^2(z)) \tag{7.15}$$

giving the differential equation for $r(z)$

$$\frac{dr}{dz} = \kappa(1 - r^2(z)) \tag{7.16}$$

For a position-independent coupling coefficient, the solution to this equation is again a tanh relation:

$$r(z) = \tanh(\kappa z) + r(0) \tag{7.17}$$

For a grating extending from $z = 0$ to $z = L$, with no reflection at $z = L$ ($r(L) = 0$), we have for the reflection at $z = 0$:

$$r(0) = -\tanh(\kappa L) \tag{7.18}$$

This agrees with the result from Section 3.3.1 except for a phase factor that is simply due to the choice of reference plane. An extensive discussion of the tanh relation and its applications is given in [3].

The following discussion of reflection from structures with a nonuniform coupling coefficient is based on [4]. We start from the coupled-mode equations discussed in Section 3.2, including a factor allowing for a phase shift of the grating with respect to the point $z = 0$ ($\phi(0) = 0$):

$$\frac{dR}{dz} + j\Delta\beta R = -j\kappa(z)S\exp(-j\phi(z)) \tag{7.19}$$

$$\frac{dS}{dz} - j\Delta\beta S = j\kappa(z)R\exp(j\phi(z)) \tag{7.20}$$

As in Chapter 3, $\Delta\beta$ is defined as

$$\Delta\beta = \beta - \beta_0 \tag{7.21}$$

where β_0 is the Bragg propagation constant.

The local reflection coefficient is given by

$$\rho(z) = \frac{S}{R}\exp(-j\phi(z)) \tag{7.22}$$

Differentiation of this with respect to z gives

$$\frac{d\rho(z)}{dz} = \left(\frac{1}{R}\frac{dS}{dz} - \frac{S}{R^2}\frac{dR}{dz} - j\frac{S}{R}\frac{d\phi(z)}{dz} \right) \exp\left(-j\phi(z)\right) \tag{7.23}$$

Use of the coupled-mode equations then gives

$$\frac{d\rho(z)}{dz} = j\kappa(z)(1 + \rho^2) + j(2\Delta\beta - \frac{d\phi(z)}{dz}) \tag{7.24}$$

For a structure extending from $z = 0$ to $z = L$, $\rho(0)$ is the reflectivity for a wave incident from the left, and we have the boundary condition $\rho(L) = 0$. Using the substitution

$$\rho(z) = \sigma(z)\exp\left(2j\Delta\beta z - j\phi(z)\right) \tag{7.25}$$

we get the following equation for σ:

$$\frac{d\sigma(z)}{dz} = j\kappa(z)\left[\exp\left(-2j\Delta\beta z + j\phi(z)\right) + \sigma^2(z)\exp\left(2j\Delta\beta z - j\phi(z)\right) \right] \tag{7.26}$$

The second term in (7.26) accounts for the depletion of the input wave.
For the simple case of a uniform grating from $z = 0$ to $z = L$ (κ constant and $\phi(z) = 0$), we have at the Bragg wavelength ($\Delta\beta = 0$)

$$\frac{d\sigma(z)}{dz} = j\kappa\left(1 + \sigma^2(z)\right) \tag{7.27}$$

which has the solution

$$\sigma(z) - \sigma(0) = j\tanh\left(\kappa z\right) \tag{7.28}$$

Using the boundary condition $\rho(L) = 0$, we find the reflection coefficient at $z = 0$

$$\rho_L = \rho(0) = -j\tanh\left(\kappa L\right) \tag{7.29}$$

in agreement with the result derived earlier.
For the case of a weak reflector, we can neglect the depletion term in (7.26); this is equivalent to the first Born approximation in scattering problems:

$$\frac{d\sigma(z)}{dz} = j\kappa(z)\exp\left(-2j\Delta\beta z + j\phi(z)\right) \tag{7.30}$$

This gives

$$\sigma(0) = \sigma(L) - j\int_0^L \kappa(z)\exp\left(-2j\Delta\beta z + j\phi(z)\right) dz \tag{7.31}$$

and we get the following expression for the spectral variation of the reflection coefficient at $z = 0$:

$$\rho(\Delta\beta) = -j \int_0^L (\kappa(z) \exp(j\phi(z))) \exp(-2j\Delta\beta z) \, dz \tag{7.32}$$

This shows that, when the depletion term is neglected, the spectral variation of the field reflection coefficient at $z = 0$ can be written as the Fourier integral of the grating function $\kappa(z) \exp(j\phi(z))$.

Looking again at a uniform grating of length L with $\kappa L \ll 1$, we have

$$\rho(\Delta\beta) = -j\kappa \int_0^L \exp(-2j\Delta\beta z) \, dz = -j\kappa L \exp(-j\Delta\beta L) \frac{\sin(\Delta\beta L)}{\Delta\beta L} \tag{7.33}$$

giving the power reflectivity

$$|\rho|^2 = (\kappa L)^2 \left(\frac{\sin(\Delta\beta L)}{\Delta\beta L} \right)^2 \tag{7.34}$$

For low values of κL, this is consistent with the results shown in Figure 3.5.

7.3   DBR-TYPE LASER STRUCTURES

In Section 7.1 we showed how a comb-like reflection spectrum can be achieved by using a cavity as reflector, and how this could be used to achieve an extended tuning range. However, the example considered in Section 7.1 is not suitable for implementation in a practical laser structure, because the relatively high values of the reflectivity cannot easily be achieved in a monolithic structure. Instead it is possible to use a structure with multiple cavities, and to use a short grating as reflector for each cavity. Several different realizations of this idea are possible.

7.3.1   Sampled Grating DBR Lasers

A comb-like reflection spectrum can be achieved by using a sampled grating, which consists of several sections of interrupted grating, as shown in Figure 7.8. Each sampling period of length L_s is equivalent to a short cavity with the discrete reflector considered in Section 7.1 replaced by a grating, and we therefore expect reflection peaks separated by

$$\Delta\lambda_s = \frac{\lambda^2}{2n_g L_s} \tag{7.35}$$

where n_g is the group index of structure.

We can analyze the sampled grating by using the results from Section 7.2. The overall grating function for a sampled grating of total length $L = N_s L_s$, where N_s is the

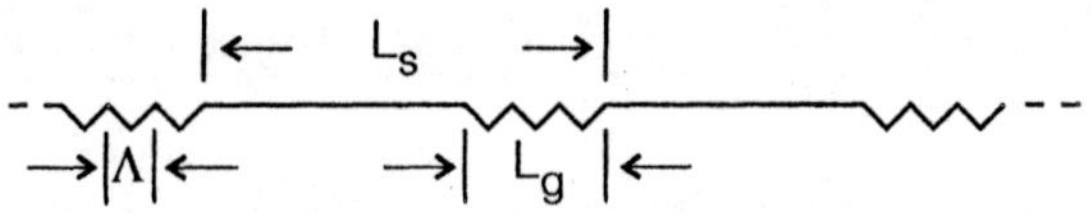

Figure 7.8 Sampled grating with sampling period L_s and grating length L_g.

number of sampling periods, can be written as the product of the original grating function and a sampling function:

$$\kappa(z) \exp\left(j\phi(z)\right) = \kappa_1(z)\kappa_2(z) \tag{7.36}$$

with

$$\kappa_1(z) = \begin{cases} \kappa & \text{if } 0 < z < L \\ 0 & \text{otherwise} \end{cases} \tag{7.37}$$

and

$$\kappa_2(z) = \begin{cases} 0 & \text{if } NL_s < z < (N+1)L_s - L_g \\ 1 & \text{if } (N+1)L_s - L_g < z < (N+1)L_s \end{cases} \tag{7.38}$$

Because the grating function can be written as a product of two functions, we can use the following properties for Fourier transforms: the Fourier transform of a product equals the convolution of the Fourier transforms of the factors. Consequently, the reflection spectrum is found as the convolution of the Fourier transforms for κ_1 and κ_2. For the uniform grating we have

$$F_1 = \mathcal{F}(\kappa_1(z)) = -j\kappa L \exp\left(-j\Delta\beta L\right)\frac{\sin\left(\Delta\beta L\right)}{\Delta\beta L} \tag{7.39}$$

giving a lobe width of $\Delta\beta_L = \pi/L$. The sampling function $\kappa_2(z)$ is periodic, and the coefficients for its Fourier series are given by

$$F_{2,N} = \frac{1}{L_s}\int_0^{L_s} \kappa_2(z) \exp\left(-j\frac{2N\pi}{L_s}z\right) dz \tag{7.40}$$

Neglecting a phase factor, which depends on the choice of reference plane, we have

$$F_{2,N} = \frac{1}{N\pi} \sin\left(\frac{N\pi L_g}{L_s}\right) \tag{7.41}$$

The terms of the Fourier series of the sampling function are spaced by $\Delta\beta_s = \pi/L_s$, giving the spectral spacing anticipated from (7.35). An example is shown in Figure 7.9. The convolution of the Fourier transforms gives a power reflection spectrum with the following properties:

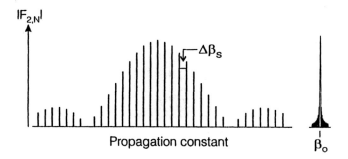

Figure 7.9   Magnitude of the Fourier coefficients for a sampled grating with $L_g = 0.1L_s$. The magnitude of the field reflection spectrum for a uniform grating with $L = 10L_s$ (and $\kappa L \ll 1$) is shown to the right on the same scale.

- The maximal power reflection occurs at β_0 with the value $(\kappa N_s L_g)^2$, where $N_s L_g$ is the total grating length (as discussed below, $\tanh^2(\kappa N_s L_g)$ is a more accurate expression for the reflectivity for high values of $\kappa N_s L_g$).

- The sampling function gives rise to subsidiary reflection peaks spaced by $\Delta\beta_s = \pi/L_s$ (corresponding to the spectral spacing $\Delta\lambda_s$ given by (7.35)), and with relative power reflectivities of $\left(\frac{L_s}{N\pi L_g}\sin\left(\frac{N\pi L_g}{L_s}\right)\right)^2$

- The number of subsidiary peaks with a power reflectivity of more than half the maximum is approximately L_s/L_g.

- Each reflection peak has sidelobes with a spacing given by $\Delta\beta_L = \pi/L$, where $L = N_s L_s$ is the total length.

    The reflection spectrum can also be calculated directly, taking advantage of the fact that the sampled grating can be described as a concatenation of N_s identical sections (see Appendix C). It turns out, however, that the simple calculation above is highly accurate, for low values of $\kappa N_s L_g$.

    The subsidiary reflection peaks occur when the reflections from the separate sampling periods are in phase; this happens at wavelengths spaced according to (7.35). As discussed in Section 7.2, these reflections will add according to the tanh rule. Consequently, the power reflectivity at peak N is given by

$$R_N \approx \tanh^2\left(|F_{2,N}|\kappa N_s L_s\right) \tag{7.42}$$

instead of $(|F_{2,N}|\kappa N_s L_s)^2$. All the major features of sampled gratings can be derived from this simple analysis.

    To take advantage of the Vernier effect, we can fabricate a laser with sampled gratings at both the front and the rear, with the sampling periods $L_{s,f}$ and $L_{s,r}$ being different. Except for the shape of the envelope determined by the subsidiary reflection peaks, this gives a situation similar to the one shown in Figure 7.4. As an example, we consider the case where the grating length L_g is the same in the front and rear gratings, $L_{s,f} = 10L_g$

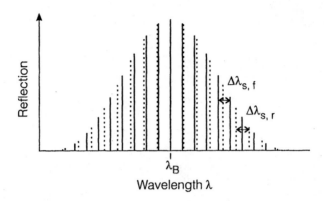

Figure 7.10   For low values of $\kappa N_s L_g$, the peaks of the power reflection curve equals the square of the magnitude of the Fourier coefficients for the sampling function. This is shown for $L_{s,f} = 10L_g$ (full lines) and $L_{s,f} = 9L_g$ (dotted lines).

and $L_{s,r} = 9L_g$. The magnitude squared of the two sets of reflection peaks are shown in Figure 7.10, assuming that both reflection spectra are centered on the Bragg wavelength.

By increasing the refractive index of the front section (which has a long sampling period), we get discontinuous tuning toward longer wavelengths, as was the case in Figure 7.5 when the refractive index of the long cavity was increased. Increasing the refractive index in the rear section (which has a short sampling period) gives discontinuous tuning toward shorter wavelength. Because of the nonuniform envelope of the reflection peaks, the lasing will eventually jump to the other side of the Bragg wavelength, because the product of the two reflectivities here will be higher. If the gain peak and the Bragg wavelength coincide, the tuning range will be symmetrical around the Bragg wavelength; and for the example shown in Figure 7.10, the tuning range will be $10\Delta\lambda_{s,f} = 9\Delta\lambda_{s,r}$. This is shown schematically in Figure 7.11.

Note that when the *front* section is tuned, the width of the wavelength jumps is determined by the reflection peak spacing of the *rear* section and vice versa. The 10% difference in spacing in Figure 7.11 is hardly discernible.

If the spacing between the reflection peaks is sufficiently small, the gaps in the tuning curve can be filled by tuning the front and rear section simultaneously. The tuning properties under such simultaneous tuning are very similar to those of a conventional DBR laser, and the continuous tuning range that can be achieved is therefore of the same order. Access to a given wavelength within the tuning range is achieved by a combination of discrete tuning and continuous tuning.

One major advantage of the SG-DBR laser is that the fabrication process is very similar to that of a conventional DBR laser (see Figures 3.27 and 3.28). The main difference is that for the same value of the peak reflectivity, the passive sections have to be longer by a factor of L_s/L_g. To implement the sampling of the grating, only one additional mask is required, and the grating can be defined either holographically or by e-beam.

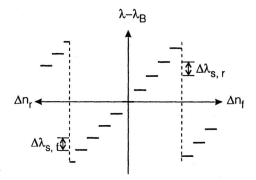

Figure 7.11   Tuning curve corresponding to the spectra shown in Figure 7.10, showing the change in wavelength when one of the refractive indices n_f or n_r of the front or rear sampled gratings is changed.

We can summarize the design rules for SG-DBR lasers as follows: To have a reasonable value for the peak power reflectivity, we should have

$$0.5 < \kappa N_s L_g < 1 \tag{7.43}$$

If the passive sampled grating has a loss coefficient α, we must require

$$\alpha N_s L_s \ll 1 \tag{7.44}$$

The wavelength jumps are given by

$$\Delta \lambda_s = \frac{\lambda^2}{2 n_{g,\text{eff}} L_s} \tag{7.45}$$

If access to all wavelengths is required, $\Delta \lambda_s$ must be sufficiently small to allow the gaps to be filled by simultaneous tuning. The full width at half maximum of the envelope of the reflection peaks is a measure for the wavelength range where there is a reasonable reflectivity, this width is approximately

$$\Delta \lambda_{\text{env}} = \Delta \lambda_s \frac{L_s}{L_g} = \frac{\lambda^2}{2 n_{g,\text{eff}} L_g} \tag{7.46}$$

Short gratings are advantageous for achieving a wide envelope, but there are practical limits on the minimal grating length, as well as the condition given by (7.43). If the front and rear sampling periods are nearly equal, with a difference ΔL_s, we have a beat period (determining the maximal tuning range) given by

$$\Delta \lambda_{\text{beat}} = \Delta \lambda_s \frac{L_s}{\Delta L_s} \tag{7.47}$$

and if the envelope width is equal to the beat period, we have

$$L_g = \Delta L_s \tag{7.48}$$

If we also require the period difference for the sampled gratings to equal the lobe width for the uniform grating reflection curve, we have

$$\frac{\pi}{L_s} \frac{\Delta L_s}{L_s} = \frac{\pi}{L} \tag{7.49}$$

which gives

$$N_s = \frac{L}{L_s} = \frac{L_s}{\Delta L_s} \tag{7.50}$$

Numerical Example: We consider a structure designed for $\lambda = 1,550$ nm with $n_{g,\text{eff}} = 3.5$. For $L_{s,f} = 50\,\mu$m and $L_{s,r} = 45\,\mu$m, we find the reflection peak separations $\Delta\lambda_{s,f} = 6.9$ nm and $\Delta\lambda_{s,r} = 7.6$ nm. Using (7.48) we find $L_g = 5\,\mu$m, and a maximal tuning range of 70 nm. For $\kappa N_s L_g = 0.7$ we require $\kappa N_s = 1,400\,\text{cm}^{-1}$, with 10 sampling periods this gives $\kappa = 140\,\text{cm}^{-1}$, which can be achieved in practice with a properly designed first-order grating. The lengths of the front and rear sampled grating regions are $500\,\mu$m and $450\,\mu$m, respectively.

In addition to the gain condition, we also have to satisfy the phase condition at the lasing wavelength. For moderate values of the coupling strength (i.e., $\kappa N_s L_g < 1$) the effective length of the sampled grating, as defined in Section 3.3.1, is close to half the physical length:

$$L_{\text{eff},s} \approx \frac{N_s L_s}{2} \tag{7.51}$$

With an active layer of length L_a placed between two sampled gratings of similar length, the mode spacing (separation between wavelengths satisfying the phase condition) is

$$\Delta\lambda_m = \frac{\lambda^2}{2n_{g,a}L_a + 4n_{g,s}L_{\text{eff},s}} \approx \frac{\lambda^2}{2n_{g,a}L_a + 2n_{g,s}N_s L_s} \tag{7.52}$$

The lobe width for the sampled grating reflection, expressed in wavelength, is

$$\Delta\lambda_{sg} = \frac{\lambda^2}{2n_{g,s}N_s L_s} \tag{7.53}$$

and it follows that, even for a short active region, there is always at least one mode within the reflection bandwidth because $\Delta\lambda_{sg} > \Delta\lambda_m$.

To ensure lasing at the wavelength where the product of the two sampled grating reflections have the highest value, a phase tuning section can be inserted, as for the three-section DBR laser described in Chapter 5. If the refractive index of the waveguide layer

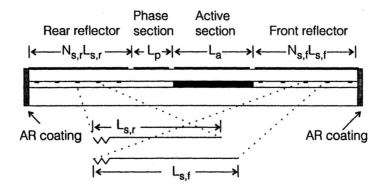

Figure 7.12   SG-DBR laser with a phase section. Note that the figure is not to scale, and that only a few sampled grating periods are shown.

in the phase tuning section can be changed by Δn_p, if the relevant confinement factor is Γ_p, and if the length is L_p, then a full 2π phase shift can be achieved if

$$\frac{2\Gamma_p\Delta n_p L_p}{\lambda} = 1 \tag{7.54}$$

A schematic diagram of an SG-DBR laser with a phase section is shown in Figure 7.12, and an example of tuning curves is shown in Figure 7.13.

The first detailed theoretical and experimental description of widely tunable DBR lasers using sampled gratings is given in [5]. In this paper, the tuning range was limited to the beat period, which was predicted to be 59 nm, against an observed tuning range of 57 nm. Also other groups have reported wide tuning ranges for SG-DBR lasers [6, 7]. In addition, a small-signal modulation bandwidth in excess of 3 GHz has been reported [8], and data transmission at 1.244 Gbit/s on four separate wavelengths each spaced by 15 nm has been demonstrated [9].

7.3.2   Superstructure Grating DBR Lasers

The analysis in Section 7.2 provides a very intuitive interpretation of the properties of sampled gratings: The uniform grating gives a spectral response with a (narrow) sidelobe spacing that is determined by the total length. The sampling function can be regarded as a modulation function, with a low spatial frequency, superimposed on the uniform grating. This modulation gives rise to sidebands (subsidiary reflection peaks) with a spacing determined by the sampling period, and magnitudes depending on the Fourier coefficients of the sampling function. The sampled grating is therefore just a special case of a much broader class of superstructure gratings. Such superstructure gratings have superperiods Λ_s equal to the period of the modulation function. Different modulation functions will give shapes of the envelope of the reflection spectrum different from the $\sin(x)/x$ obtained for the sampled grating.

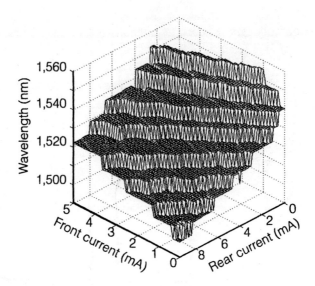

Figure 7.13   Lasing wavelength as a function of the front and rear tuning currents for an SG-DBR laser. The phase control contact was not used. (Reprinted with permission from GEC-Marconi Materials Technology Limited.)

The first example of a superstructure grating we will examine is the chirped grating. In this structure each superperiod consists of a grating with the grating period varying linearly as shown schematically in Figure 7.14.

The modulation function for a linearly chirped grating has a magnitude of 1 and a quadratic phase term. As a result, the Fourier coefficients are given in terms of Fresnel integrals [10]. As expected, the reflection peaks for this structure are fairly pronounced in the wavelength interval determined by the maximal and minimal period, and tail off outside this interval; the example from [10] is shown in Figure 7.15. It is noticeable from Figure 7.15 that the envelope of the reflection peaks is significantly more uniform than the one for the sampled grating.

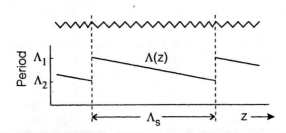

Figure 7.14   Superstructure grating with superperiod Λ_s. The grating period varies linearly from Λ_1 to Λ_2 over each superperiod.

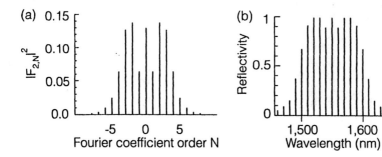

Figure 7.15   (a) Magnitude squared of the Fourier coefficients for the chirped grating. (b) Resulting power reflectivity (only the peaks are shown), calculated directly from the coupled-mode equations. The parameters used are: superperiod $\Lambda_s = 35.7\,\mu$m, number of superperiods $N_s = 20$, coupling coefficient $\kappa = 100\,$cm^{-1}, the maximal and minimal periods correspond to wavelengths of 1,600 nm and 1,500 nm, respectively. (Reprinted with permission from *IEEE Photonics Technology Letters*, Vol. 5, pp. 393–395, ©1993 IEEE.)

In practice, a stepwise change in the grating period is used rather than a linear chirp. Single-mode operation over an 83-nm tuning range has been reported for such a laser [11]. Full wavelength access over a 34-nm range has also been achieved [12].

As already mentioned, a linear chirp in the grating period is equivalent to a quadratic change in grating phase. It is therefore possible to have a fixed grating period, but insert phaseshifts with a quadratically varying density. Such a structure is described in [13]; here 18 phaseshifts each of $\lambda/10$ are used for each 35.7-μm superperiod. A tuning range of 105 nm was achieved, the *SSR* was over 30 dB across the tuning range, and 4 Gbit/s modulation was demonstrated at both ends of the tuning range.

Ideally, the envelope of the reflection peaks should be rectangular, with uniform values within the desired tuning range and near-zero values outside. A grating modulation function with this property can be synthesised using the general theory from Section 7.2. Assuming that the magnitude of the coupling coefficient is constant over the superperiod, the design problem consists of finding a phase variation $\phi(z)$ that satisfies

$$\frac{1}{\Lambda_s} \int_0^{\Lambda_s} \exp\left(j\phi(z)\right) \exp\left(-j\frac{2N\pi}{\Lambda_s}z\right) dz = \begin{cases} C_N & \text{if } |N| \leq N_{\max} \\ 0 & \text{if } |N| > N_{\max} \end{cases} \tag{7.55}$$

where the magnitude of C_N is independent of N.

As an example, we examine the case corresponding to pure frequency modulation of the grating with a modulation index A:

$$\phi(z) = A \sin\left(\frac{2\pi}{\Lambda_s}z + \psi\right) \tag{7.56}$$

In this case, the Fourier coefficients can be found analytically:

$$|F_{2,N}| = |J_N(A)| \tag{7.57}$$

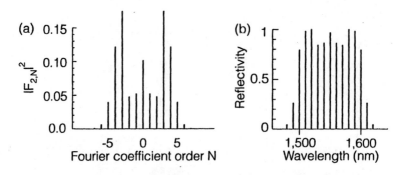

Figure 7.16   (a) Magnitude squared of the Fourier coefficients for the frequency-modulated grating with $A = 4.5$. (b) Resulting power reflectivity (without sidelobes), calculated from (7.42), using $\kappa N_s \Lambda_s = 7$ (close to the value used in Figure 7.15), assuming that the reflectivity curve is centered at 1,550 nm, with a superperiod giving a 10-nm spacing.

where J_N is the Bessel function of order N. An examination of a table of Bessel functions shows that a high degree of uniformity is achieved for $A = 4.5$. The results are shown in Figure 7.16.

An even higher degree of uniformity for the reflection peaks can be found by numerical optimization of the grating phase. The result of such an optimization was first presented in [14] with more detail given in [15] and [16]; the results are shown in Figure 7.17.

The tuning curve from [14] is shown in Figure 7.18.

In [15], the tuning was accomplished by thermal tuning using thin-film heaters. The resulting tuning range was 40 nm and the linewidth was below 400 kHz over the

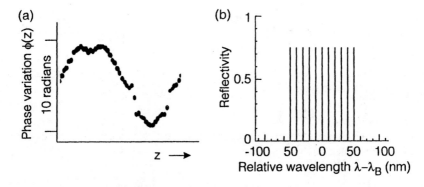

Figure 7.17   (a) Phase variation over a superperiod, 50 phaseshifts are used. Note that the phase variation is very close to that given by (7.56) with $A = 4.5$. (b) Calculated reflection spectrum shown without sidelobes. (Reprinted with permission from *IEEE Journal of Selected Topics in Quantum Electronics*, Vol. 1, pp. 401–407, ©1995 IEEE.)

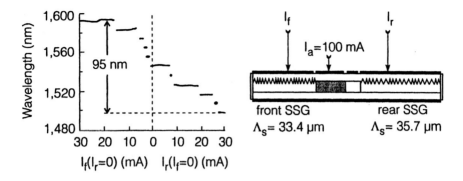

Figure 7.18   Tuning curve for a SSG-DBR laser. (Reprinted with permission from *Electronics Letters*, Vol. 30, pp. 1141–1142, ©1994 IEE.)

whole tuning range. In [17] full wavelength access over a 62.4-nm range was achieved using a similar laser structure.

An alternative grating design is described in [18]. Here the grating period is piecewise constant, corresponding to a piecewise linear phase. Using five different grating periods over a 45-nm superperiod, a near-uniform reflection peak envelope with a 60-nm width is obtained.

Gratings with multiple reflection peaks can also be fabricated by a multiple-exposure technique, as described in [19].

It is possible to use superstructure gratings in DFB lasers as well [20]. Since no active/passive integration is required in the DFB structure, the fabrication is easier than that of a DBR structure. The advantage of this approach is that a narrow linewidth is possible under tuning, without the disadvantage of the slow tuning speed in thermally tuned structures. The disadvantage is that all sections of the laser are active, the change of any of the laser currents will lead to a change in both the gain and the refractive index. This means that power and wavelength cannot be controlled independently.

In the discussion of SG-DBR and SSG-DBR lasers, we quoted a couple of results demonstrating that direct digital modulation at Gbit/s rates is possible for these laser types. Another important issue is the switching time from one wavelength to another. For lasers with thermal tuning, the switching time can be expected to be dominated by the thermal response time, and according to the discussion in Section 4.7, we can expect the switching time to be in the microsecond range. For lasers with electronic tuning, on the other hand, the carrier lifetime will dominate and we can expect much faster wavelength switching. A switching time of 2 ns has been reported for an SSG-DBR laser [21].

7.4   INTERFEROMETRIC STRUCTURES

In Section 7.1 we showed how the Vernier effect could be used to achieve enhanced tuning if the reflection at each end of a laser had a comb spectrum, with the two periods being different. In the example in Section 7.1, this was achieved by replacing the usual discrete reflector by a (two-reflector) cavity.

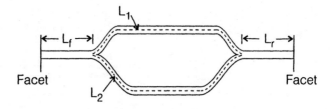

Figure 7.19   Mach–Zehnder interferometer with arm lengths L_1 and L_2.

There are a number of ways to create a structure that consists of two interfering cavities. Examples of interferometric and ring laser structures were examined in [22], the case of two laterally coupled active regions of different lengths was studied in [23], and multibranch lasers were analyzed in [24]. To understand the spectral properties of these structures, we start by examining the Mach–Zehnder (MZ) interferometer shown in Figure 7.19.

The arms in the MZ interferometer form two cavities, and if the refractive indices are identical, the corresponding phase conditions are

$$\frac{2\pi}{\lambda_{i,1}} n'_{\text{eff}}(\lambda_{i,1})(L_1 + L_f + L_r) = N_1 \pi \tag{7.58}$$

and

$$\frac{2\pi}{\lambda_{i,2}} n'_{\text{eff}}(\lambda_{i,2})(L_2 + L_f + L_r) = N_2 \pi \tag{7.59}$$

where N_1 and N_2 are integers. Constructive interference at the power splitters requires

$$\frac{2\pi}{\lambda_i} n'_{\text{eff}}(\lambda_i)(L_2 - L_1) = N \pi \tag{7.60}$$

For $L_2 - L_1 \ll L_1 < L_2$, this shows the Vernier effect, giving a separation between the resonant wavelengths, which is much wider than the cavity modespacing.

The same effect is used in a slightly simpler form in the "multibranch" or "Y" laser structures that correspond to a "half" MZ structure, as shown in Figure 7.20. If the refractive index is the same throughout the structure, and if the branch length difference is ΔL, then the spacing of the wavelengths corresponding to constructive interference (also known as the "free spectral range") is, using the group index to account for dispersion:

$$\Delta \lambda_{\text{MZ}} = \frac{\lambda^2}{2 n_{g,\text{eff}} \Delta L} \tag{7.61}$$

7.4.1   Lateral Integration: The Y-Laser

To use an interferometric laser structure for wavelength tuning a mechanism for changing the refractive index must be provided. In principle, this can be achieved if the laser

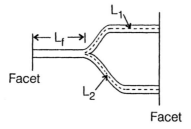

Figure 7.20   Y-laser structure equivalent to a folded MZ interferometer (top view).

consists of several sections, because this will allow the refractive index of one or more regions to be changed electronically or thermally [25]. For an ideal Y-junction with no losses, the interference will give rise to a wavelength dependent factor in the cavity gain

$$C_{MZ}(\lambda) = \cos^2\left(2\pi\frac{n_2(\lambda)L_2 - n_1(\lambda)L_1}{\lambda}\right) \tag{7.62}$$

The resulting spectral properties are illustrated in Figure 7.21.

To have an unambiguous wavelength selection, the value of $\Delta\lambda_{MZ}$ cannot be too small because the variation in material gain at the different wavelengths selected by the interferometer must be sufficient to suppress unwanted wavelengths, and it is clear that the tuning range cannot exceed $\Delta\lambda_{MZ}$.

Numerical Example: For $\lambda = 1{,}550$ nm, $n_{g,\text{eff}} = 4$, and $\Delta\lambda_{MZ} = 30$ nm, we find from (7.61) that an arm's length difference of $\Delta L = 10\,\mu$m is required. If the total cavity length is $1{,}000\,\mu$m, the cavity modespacing is 0.3 nm, which is only 1% of $\Delta\lambda_{MZ}$. Assuming that the gain filtering curve given by (7.62) is centered exactly on a cavity mode ($C_{MZ} = 1.0$), we find that the value of this function at the next neighboring cavity mode is 0.9995. We conclude that in this case, the side-mode suppression provided by the MZ characteristic may not be sufficient to ensure single-mode operation. This problem is particularly pronounced for large values of $\Delta\lambda_{MZ}$.

An improved side-mode suppression is possible by having separate coarse and fine wavelength control as in the Y-3 laser, [26], shown schematically in Figure 7.22. In the Y-3 laser, the interferometer with a large free-spectral range selects a particular wavelength region within the gain bandwidth, but this interferometer does not provide sufficient discrimination between neighboring cavity modes. The second interferometer, which has a small free-spectral range, then selects a particular cavity mode within the wavelength region selected by the first interferometer. Design details of the Y-3 laser are given in [27].

Several very high values for the tuning range of Y-lasers have been reported: 38 nm with better than 20-dB side-mode suppression [28] and 45 nm with over 25 dB side-mode suppression [26]. The highest value reported for the tuning range is 51 nm [29].

Wavelength control and stability is a particular problem for interferometric lasers consisting of a number of active sections because changes in the carrier density in a region leads to changes of both the refractive index and the gain of that region. At least two

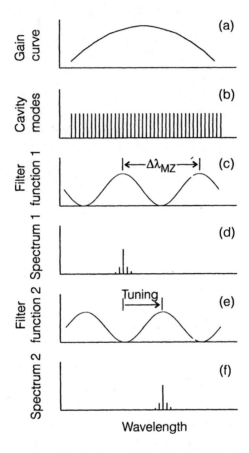

Figure 7.21   Spectral properties of tunable Y-laser. (a) Material gain. (b) Positions of cavity modes. (c,d) Interference factor (7.62) and resulting spectrum. (e,f) Interference factor and spectrum under a different tuning condition.

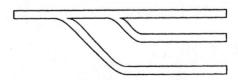

Figure 7.22   Principle of the Y-3 laser. The structure consists of separate sections, forming two interferometers with different free-spectral ranges.

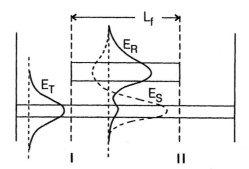

Figure 7.23   VMZ laser structure, side view. (Reprinted with permission from *Electronics Letters*, Vol. 30, pp. 2047–2049, ©1994 IEE.)

control currents are required to have control of both optical power and wavelength, and these controls are not independent. An analysis of a particular tuning scheme is presented in [30].

The wavelength switching time for Y-lasers has been investigated experimentally [31]. As the switching is electronic, switching times in the nanosecond range are expected. The reported times are 4 ns for switching off and 10 ns for switching on; switching is faster for widely separated wavelengths than for closely spaced wavelengths.

7.4.2   Transverse Integration: The VMZ Laser

In the vertical Mach–Zehnder (VMZ) laser [32], two waveguide *layers* rather than two waveguide *branches* are used.

Referring to Figure 7.23, the VMZ laser works as follows: At plane I the right-propagating mode T with field distribution E_T excites two modes R and S with field distributions E_R and E_S and propagation constants $\beta_R = 2\pi n_R/\lambda$ and $\beta_S = 2\pi n_S/\lambda$. These field distributions and propagation constants can be found by solving the wave equation for the layer structure between plane I and plane II. The modes will recombine to the filed distribution T at plane II if

$$|\beta_R - \beta_S|L_f = 2\pi N \tag{7.63}$$

where N is an integer. This means that constructive interference occurs for wavelengths given by

$$\lambda = \frac{\Delta n L_f}{N} \tag{7.64}$$

where

$$\Delta n = |n_R - n_S| \tag{7.65}$$

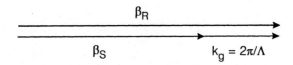

Figure 7.24   Vector diagram for codirectional coupling between modes with propagation constants β_r and β_s in a structure with a period Λ.

This gives the free-spectral range

$$\Delta\lambda_{VMZ} = \frac{\lambda^2}{\Delta n L_f F} \tag{7.66}$$

where F accounts for the dispersion of Δn. (The value of F can be as high as 2 to 3 [32]; see also the last part of Section 7.5.1.) This expression is analogous to (7.61) for the Y-laser.

Because of the characteristics of the filtering function, there is again a tradeoff between the tuning range, which cannot exceed $\Delta\lambda_{VMZ}$, and the side-mode suppression, which deteriorates for large values of $\Delta\lambda_{VMZ}$. It is possible to use a structure with two concatenated interferometers. Coarse tuning and selection of a single-wavelength region within the gain band is achieved with a short interferometer, and the fine tuning and suppression of neighboring modes is achieved with a long interferometer. This is completely analogous to the Y-3 laser.

In [32], a 30-nm tuning range is reported for a structure with $L_{f1} = 456\,\mu m$ ($N = 40$), $L_{f2} = 114\,\mu m$ ($N = 10$), and a total cavity length of $600\,\mu m$.

In contrast to the Y-laser, not all the interferometer sections are active; this leads to an easier control.

7.5   CODIRECTIONALLY COUPLED LASER DIODES

In the periodic structures considered in Chapter 3, the grating provides coupling between a right-propagating and a left-propagating mode. These modes have the same transverse field distribution, and their propagation constants are identical (but the propagation vectors are in opposite directions). A periodic structure can also provide coupling between two modes propagating in the same direction with different propagation constants and with different transverse field distributions. Coupling takes place at the wavelength where the periodic structure provides phase-matching between the modes (see Figure 7.24).

The phase-matching condition that defines the coupling wavelength λ_c can be expressed

$$\frac{2\pi n_R}{\lambda_c} = \frac{2\pi n_S}{\lambda_c} + \frac{2\pi}{\Lambda} \tag{7.67}$$

where n_R and n_S are the effective indices of the two modes, and Λ is the period. The coupling wavelength is then

$$\lambda_c = \Lambda(n_R - n_S) \tag{7.68}$$

Because $(n_R - n_S) \ll n_R$, it is clear that the period required for codirectional coupling is generally much longer than the period required for contradirectional coupling (c.f., (3.4)).

The mode-coupling is only effective close to the phase-matching wavelength, and this wavelength dependence can be used as the basis for tunable filters and detectors [33–36]. As the phase-matching wavelength depends on the *difference* of the effective indices of the modes, small changes of n_R and/or n_S can give rise to a comparatively large wavelength change

$$\Delta\lambda = \lambda_c \frac{\Delta(n_R - n_S)}{n_R - n_S} \tag{7.69}$$

Codirectional coupling therefore has the potential of making very large tuning ranges possible.

7.5.1   Theory for Codirectional Coupling

In most practical coupler structures, there are two high-refractive index waveguide regions, and if these waveguides are different, one mode will have most of its power in one of the waveguides, and the other mode will have most of its power in the other waveguide. Usually the mode with the highest effective refractive index will be concentrated in the waveguide that provides the strongest guiding. If the waveguides are weakly coupled, the modes of the coupler structure can be found as superpositions of the two modes defined by the separate waveguides. More precise results, however, are obtained by calculating the modes of the whole structure directly.

Codirectional coupling can be analyzed by coupled-mode theory by regarding the grating as a perturbation to a DC structure without grating. Similar to the situation in Chapter 3, a coupling coefficient can be defined based on the overlap integral of the two modes, with the integration interval extending over the grating. The coupling between the modes results in power transfer between them, and if each mode is largely confined to one of the waveguide regions, the result is power transfer between the waveguides.

A large number of papers have been published on coupled-mode theory for grating assisted couplers [37–41]. Here, we will first use a more intuitive eigenmode propagation description [42] before quoting the main results from coupled-mode theory. The two approaches can be shown to agree for moderate coupling and moderate detuning from the coupling wavelength.

For the study of a grating-assisted coupler, we refer to the schematic outline in Figure 7.25. Each section supports two modes; in section A, the (normalized) field distributions are given by $E_{R,A}$ and $E_{S,A}$ with amplitudes R_A and S_A, and in section B, they are $E_{R,B}$ and $E_{S,B}$ with amplitudes R_B and S_B. The corresponding propagation constants are $\beta_{R,A}$, $\beta_{S,A}$, $\beta_{R,B}$, and $\beta_{S,B}$. Both the fields and the propagation constants can be found by direct solution of the field equation for regions A and B.

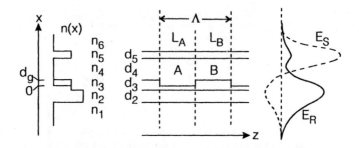

Figure 7.25   Codirectional coupler with period Λ, consisting of two regions of lengths L_1 and L_2, and six layers with refractive indices $n_i, i = 1, \ldots, 6$, and center layer thicknesses of $d_j, j = 2, 3, 4, 5$ (note that here d_3 is the thickness in region B). The grating thickness is d_g. Also indicating the field profiles for modes R and S in the unperturbed structure.

At the boundary between regions A and B, we can expand the modes in region B in terms of the modes of region A. The equation for the field amplitudes can be expressed in matrix form:

$$\begin{pmatrix} R_B \\ S_B \end{pmatrix} = \begin{pmatrix} C_{11} & C_{12} \\ C_{21} & C_{22} \end{pmatrix} \begin{pmatrix} R_A \\ S_A \end{pmatrix} = \mathbf{C} \begin{pmatrix} R_A \\ S_A \end{pmatrix} \tag{7.70}$$

The transition from B to A is given by the transpose of $\mathbf{C}$. The matrix elements are found from standard first-order perturbation theory; the result can be expressed as

$$C_{11} = C_{22} = \sqrt{1 - \epsilon^2} \tag{7.71}$$

$$C_{12} = -C_{21} = \epsilon \tag{7.72}$$

where ϵ is given by the overlap integral

$$\epsilon = \frac{k_0^2}{\beta_{R,A}^2 - \beta_{S,A}^2} \int_{-\infty}^{\infty} (n_B^2(x) - n_A^2(x)) E_{R,A} E_{S,A} \, dx \tag{7.73}$$

(Note that the fields $E_{R,A}$ and $E_{S,A}$ are assumed to be normalized; i.e., the integrals from $-\infty$ to ∞ of the square of the fields equal 1.) For small refractive index differences:

$$\epsilon \approx \frac{k_0}{\beta_{R,A} - \beta_{S,A}} \int_0^{d_g} (n_B(x) - n_A(x)) E_{R,A} E_{S,A} \, dx \tag{7.74}$$

here $k_0 = 2\pi/\lambda$, and $n_A(x)$ and $n_B(x)$ are the refractive index profiles in regions A and B. In analogy with Chapter 3, we define the coupling coefficient

$$\kappa = \frac{2}{\lambda} \int_0^{d_g} (n_B(x) - n_A(x)) E_{R,A} E_{S,A} \, dx \tag{7.75}$$

If the fields are nearly constant in the grating region $0 < x < d_g$, we have

$$\kappa \approx \frac{2}{\lambda} \Delta n_g \sqrt{\Gamma_{R,g} \Gamma_{S,g}} \tag{7.76}$$

where Δn_g is the difference in refractive index of the two layers forming the grating, and $\Gamma_{R,g}$ and $\Gamma_{S,g}$ and the confinement factors for modes R and S in the grating region (we note that to first order these confinement factors are the same for region A and region B).

Near the coupling wavelength we have

$$(\beta_{R,A} - \beta_{S,A})L_A = \pi + 2\delta_A L_A \tag{7.77}$$

and

$$(\beta_{R,B} - \beta_{S,B})L_B = \pi + 2\delta_B L_B \tag{7.78}$$

This defines the detuning parameters δ_A and δ_B, which are both zero at the coupling wavelength, and L_A and L_B are both close to one half of the period Λ. This gives

$$\epsilon = \frac{\kappa \Lambda}{2} \tag{7.79}$$

In region A, the propagation can be described by

$$\begin{pmatrix} R_A(L_A) \\ S_A(L_A) \end{pmatrix} = \mathbf{T_A} \begin{pmatrix} R_A(0) \\ S_A(0) \end{pmatrix} \tag{7.80}$$

where

$$\mathbf{T_A} = \begin{pmatrix} \exp\left(-j\beta_{R,A}L_A\right) & 0 \\ 0 & \exp\left(-j\beta_{S,A}L_A\right) \end{pmatrix} \tag{7.81}$$

with a similar expression for region B, with $\beta_{R,A}$, $\beta_{S,A}$, and L_A replaced by $\beta_{R,B}$, $\beta_{S,B}$, and L_B.

The propagation through a full period is given by the matrix product

$$\mathbf{M} = \mathbf{C^t T_B C T_A} \tag{7.82}$$

This is similar to the transfer matrices used in Chapter 3, but here the two modes propagate in the same direction. The transfer matrix for a structure consisting of a number of identical periods the matrix $\mathbf{M}$ can be raised to the appropriate power using the method described in Appendix C. All that is required to calculate the transfer matrix for a given structure is the overlap integral given by (7.73) and the propagation constants.

As noted in [42], near the coupling wavelength the transfer matrix corresponds to a rotation matrix for a rotation angle α given by

$$\alpha = \arctan(2\epsilon) \tag{7.83}$$

Full power transfer is obtained after N periods with

$$N\alpha = \frac{\pi}{2} \tag{7.84}$$

using (7.79), this gives a coupling length of

$$L_c = N\Lambda = \frac{\pi}{2\kappa} \tag{7.85}$$

Coupled-mode equations for the field amplitudes R and S of the two modes E_R and E_S of the unperturbed structure can be written in a way similar to the ones for contradirectional coupling (3.9) and (3.10). Since the modes propagate in the same direction, we change the sign on the two terms on the left-hand side of (3.10), and for notational convenience we replace S by jS. This leads to

$$\frac{dR}{dz} + j\delta R = \kappa S \tag{7.86}$$

and

$$\frac{dS}{dz} - j\delta S = -\kappa R \tag{7.87}$$

The detuning δ is found by using

$$(\beta_{R,A} - \beta_{S,A})L_A + (\beta_{R,B} - \beta_{S,B})L_B = (\beta_R - \beta_S)\Lambda \tag{7.88}$$

and

$$(\delta_A L_A + \delta_B L_B) = \delta\Lambda \tag{7.89}$$

This gives

$$\delta = \frac{\beta_R - \beta_S}{2} - \frac{\pi}{\Lambda} \tag{7.90}$$

where β_R and β_S are the propagation constants for the unperturbed structure without the grating. The coupling coefficient κ can be found from (7.75), using the field distributions E_R and E_S for the unperturbed structure.

The general solution to these coupled-mode equations is of a structure similar to the contradirectional case (3.23) and (3.24):

$$R(z) = \left(\cos(\gamma z) - \frac{j\delta}{\gamma} \sin(\gamma z) \right) R(0) + \frac{\kappa}{\gamma} \sin(\gamma z)S(0) \tag{7.91}$$

$$S(z) = -\frac{\kappa}{\gamma} \sin(\gamma z)R(0) + \left(\cos(\gamma z) + \frac{j\delta}{\gamma} \sin(\gamma z) \right) S(0) \tag{7.92}$$

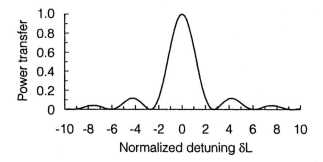

Figure 7.26   Power transfer as function of the detuning δL for the case $\kappa L = \pi/2$.

where

$$\gamma^2 = \kappa^2 + \delta^2 \tag{7.93}$$

At the coupling wavelength, the detuning δ is zero and the solution can be interpreted as a rotation matrix corresponding to a rotation angle κz (note that this agrees with the eigenmode propagation method because $\kappa\Lambda = 2\epsilon$, and with the result (7.85) for the coupling length). If the input to the coupler is given by $R(0) = 1$ and $S(0) = 0$, we have after one coupling length $R(L_c) = 0$ and $S(L_c) = 1$, and the physical interpretation of the rotation becomes obvious if we represent the total field by the vector $(R(z), S(z))$.

With the input given by $R(0) = 1$ and $S(0) = 0$, and for a finite detuning, we have the following expression for the amount of power transferred to the other mode after a distance L:

$$|S(L)|^2 = \frac{\kappa^2}{\kappa^2 + \delta^2} \sin^2\left(\sqrt{\kappa^2 + \delta^2}\, L\right) \tag{7.94}$$

This is shown in Figure 7.26 for the case where the length equals the coupling length given by (7.85). The power transfer has dropped to half when $\delta L = \pm 1.254$.

From (7.94) we can work out the bandwidth of the coupler [33]. We write the detuning caused by a wavelength deviation $\Delta\lambda$ from the desired coupling length λ_c as

$$\delta = \frac{\Delta\lambda}{2}\frac{\mathrm{d}\Delta\beta}{\mathrm{d}\lambda}\bigg|_{\lambda=\lambda_c} \tag{7.95}$$

Carrying out the differentiation and taking into account that the refractive index may be wavelength dependent, we get by using (7.68):

$$\delta = -\frac{\Delta\lambda}{\lambda}\frac{\pi}{\Lambda}F \tag{7.96}$$

Here, we have introduced the dispersion factor F:

$$F = 1 - \Lambda \frac{d\Delta n_{RS}}{d\lambda} \qquad (7.97)$$

where

$$\Delta n_{RS} = n_R - n_S \qquad (7.98)$$

is the difference in effective refractive index for the two modes. The dispersion factor can be very significant if Δn_{RS} is small and the two modes have different dispersion properties. The dispersion factor can also be written

$$F = \frac{\Delta n_{RS,g}}{\Delta n_{RS}} \qquad (7.99)$$

where $\Delta n_{RS,g}$ is the group index difference between the modes.

Defining $\Delta\lambda_{3dB}$ as the full width of the wavelength interval where more than half of the power is transferred, we have for a coupler of length L_c, using (7.96) with $\delta L_c = 1.254$

$$\Delta\lambda_{3dB} = \frac{2.508}{\pi} \frac{\lambda\Lambda}{L_c F} \qquad (7.100)$$

As L_c/Λ equals the number of periods N, we see that the relative bandwidth is proportional to $1/N$. This is different from the contradirectional case where the relative bandwidth is proportional to the relative refractive index variation in the grating (3.37).

   Numerical Example: We consider an example based on the filter structure in [34]. Referring to Figure 7.25, the parameters are $n_1 = 3.18$, $n_2 = 3.40$, $n_3 = 3.129$, $n_4 = 3.18$, $n_5 = 3.29$, $n_6 = 3.18$, $d_2 = 0.3\,\mu m$, $d_3 = 0.5\,\mu m$, $d_4 = 1.5\,\mu m$, $d_5 = 0.2\,\mu m$. The grating height is $0.06\,\mu m$, and we assume operation at a 1,500-nm wavelength. By solving the six-layer problem, we find the effective refractive indices in region A as $n_{R,A} = 3.28627$ and $n_{S,A} = 3.19200$, in region B the values are $n_{R,B} = 3.28780$ and $n_{S,B} = 3.19225$. Using (7.77) and (7.78), this gives $L_A = 7.9\,\mu m$ and $L_B = 7.8\,\mu m$, giving a period of $15.7\,\mu m$. The overlap integral (7.73) gives $\epsilon \approx 0.008$ and a coupling coefficient (7.79) of $1\,mm^{-1}$. Using (7.85), the coupling length is $1.6\,mm$, corresponding to about 100 periods. Calculating the effective refractive indices at a slightly different wavelength, and taking the material dispersion into account allows the calculation of the dispersion factor. From (7.97), this gives a value of $F = 2.7$. Using (7.100) we find a bandwidth of $6\,nm$. If dispersion is neglected (corresponding to $F = 1$), the estimated bandwidth would be $16\,nm$.

7.5.2   Tuning and Modespacing

From the results of the previous subsection, it follows that the relative change in the coupling wavelength for a grating-assisted codirectional coupler is related to the relative change in the difference in effective index between the two modes in the coupler. Including the dispersion factor F, this can be written

$$\frac{\Delta\lambda}{\lambda} = \frac{\Delta(n_R - n_S)}{(n_R - n_S)F} \tag{7.101}$$

By changing the refractive index in one layer, the tuning layer, by the amount Δn_t, we find, using $\lambda = \Lambda(n_R - n_S)$, that the coupling wavelength changes by

$$\Delta\lambda = (\Gamma_R - \Gamma_S)\Delta n_t \frac{\Lambda}{F} \tag{7.102}$$

Here Γ_R and Γ_S are the confinement factors for the two modes in the tuning layer. The tuning layer is usually one of the high-index waveguide layers, and the two confinement factors are very different, with one of them being very small compared with the other (see Figure 7.25).

We now recall the corresponding result for a DBR structure from Chapter 3. For this case, the relative wavelength change is

$$\frac{\Delta\lambda}{\lambda} = \frac{\Delta n}{n_{g,\text{eff}}} \tag{7.103}$$

giving a tuning of

$$\Delta\lambda = \Gamma_t \Delta n_t \frac{\lambda}{n_{g,\text{eff}}} \tag{7.104}$$

By comparing (7.102) with (7.104), we find the tuning enhancement of the grating-assisted coupler relative to the DBR, for the same amount of change of the refractive index of the tuning layer (assuming $\Gamma_t \approx \Gamma_R - \Gamma_S$):

$$\frac{\Lambda n_{g,\text{eff}}}{\lambda F} = \frac{n_{g,\text{eff}}}{n_R - n_S} \frac{1}{F} \tag{7.105}$$

The modespacing in a structure with total length L_{tot} and an average group index $n_{g,\text{eff}}$ is

$$\Delta\lambda_m = \frac{\lambda^2}{2n_{g,\text{eff}}L_{\text{tot}}} \tag{7.106}$$

Using the bandwidth for a coupler of length L_c (7.100), we find the following expression for the ratio of bandwidth to modespacing:

$$\frac{\Delta\lambda_{3dB}}{\Delta\lambda_m} = 1.6\frac{\Lambda n_{g,\text{eff}}}{\lambda F}\frac{L_{\text{tot}}}{L_c} \tag{7.107}$$

For a DBR laser with a relatively short active region and a moderate value of κL, this ratio has a value near unity (c.f., (3.37) and (3.38)). For a structure with a grating-assisted coupler, the ratio is increased by two factors, the first being the tuning enhancement factor

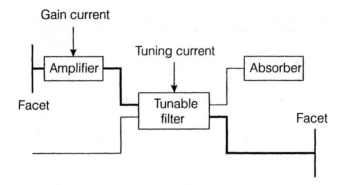

Figure 7.27   Principle of tunable laser with a tunable filter based on a grating-assisted coupler. At the coupling wavelength, a laser cavity is formed between the facets. For wavelengths away from the coupling wavelength, the coupling is incomplete and some part of the light is lost in the absorber, thus preventing lasing away from the coupling wavelength.

(7.105) and the second being the ratio of the total length to the coupler length. (We have assumed that the group index for the DBR equals the average group index for the structure with the coupler.)

The bandwidth-to-modespacing ratio clearly shows a tradeoff between enhanced tuning and suppression of side modes. This situation is studied in [43]; the result is that the *SSR* contains a factor proportional to the inverse of the square of the expression given in (7.107).

7.5.3 Longitudinally Integrated Structures

The principle of the use of a grating assisted coupler in a tunable laser structure is shown in Figure 7.27.

An example of the implementation of this idea into a laser is shown in Figure 7.28 [44]. In this case, the laser is based on the TTG structure (see Section 5.2.1 for details).

The main parameters of this laser are: period 35 μm, active region length 200 μm, coupler length 200 μm, and absorber length 200 μm. The coupler bandwidth is estimated to be about 60 nm and the modespacing is about 0.5 nm. In spite of the high ratio between bandwidth and modespacing (over 100), an *SSR* of over 25 dB was found for some wavelength ranges. The measured total tuning range was about 30 nm.

A different approach was presented in [45]; this vertical coupler filter (VCF) laser is shown in Figure 7.29. In this case, any uncoupled light is lost because of diffraction in the window region. The following values were used: priod 16 μm, active region length 600 μm, coupler length 1.3 mm, and window length 600 μm. The coupler bandwidth is estimated to be about 5 nm and the modespacing is about 0.15 nm. The improved bandwidth-to-modespacing ratio compared with the previous example resulted in an *SSR* of typically 25 dB, with values up to 30 dB, over the 42-nm tuning range (57 nm under pulsed operation).

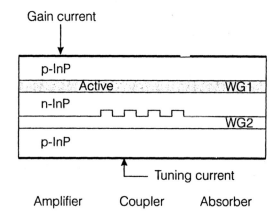

Gain current

Figure 7.28   The ACA (amplifier-coupler-absorber) laser. (Reprinted with permission from *Electronics Letters*, Vol. 27, pp. 2207–2209, ©1991 IEE.)

In [46] a similar structure is presented, but the periodic index variation is formed by varying the width rather than the thickness of the waveguide layer. A tuning range of 58 nm is achieved.

A modified structure, including a buried grating and an absorber region, is described in [47] (see Figure 7.30). The dimensions are: period 11 μm, active region length 565 μm, coupler length 840 μm, and absorber length 85 μm. The coupler bandwidth is estimated to be about 5 nm and the modespacing is about 0.24 nm. In this case, an *SSR* of over 25 dB is obtained over a tuning range of 74 nm.

More details on design issues for lasers incorporating grating-assisted couplers can be found in [43, 48].

It has been observed that not all cavity modes of a codirectionally coupled laser are accessed during tuning, thus preventing complete wavelength coverage. It is believed that internal reflections from the grating may be responsible for this [47]. A possible way

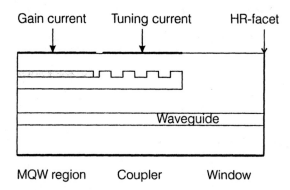

Figure 7.29   Vertical coupler filter (VCF) structure laser with MQW active region.

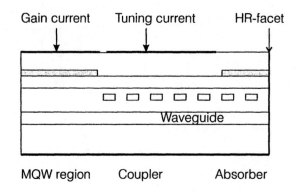

Figure 7.30   Vertical coupler filter laser with buried grating and absorber region.

of reducing these reflections is the use of a tilted grating [49]. This approach was also used for the VMZ laser structure [32].

7.5.4   Transversely Integrated Structures

As we have seen, the spectral selectivity of laser using grating assisted couplers for enhanced tuning is deteriorated because of the unfavorable ratio between the filter bandwidth and the modespacing. This problem can, at least partly, be alleviated if the ratio between coupler length and total length is increased; ultimately, the coupler length should be equal to the total length. This is the idea behind the distributed forward coupled (DFC) structure shown in Figure 7.31.

As in the grating-assisted structures, two modes, R and S, are supported by the unperturbed structure, but in the DFC laser, the grating is present along the whole length of the device.

The analysis of the DFC is based on the eigenmode propagation description introduced in Section 7.5.1. Here we outline the main elements of the theory, based on [50] with some modifications in the notation to make it consistent with the description of the other codirectionally coupled structures.

The transfer matrix for one period, of length Λ, of the DFC can be written

$$M = \begin{pmatrix} \exp(-j\delta\Lambda) & j\Lambda\kappa \\ j\Lambda\kappa & \exp(j\delta\Lambda) \end{pmatrix} \exp(-j\beta_{av}\Lambda) \tag{7.108}$$

where the average propagation constant is

$$\beta_{av} = \frac{1}{2\Lambda} \left((\beta_{R,A} + \beta_{S,A})L_A + (\beta_{R,B} + \beta_{S,B})L_B \right) \tag{7.109}$$

here $\beta_{i,J}$ is the propagation constant for mode i in section J. The detuning is given by

$$\delta = \frac{1}{2\Lambda} \left((\beta_{R,A} - \beta_{S,A})L_A + (\beta_{R,B} - \beta_{S,B})L_B \right) - \frac{\pi}{\Lambda} \tag{7.110}$$

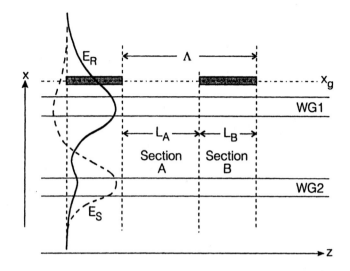

Figure 7.31   Principle of the distributed forward coupled structure. The grating perturbation is shown in black. (Reprinted with permission from *IEEE Journal of Selected Topics in Quantum Electronics*, Vol. 1, pp. 387–395, ©1995 IEEE.)

We consider the case where the perturbation is purely imaginary, corresponding to gain or loss. In this case the real part of the propagation constant difference has the same value in both sections, corresponding to a difference in the real part of the effective indices for the two modes of $\Delta n'$. This gives a coupling wavelength of

$$\lambda_c = \Lambda \Delta n' \tag{7.111}$$

In (7.108) κ is the coupling coefficient given by (see also (7.79))

$$\kappa = \frac{2\epsilon}{\Lambda} \sin\left(\pi \frac{L_B}{\Lambda}\right) \tag{7.112}$$

where ϵ depends on the overlap integral of the field distributions E_R and E_S (for the unperturbed structure without a grating). For a gain (or loss) perturbation g_α we have, in analogy with (7.74),

$$\epsilon = j \frac{g_\alpha}{4\pi} \Lambda \int_0^{d_g} E_R E_S \, dx \tag{7.113}$$

where the integration is carried out over the grating region, and the field distributions are again assumed to be normalized. For the case where the fields are nearly constant in the grating region we have

$$\kappa \approx j \frac{g_\alpha}{4\pi} \sin\left(\pi \frac{L_B}{\Lambda}\right) \sqrt{\Gamma_{R,g} \Gamma_{S,g}} \tag{7.114}$$

where $\Gamma_{R,g}$ and $\Gamma_{S,g}$ are the confinement factors for modes R and S in the grating region.

In the presence of the periodic perturbation, the structure will have eigenmodes U and V. These are linear combinations of R and S and can be found from the eigenvectors of $\mathbf{M}$. The corresponding propagation constants are found from the eigenvalues of $\mathbf{M}$. If the perturbation contains an imaginary part, the modal gain of one of the eigenmodes will be increased in a certain wavelength interval (hence this mode will dominate), the modal gain of the other mode will decrease in this interval. This filtering mechanism works best if the perturbation is purely imaginary [50]. The filtering also works best if the modes R and S of the unperturbed structure have identical values for the longitudinally averaged gain

$$g_{I,av} = \frac{g_{I,A}L_A + g_{I,B}L_B}{\Lambda} \tag{7.115}$$

where I is R or S, and $g_{I,J}$ is the modal gain for mode I in section J. In principle, the section lengths can be designed to achieve this.

For the optimized structure, with a purely imaginary perturbation and identical values for the longitudinally averaged gain of the two modes, the gain variation around the coupling wavelength λ_c for modes U and V is given by

$$g_{U,V} = \begin{cases} g_{av} \pm \Delta g \sqrt{1 - \left(\frac{\lambda - \lambda_c}{\Delta\lambda_f/2}\right)^2} & \text{if } |\lambda - \lambda_c| \leq \Delta\lambda_f/2 \\ g_{av} & \text{if } |\lambda - \lambda_c| > \Delta\lambda_f/2 \end{cases} \tag{7.116}$$

Here the upper sign applies to mode U, the lower sign to mode V.

The amplitude of the gain variation is given by

$$\Delta g = \frac{|g_\alpha|}{\pi} \sin\left(\pi\frac{L_B}{\Lambda}\right) \int_0^{d_g} E_R E_S \, dx \approx \frac{|g_\alpha|}{\pi} \sin\left(\pi\frac{L_B}{\Lambda}\right)\sqrt{\Gamma_{R,g}\Gamma_{S,g}} \tag{7.117}$$

and the bandwidth is

$$\Delta\lambda_f = \frac{\lambda\Lambda}{\pi F}\Delta g \tag{7.118}$$

where F is the dispersion factor (7.97). The gain variation of the two modes is shown in Figure 7.32.

The physics of the gain variation can be explained in the following way: The modes U and V are formed as (different) linear combinations of the modes R and S of the unperturbed structure. For a wavelength within the coupling bandwidth, the different values of the propagation constants β_R and β_S lead to beating, giving power variations when we look at a plane $x = constant$ in the structure. In particular, the power in the grating layer shows a longitudinal variation; if the perturbation is in the form of absorbers one mode (say U) attains a higher average modal gain because its power maxima are between the absorbers, whereas the other mode (V) has maxima coinciding with the absorbers. This is illustrated in Figure 7.33.

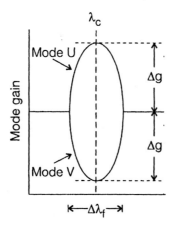

Figure 7.32   Wavelength dependence of the composite modes U and V for the case where the longitudinally averaged gain values for the modes R and S are identical.

The bandwidth to modespacing ratio is given by

$$\frac{\Delta\lambda_f}{\Delta\lambda_m} = \frac{\lambda\Lambda}{\pi F}\Delta g\frac{2n_{g,\mathrm{eff}}L}{\lambda^2} = \frac{\Lambda n_{g,\mathrm{eff}}}{\lambda F}\frac{2}{\pi}\Delta gL \tag{7.119}$$

Since the value of ΔgL is of the order of unity, we see that compared with the grating-assisted coupler, the factor from the ratio between the total length and the coupler length has disappeared. This improvement is significant for the *SSR*, which depends on the square of this factor.

We have only outlined the theory for the ideal structure. The difference in the values of the longitudinally averaged gain for modes R and S becomes significant if it cannot be neglected compared with Δg, leading to reduced discrimination against modes

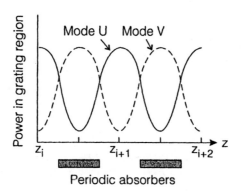

Figure 7.33   Power evolution in the grating layer for modes U and V.

far from the coupling wavelength. The filter characteristic becomes flatter and wider if the perturbation contains a real part in addition to the imaginary part. Usually an absorbing layer will have a high value of the real part of the refractive index, but this can be compensated by adding a low index layer on top of it. Finally, the structure should be cleaved exactly at the center of periods. The relative tolerance is about 10% of the period length, corresponding to a few micrometers, which can be achieved in practice.

Tuning can be accomplished by changing the refractive index in one of the waveguide layers. If we assume that the magnitude of the α_H factor for the tuning layer is much higher than the α_H factor for the active layer, we find that the tuning is given by the same expression as for the grating-assisted coupler, (7.102). Consequently, it should be possible to achieve comparable tuning ranges.

A more general expression for the wavelength change due to an index change of the tuning layer is derived in [50], based on the fact that the mode gain is clamped and using a procedure similar to the one used in Section 5.1. The result can be written

$$\Delta\lambda = (\Gamma_{R,t} - \Gamma_{S,t})\Delta n_t \frac{\Lambda}{F}\left(1 - \frac{\Gamma_{R,a} - \Gamma_{S,a}}{\Gamma_{R,t} - \Gamma_{S,t}}\frac{\alpha_{H,a}}{\alpha_{H,t}}\frac{\Gamma_{R,t} + \Gamma_{S,t}}{\Gamma_{R,a} + \Gamma_{S,a}}\right) \tag{7.120}$$

Here $\Gamma_{I,j}$ is the confinement factor for mode I in layer j (a for active and t for tuning), and $\alpha_{H,j}$ is the α_H factor for layer j.

Experimental results are limited to [51], which reports a tuning range of 16.5 nm.

7.6 COMPARISON OF WIDELY TUNABLE LASER STRUCTURES

To compare the relative merits of the various schemes for widely tunable lasers, we identify the main dependencies for a number of important performance parameters. In this comparison, numerical factors of the order of unity are neglected.

Tuning Range: The ultimate limitation is the width of the gain curve. From this point of view, a tuning well in excess of 100 nm can be expected. In this context it is interesting to note that a tuning range of 242 nm has been achieved by using a grating reflector in an external cavity configuration [52]. The width of the gain curve may be increased by using a combination of first- and second-quantized-state lasing in a quantum-well laser [53], or by using a quantum-well structure with wells of different widths [54]. In principle, a grating-assisted coupler (GAC) can be designed to cover any range, but for superstructure grating (SSG) and interferometric (MZ)-type lasers, there is an additional limitation to the tuning range because of the inherent beat period. For the SSG case, we have from (7.47):

$$\Delta\lambda_{\text{max,SSG}} = \Delta\lambda_s \frac{L_s}{\Delta L_s} \tag{7.121}$$

where $\Delta\lambda_s$ is the reflection peak spacing, L_s is the superstructure period, and $\Delta\lambda_s$ is the difference in superstructure period. For the MZ case we have from (7.61):

$$\Delta\lambda_{\text{max,MZ}} = \frac{\lambda^2}{2n_{g,\text{eff}}\Delta L} \tag{7.122}$$

where $n_{g,\text{eff}}$ is the effective group index and ΔL is the arm's-length difference.

Tuning Enhancement Factor: For "ordinary" tunable laser structures, the maximal continuous tuning range from electronic or thermal effects is of the order 10 nm. The tuning of a refractive index difference gives rise to an enhancement of the tuning. For the SSG and MZ cases, this factor follows directly from the Vernier effect

$$T_{\text{SSG}} = \frac{L_s}{\Delta L_s} \tag{7.123}$$

and

$$T_{\text{MZ}} = \frac{L}{\Delta L} \tag{7.124}$$

For the GAC, we have from (7.105):

$$T_{\text{GAC}} = \frac{n_{g,\text{eff}}}{n_R - n_S} \frac{1}{F} = \frac{n_{g,\text{eff}}}{\Delta n_{RS,g}} \tag{7.125}$$

where n_R and n_S are the effective refractive indices of the two modes in the coupler, and F is the dispersion factor (7.97).

Filter Width: The lobe width for an SSG is determined by the effective length of the SSG. If the lobe is wide compared with the difference in the reflection peak periods, there may not be sufficient discrimination against competing modes. If, on the other hand, the lobe is narrow compared with the difference in the reflection peak periods, the potential tuning range will be reduced. It seems that a good compromise is a lobe width comparable to the difference in the reflection peak periods. For the MZ case, the filter width is given by (7.61) (to within a numerical factor of the order of unity):

$$\Delta\lambda_{\text{f,MZ}} \approx \frac{\lambda^2}{2n_{g,\text{eff}}\Delta L} \tag{7.126}$$

The corresponding expression for the GAC (7.100) is

$$\Delta\lambda_{\text{f,GAC}} \approx \frac{\lambda\Lambda}{L_c F} \tag{7.127}$$

where Λ is the period and L_c is the coupler length. For the DFC structure, the result (7.118) is

$$\Delta\lambda_{\text{f,DFC}} = \frac{\lambda\Lambda}{\pi F}\Delta g \tag{7.128}$$

where Δg is the amplitude of the gain variation (7.117).

Modespacing: For all structures the cavity modespacing is given by the Fabry–Perot expression

$$\Delta\lambda_m = \frac{\lambda^2}{2n_{g,\text{eff}}L_{\text{tot}}} \tag{7.129}$$

Here $n_{g,\text{eff}}$ is the *average* effective group index of the structure, and in the total length L_{tot} the effective lengths must be used for grating regions.

Filter-Width-to-Modespacing Ratio: For the SSG case, this ratio is of the order of unity. For the MZ case (7.126) and (7.129) give

$$R_{\text{MZ}} \approx \frac{L}{\Delta L} \qquad\qquad (7.130)$$

For the GAC, we have using (7.127):

$$R_{\text{GAC}} \approx \frac{\Lambda n_{g,\text{eff}}}{\lambda F} \frac{L_{\text{tot}}}{L_c} \qquad\qquad (7.131)$$

and for the DFC, the result is

$$R_{\text{DFC}} \approx \frac{\Lambda n_{g,\text{eff}}}{\lambda F} \Delta g L_{\text{tot}} \qquad\qquad (7.132)$$

Side-Mode Suppression Ratio: The value of the *SSR* depends on the cavity gain difference between the lasing mode and the next competing mode. For the SSG case, assuming that the distance between the SSGs is small compared with the effective lengths of the reflectors, we expect values comparable to those of a DBR laser, *provided* the laser is tuned in such a way that the front and rear reflection peaks coincide at the desired wavelength, and that the phase control section is tuned to ensure that the phase condition is satisfied at this wavelength.

The other structures rely on various filter functions. Near their respective peaks these functions have (to first order) a parabolic shape. It follows from this that the gain discrimination against neighboring modes depends on R^{-2}, where R is the filter-width-to-modespacing ratio. Consequently, the *SSRs* for these structures are all *reduced* (to within a numerical factor of the order unity) by R^2, where the relevant value of R is found from (7.130), (7.131), or (7.132).

Wavelength Coverage and Access: The price for the favorable *SSR* properties of the SSG lasers is a more cumbersome tuning procedure. To achieve maximal optical power at a specified wavelength, both SSG regions have to be tuned to have a reflection peak at the requested wavelength; in addition, the phase control section has to be tuned to ensure that the roundtrip condition is satisfied at this wavelength. If the continuous tuning range for both reflectors exceeds the spacing of the reflection peaks, it will be possible, at least in principle, to access any wavelength within the tuning range. The challenge is therefore to implement a robust and reliable tuning procedure. this procedure should also be able to cope with any changes to the laser properties during its lifetime.

For a GAC structure, the tuning concept is simpler because a wavelength corresponding to a cavity mode is selected by tuning the coupling wavelength. However, experience seems to indicate that lasing does not take place at all the possible wavelengths. The explanation for this may be that subcavities are created by internal reflections.

Structures with multiple active sections, such as the Y-laser, pose particular problems because changes of the carrier density in one region leads to changes of both the refractive index and the gain. Control of wavelength and power is therefore interrelated, leading to complicated tuning procedures.

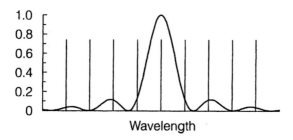

Figure 7.34   Superposition of the power transfer function of a grating-assisted coupler and the reflection peaks for a superstructure grating with uniform envelope (only the main peaks are shown).

Efficiency: The MZ- and GAC-type structures have the advantage that the optical power is emitted from the front facet directly from the active region. In principle, the reflectivity of this facet can be adjusted (by coating) to obtain the highest possible power for a given drive current. For SSG lasers, on the other hand, the optical power passes through a passive region, that may be quite long, giving rise to absorption losses. In addition, the SSG designs that give a high degree of uniformity for the reflection peaks lead to rather high reflectivities, which reduce the laser efficiency. A possible solution is to integrate an amplifier near the output facet; this amplifier can also act as a modulator [55]. A simpler alternative may be to use a high-reflectivity SSG as rear reflector and a short, low-reflectivity simple sampled grating at the front.

In Section 7.8 we compare the results reported for a number of different widely tunable lasers.

7.7 COMBINATION OF TECHNIQUES

None of the laser structures discussed in Section 7.5 can give simple tuning, a high *SSR*, and a high efficiency simultaneously. It is therefore relevant to look at possible combinations of the various tuning and mode selectivity features to design a combined structure that has all the desirable features. In [56], it was proposed to combine the wide tuning capabilities of a grating-assisted coupler with the spectral selectivity provided by a sampled grating reflector. The basic idea behind this proposal is that the spacing of the reflection peaks from the SG reflector is comparable to the filter width of the GAC. In this manner, the GAC selects one of the SG reflection peaks only. This is illustrated in Figure 7.34. If the reflection peak spacing for the SG is suitably tailored to the power transfer function for the GAC, and if the total length of the gain and coupler sections is small compared with the reflector length, we can expect this structure to have an *SSR* comparable to that of a DBR laser.

The reflection peak spacing for an SG is given by (7.35), and (7.96) gives the relation between wavelength change and detuning for a GAC with the period Λ. The example shown in Figure 7.34 is for the case where the reflection peak spacing corresponds to a normalized detuning of 2 (c.f., Figure 7.26).

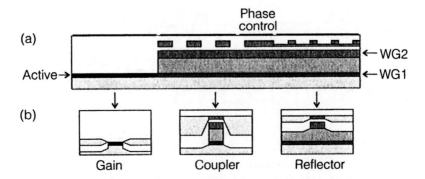

Figure 7.35   Schematic diagram of the GCSR laser, showing the longitudinal (a) and transverse (b) cross-sections of the different elements. (Reprinted with permission from *IEEE Photonics Technology Letters*, Vol. 7, pp. 697–699, ©1995 IEEE.)

An experimental realization of a grating-assisted codirectional coupler laser with rear sampled grating reflector (GCSR, for short), was reported in [57]. A tuning range of 74 nm is achieved with an *SSR* in excess of 30 dB over most of this range. An improved design giving a 114-nm tuning range is reported in [58]. In this case, the reflector is a superstructure grating with a 45-nm period, giving a 7-nm separation between the reflection peaks. Each superperiod consists of 5 subsections, each having a constant grating period. The resulting envelope of the reflection peaks has a dip in the center, thereby compensating for the spectral gain variation. More detail about characterization of GCSR lasers can be found in [18]. An outline of the GCSR structure is shown in Figure 7.35.

In [59], a near complete 100-nm coverage is reported. By tuning the coupler only, 20 reflection peaks with a separation around 5 nm can be selected (coarse tuning), as shown in Figure 7.36. If the coupler and reflector are tuned simultaneously, a coverage of 6.5 nm is possible for each of the reflection peaks (medium tuning). Because this exceeds

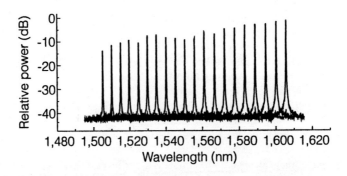

Figure 7.36   Superimposed spectra obtained for a GCSR laser by tuning of the coupler section. Each spectrum corresponds to alignment of the coupling wavelength with a reflection peak. (Reprinted with permission from *IEEE Photonics Technology Letters*, Vol. 7, pp. 1249–1251, ©1995 IEEE.)

the peak separation, full wavelength access is possible. Finally, by using the phase section as well, each cavity mode can be tuned across the 0.2-nm modespacing (fine tuning). As an example, it is shown that 16 wavelengths can be selected on a 1-nm grid.

Fast wavelength switching of GCSR lasers has been demonstrated [60], with switching times between wavelengths being of the order of 5 ns.

An alternative widely tunable laser structure is described in [61], based on the codirectional coupled filter laser from [46]. It is similar to the structure shown in Figure 7.29 (except that the coupler has a width rather than a thickness variation), in addition there is a superstructure grating in the active section, thus effectively forming a combination of an SSG-DFB laser and a tunable codirectional coupler. The grating design is described in more detail in [62]. The tuning range reported in [61] is 44 nm.

7.8   SUMMARY OF WIDELY TUNABLE LASER RESULTS

To summarize the present state of the art for monolithic widely tunable diode lasers, an overview of published results is presented in Table 7.1. The various laser types are

Table 7.1
Reported results on tuning range for various widely tunable laser structures.

Type	Range (nm)	Comment	Ref.
Superstructures (7.3)			
SG-DBR	57	First detailed SG study	[5]
SSG-DBR	83	Chirped grating	[11]
	34	Chirped grating, full cover	[12]
	105	Quadratic phase variation	[13]
	95	Optimized phase variation	[14]
	40	Thermal tuning, linewidth < 400 kHz	[15]
	62	Full cover	[17]
SSG-DFB	86	Linewidth < 5 MHz over 50 nm	[20]
Interferometric (7.4)			
Y-laser	51	Low *SSR*	[29]
Y3-laser	45	Improved control	[26]
VMZ	30	Vertical MZ	[32]
Codirectional (7.5)			
ACA	51	TTG structure	[44]
VCF	57	Pulsed operation, 42 nm for CW	[45]
	58	Lateral grating	[46]
	74	Buried grating	[47]
DFC	16	Transverse integration, improved *SSR*	[51]
Combinations (7.7)			
SSG-DBR/Codirectional	114	Record for monolithic structure	[58]
	100	Access to all reflection peaks	[59]
SSG-DFB/Codirectional	44	Lateral grating in coupler	[61]

listed in the order they have been discussed in this Chapter 7. For further details on the various laser types, consult the relevant sections or the original references. Results for tunable external cavity lasers (including vertical cavity structures), laser arrays, and multiwavelength lasers can be found in Sections 8.1 and 8.2.

REFERENCES

[1] Öberg, M., Nilsson, S., Klinga, T., and Ojala, P., "A three-electrode distributed Bragg reflector laser with 22 nm wavelength tuning range," *IEEE Photonics Technology Letters*, Vol. 3, 1991, pp. 299–301.

[2] Mori, A., Ohishi, Y., Yamada, M., Ono, H., Nishida, Y., Oikawa, K., and Sato, S., "1.5 μm broadband amplification by tellurite-based EDFAs," *Optical Fiber Communications (OFC'97)*, pp. PD1–1 to PD1–4, Dallas, TX, 1997.

[3] Corzine, S. W., Yan, R. H., and Coldren, L. A., "A tanh substitution technique for the analysis of abrupt and graded interface multilayer dielectric stacks," *IEEE Journal of Quantum Electronics*, Vol. 27, 1991, pp. 2086–2090.

[4] Kogelnik, H., "Filter response of nonuniform almost-periodic structures," *Bell System Technical Journal*, Vol. 55, 1976, pp. 109–126.

[5] Jayaraman, V., Chuang, Z.-M., and Coldren, L. A., "Theory, design, and performance of extended tuning range semiconductor lasers with sampled gratings," *IEEE Journal of Quantum Electronics*, Vol. 29, 1993, pp. 1824–1834.

[6] Gardiner, C. K., Plumb, R. G. S., Williams, P. J., and Reid, T. J., "Three-section sampled grating DBR lasers: modelling and measurements," *IEE Proceedings*, Part J, Vol. 143, 1996, pp. 24–30.

[7] Ougier, C., Talneau, A., Delorme, F., Slempkes, S., and Mathoorasing, D., "High number of wavelength channels demonstrated by a widely tunable sampled-grating DBR laser," *IEE Proceedings*, Part J, Vol. 143, 1996, pp. 77–80.

[8] Ougier, C., Talneau, A., Delorme, F., Raffle, Y., Landreau, J., and Mathoorasing, D., "Sampled-grating DBR lasers with 80 addressable wavelengths over 33 nm for 2.5 Gbit/s WDM applications," *Electronics Letters*, Vol. 32, 1996, pp. 1592–1593.

[9] Mason, B., Lee, S.-L., Heimbuch, M. E., and Coldren, L. A., "Directly modulated sampled grating DBR lasers for long-haul WDM communication systems," *IEEE Photonics Technology Letters*, Vol. 9, 1997, pp. 377–379.

[10] Ishii, H., Tohmori, Y., Tamamura, T., and Yoshikuni, Y., "Super structure grating (SSG) for broadly tunable DBR lasers," *IEEE Photonics Technology Letters*, Vol. 5, 1993, pp. 393–395.

[11] Tohmori, Y., Yoshikuni, Y., Ishii, H., Kano, F., Tamamura, T., Kondo, Y., and Yamamoto, M., "Broad-range wavelength-tunable superstructure grating (SSG) DBR lasers," *IEEE Journal of Quantum Electronics*, Vol. 29, 1993, pp. 1817–1823.

[12] Ishii, H., Kano, F., Tohmori, Y., Kondo, Y., Tamamura, T., and Yoshikuni, Y., "Broad range (34 nm) quasi-continuous wavelength tuning in super-structure-grating DBR lasers," *Electronics Letters*, Vol. 30, 1994, pp. 1134–1135.

[13] Ishii, H., Tohmori, Y., Yoshikuni, Y., Tamamura, T., and Kondo, Y., "Multiple-phase-shift super structure grating DBR lasers for broad wavelength tuning lasers," *IEEE Photonics Technology Letters*, Vol. 5, 1993, pp. 613–615.

[14] Ishii, H., Tohmori, Y., Yamamoto, Y., Tamamura, T., and Yoshikuni, Y., "Modified multiple-phase-shift super-structure-grating DBR lasers for broad wavelength tuning," *Electronics Letters*, Vol. 30, 1994, pp. 1141–1142.

[15] Ishii, H., Kano, F., Tohmori, Y., Kondo, Y., Tamamura, T., and Yoshikuni, Y., "Narrow spectral linewidth under wavelength tuning in thermally tunable super-structure-grating (SSG) DBR lasers," *IEEE Journal of Selected Topics in Quantum Electronics*, Vol. 1, 1995, pp. 401–407.

[16] Ishii, H., Tanobe, H., Kano, F., Tohmori, Y., Kondo, Y., and Yoshikuni, Y., "Quasicontinuous wavelength tuning in super-structure-grating (SSG) DBR lasers," *IEEE Journal of Quantum Electronics*, Vol. 32, 1996, pp. 433–441.

[17] Ishii, H., Tanobe, T., Kano, F., Tohmori, Y., Kondo, Y., and Yoshikuni, Y., "Broad-range wavelength coverage (62.4 nm) with superstructure-grating DBR laser," *Electronics Letters*, Vol. 32, 1996, pp. 454–455.

[18] Öberg, M., Rigole, P.-J., Nilsson, S., Klinga, T., Bäckbom, L., Streubel, K., Wallin, J., and Kjellberg, T., "Complete single mode wavelength coverage over 40 nm with a super structure grating DBR laser," *IEEE Journal of Lightwave Technology*, Vol. 13, 1995, pp. 1892–1898.

[19] Talneau, A., Charil, J., and Ougazzaden, A., "Superimposed Bragg gratings on semiconductor material," *Electronics Letters*, Vol. 32, 1996, pp. 1884–1885.

[20] Tohmori, Y., Kano, F., Ishii, H., Yoshikuni, Y., and Kondo, Y., "Wide tuning with narrow linewidth in DFB lasers with superstructure grating (SSG)," *Electronics Letters*, Vol. 29, 1993, pp. 1350–1352.

[21] Kano, F., Ishii, H., Tohmori, Y., Yamamoto, Y., and Yoshikuni, Y., "Broad range wavelength switching in superstructure grating distributed Bragg reflector lasers," *Electronics Letters*, Vol. 29, 1993, pp. 1091–1092.

[22] Wang, S., Choi, H. K., and Fattah, I. H. A., "Studies of semiconductor lasers of the interferometric and ring types," *IEEE Journal of Quantum Electronics*, Vol. 18, 1982, pp. 610–617.

[23] Lang, R. J., Yariv, A., and Salzman, J., "Laterally coupled-cavity semiconductor lasers," *IEEE Journal of Quantum Electronics*, Vol. 23, 1987, pp. 395–400.

[24] Miller, S. E., "Multibranch frequency-selective reflectors and application to tunable single-mode semiconductor lasers," *IEEE Journal of Lightwave Technology*, Vol. 7, 1989, pp. 666–673.

[25] Schilling, M., Schweitzer, H., Dütting, K., Idler, W., Kühn, E., Nowitzki, A., and Wünstel, K., "Widely tunable Y-coupled cavity integrated interferometric injection laser," *Electronics Letters*, Vol. 26, 1990, pp. 243–244.

[26] Kuznetsov, M., Verlangieri, P., Dentai, A. G., Joyner, C. H., and Burrus, C. A., "Widely tunable (45 nm, 5.6 THz) multi-quantum-well three-branch Y3-lasers for WDM networks," *IEEE Photonics Technology Letters*, Vol. 5, 1993, pp. 879–882.

[27] Kuznetsov, M., "Design of widely tunable semiconductor three-branch lasers," *IEEE Journal of Lightwave Technology*, Vol. 12, 1994, pp. 2100–2106.

[28] Idler, W., Schilling, M., Baums, D., Laube, G., Wünstel, K., and Hildebrand, O., "Y laser with 38 nm tuning range," *Electronics Letters*, Vol. 27, 1991, pp. 2268–2270.

[29] Hildebrand, O., Schilling, M., Baums, D., Idler, W., Dütting, K., Laube, G., and Wünstel, K., "The Y-laser: A multifunctional device for optical communication systems and switching networks," *IEEE Journal of Lightwave Technology*, Vol. 11, 1993, pp. 2066–2075.

[30] Dütting, K., Hildebrand, O., Baums, D., Idler, W., Schilling, M., and Wünstel, K., "Analysis and simple tuning scheme of asymmetric Y-lasers," *IEEE Journal of Quantum Electronics*, Vol. 30, 1994, pp. 654–659.

[31] Kuznetsov, M., Shankaranarayanan, N. K., Verlangieri, P., and Dentai, A. G., "Dynamics of frequency switching in tunable asymmetric Y-branch lasers," *IEEE Photonics Technology Letters*, Vol. 5, 1993, pp. 625–627.

[32] Borchert, B., Illek, S., Wolf, T., Rieger, J., and Amann, M.-C., "Vertically integrated Mach-Zehnder interferometer (VMZ) widely tunable laser diode with improved wavelength access," *Electronics Letters*, Vol. 30, 1994, pp. 2047–2049.

[33] Heismann, F., and Alferness, R. C., "Wavelength-tunable electrooptic polarization conversion in birefringent waveguides," *IEEE Journal of Quantum Electronics*, Vol. 24, 1988, pp. 83–93.

[34] Alferness, R. C., Koch, T. L., Buhl, L. L., Storz, F., Heismann, F., and Martyak, M. J. R., "Grating-assisted InGaAsP/InP vertical codirectional coupler filter," *Applied Physics Letters*, Vol. 55, 1989, pp. 2011–2013.

[35] Alferness, R. C., Buhl, L. L., Koren, U., Miller, B. I., Young, M., and Koch, T. L., "Vertically coupled InGaAsP/InP buried rib waveguide filter," *Applied Physics Letters*, Vol. 59, 1991, pp. 2573–2575.

[36] Sakata, H., Takeuchi, S., and Hiroki, T., "Codirectional grating-coupled filter for wavelength selective photodetection," *Electronics Letters*, Vol. 28, 1992, pp. 749–751.

[37] Marcuse, D., "Directional couplers made of nonidentical asymmetric slabs. Part II: Grating-assisted couplers," *IEEE Journal of Lightwave Technology*, Vol. 5, 1987, pp. 268–273.

[38] Huang, W.-P., and Haus, H. A., "Power exchange in grating-assisted couplers," *IEEE Journal of Lightwave Technology*, Vol. 7, 1989, pp. 920–924.

[39] Griffel, G., Itzkovitz, M., and Hardy, A. A., "Coupled mode formulation for directional couplers with longitudinal perturbation," *IEEE Journal of Quantum Electronics*, Vol. 27, 1991, pp. 985–994.

[40] Huang, W., and Lit, J. W. Y., "Nonorthogonal coupled-mode theory of grating-assisted codirectional couplers," *IEEE Journal of Lightwave Technology*, Vol. 9, 1991, pp. 845–852.

[41] Huang, W. P., Little, B. E., and Xu, C. L., "On phase matching and power coupling in grating-assisted couplers," *IEEE Photonics Technology Letters*, Vol. 4, 1992, pp. 151–153.

[42] Nolting, H.-P., and Sztefka, G., "Eigenmode matching and propagation theory of square meander-type couplers," *IEEE Photonics Technology Letters*, Vol. 4, 1992, pp. 1386–1389.

[43] Chuang, Z.-M., and Coldren, L. A., "Design of widely tunable semiconductor lasers using grating-assisted codirectional-coupler filters," *IEEE Journal of Quantum Electronics*, Vol. 29, 1993, pp. 1071–1080.

[44] Illek, S., Thulke, W., and Amann, M.-C., "Codirectionally coupled twin-guide laser diode for broadband electronic wavelength tuning," *Electronics Letters*, Vol. 27, 1991, pp. 2207–2209.

[45] Alferness, R. C., Koren, U., Buhl, L. L., Miller, B. I., Young, M. G., Koch, T. L., Raybon, G., and Burrus, C. A., "Broadly tunable InGaAsP/InP laser based on a vertical coupler filter with 57-nm tuning range," *Applied Physics Letters*, Vol. 60, 1992, pp. 3209–3211.

[46] Lealman, I. F., Okai, M., Robertson, M. J., Rivers, L. J., Perin, S. D., and Marshall, P., "Lateral grating vertical coupler filter laser with 58 nm tuning range," *Electronics Letters*, Vol. 32, 1996, pp. 339–340.

[47] Kim, I., Alferness, R. C., Koren, U., Buhl, L. L., Miller, B. I., Young, M. G., Chien, M. D., Koch, T. L., Presby, H. M., Raybon, G., and Burrus, C. A., "Broadly tunable vertical-coupler filtered tensile-strained InGaAs/InGaAsP multiple quantum well laser," *Applied Physics Letters*, Vol. 64, 1994, pp. 2764–2766.

[48] Amann, M.-C., and Illek, S., "Tunable laser diodes utilizing transverse tuning scheme," *IEEE Journal of Lightwave Technology*, Vol. 11, 1993, pp. 1168–1182.

[49] Amann, M.-C., Borchert, B., Illek, S., and Steffens, W., "Widely tunable laser diodes with tapered index perturbations for reduced internal reflections and improved wavelength access," *Electronics Letters*, Vol. 32, 1996, pp. 221–222.

[50] Amann, M.-C., Borchert, B., Illek, S., and Wolf, T., "Distributed forward coupled (DFC) laser," *IEEE Journal of Selected Topics in Quantum Electronics*, Vol. 1, 1995, pp. 387–395.

[51] Amann, M.-C., Borchert, B., Illek, S., and Wolf, T., "Widely tunable distributed forward coupled (DFC) laser," *Electronics Letters*, Vol. 29, 1993, pp. 793–794.

[52] Bagley, M., Wyatt, R., Elton, D. J., Wickes, H. J., Spurdens, P. C., Seltzer, C. P., Cooper, D. M., and Devlin, W. J., "242 nm continuous tuning from a GRIN-SC-MQW-BH InGaAsP laser in an extended cavity," *Electronics Letters*, Vol. 26, 1990, pp. 267–269.

[53] Mehuys, D., Mittelstein, M., Yariv, A., Sarfaty, R., and Ungar, J. E., "Optimised Fabry-Perot (AlGa)As quantum-well lasers tunable over 105 nm," *Electronics Letters*, Vol. 25, 1989, pp. 143–145.

[54] Gingrich, H. S., Chumney, D. R., Sun, S.-Z., Hersee, S. D., Lester, L. F., and Brueck, S. R. J., "Broadly tunable external cavity laser diodes with staggered thickness multiple quantum wells," *IEEE Photonics Technology Letters*, Vol. 9, 1997, pp. 155–157.

[55] Lee, S.-L., Heimbuch, M. E., Cohen, D. A., Coldren, L. A., and DenBaars, S. P., "Integration of semiconductor laser amplifiers with sampled grating tunable lasers for WDM applications," *IEEE Journal of Selected Topics in Quantum Electronics*, Vol. 3, 1997, pp. 615–627.

[56] Willems, J., Morthier, G., and Baets, R., "Novel widely tunable integrated optical filter with high spectral selectivity," *18th European Conference on Optical Communication (ECOC'92)*, pp. 413–416, Berlin, Germany, 1992.

[57] Öberg, M., Nilsson, S., Streubel, K., Wallin, J., Bäckbom, L., and Klinga, T., "74 nm wavelength tuning range of an InGaAsP/InP vertical grating assisted codirectional coupler laser with rear sampled grating reflector," *IEEE Photonics Technology Letters*, Vol. 5, 1993, pp. 735–738.

[58] Rigole, P.-J., Nilsson, S., Bäckbom, L., Klinga, T., Wallin, J., Stålnacke, B., Berglind, E., and Stoltz, B., "114 nm wavelength tuning range of a vertical grating assisted codirectional coupler laser with a super structure grating distributed Bragg reflector," *IEEE Photonics Technology Letters*, Vol. 7, 1995, pp. 697–699.

[59] Rigole, P.-J., Nilsson, S., Bäckbom, L., Klinga, T., Wallin, J., Stålnacke, B., Berglind, E., and Stoltz, B., "Access to 20 evenly distributed wavelengths over 100 nm using only a single current tuning in a four-electrode monolithic semiconductor laser," *IEEE Photonics Technology Letters*, Vol. 7, 1995, pp. 1249–1251.

[60] Rigole, P.-J., Shell, M., Nilsson, S., Blumenthal, D. J., and Berglind, E., "Fast wavelength switching in a widely tunable GCSR laser using a pulse pre-distortion technique," *Optical Fiber Communications (OFC'97)*, pp. 231–232, Dallas, TX, 1997.

[61] Okai, M., Lealman, I. F., Rivers, L. J., Dix, C., Armes, D., Perin, S. D., Marshall, P., and Robertson, M. J., "Wavelength tunable in-line Fabry-Perot laser with lateral-grating assisted vertical codirectional coupled filter," *Electronics Letters*, Vol. 33, 1997, pp. 59–61.

[62] Okai, M., Lealman, I. F., Rivers, L. J., Dix, C., and Robertson, M. J., "In-line Fabry-Perot optical waveguide filter with quasi-chirped gratings," *Electronics Letters*, Vol. 32, 1996, pp. 108–109.

Chapter 8

Related Components

In the preceding Chapters 4 through 7 we have considered the tuning and spectral properties of *monolithic* semiconductor lasers. A number of other components are related in function, technology, or application: Tuning of diode lasers can be accomplished by the use of an external cavity, lasing at different wavelengths can be achieved by using arrays or multiwavelength structures, complementary structures form tunable or multiwavelength detectors, and tuning is also possible for other laser types.

It is the purpose of Chapter 8 to give a brief introduction to these components. It must be stressed, however, that this chapter serves as an introduction only; several of the topics discussed here are, or could be, the subject of whole books.

8.1 TUNABLE EXTERNAL CAVITY DIODE LASERS

Lasers in which the wavelength selection and tuning functions are external to the semiconductor structure are an obvious alternative to monolithic tunable diode lasers, where these functions are integrated in the semiconductor structure. In general, the behavior of a diode laser in an external cavity can be highly complicated, with the details depending on the external cavity length, the feedback level, the diode laser parameters, and on the optical power level. In an attempt to classify the behavior, five distinct operating regimes have been identified [1]; see also [2] for an updated and more detailed discussion.

8.1.1 Grating External Cavities

To ensure stable operation of external cavity diode lasers, it is necessary to provide an antireflection (AR) coating to the laser facet facing the cavity. Such a coating prevents the laser from operating in a mode determined purely by the facets and forces it to operate in a mode determined by the external reflector. A simple external cavity configuration is outlined in Figure 8.1.

In the structure shown in this figure, feedback (in the first diffracted order) occurs for the wavelength λ when

$$\lambda = 2\Lambda \sin \theta \tag{8.1}$$

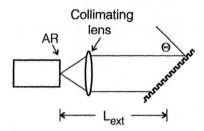

Figure 8.1   Laser in an external cavity with a diffraction grating used as external reflector.

where Λ is the grating period.

External cavity lasers have very attractive linewidth properties. Recalling the discussion in Section 3.6, the linewidth is proportional to the spontaneous emission rate, and it is in inverse proportion to the number of photons in the laser cavity. Here we assume that the external cavity length L_{ext} is much longer than the original laser. The spontaneous emission rate is the number of photons emitted into the lasing mode per unit time. Because the modespacing varies as $1/L_{ext}$, the spontaneous emission rate also varies as $1/L_{ext}$. The number of photons, on the other hand, is proportional to L_{ext}. As a consequence of these relations, the linewidth for an external cavity laser is proportional to the inverse square of the external cavity length. The result is that even for relatively short cavities (centimeter range) very narrow linewidths (low kilohertz range) can be obtained.

The main problem with external cavity configurations is mechanical and thermal stability. To avoid mode-hopping, the external cavity length L_{ext} must remain constant to within a small fraction of a wavelength.

External cavity lasers are available from several manufactures, and very compact designs have been reported; for example, miniature packaged lasers with dimensions 3 cm × 3 cm × 5 cm [3].

Tuning of an external cavity laser with grating feedback is achieved simply by rotating the grating. According to (8.1), a change in the incidence angle Θ leads to a change in the wavelength λ.

Some examples of grating external cavity tunable lasers are

- 35-nm tuning around 850 nm with 1 W CW power [4].

- 55-nm tuning range around 1,500 nm with a 10-kHz linewidth [5].

- 105-nm tuning range around 800 nm [6].

- The highest tuning range for any diode laser is 242 nm (from 1,320 nm to 1,562 nm) [7], a range of 240 nm is reported in [8].

There has also been a report of tuning achieved by using a micromachined external mirror [9]. The tuning range was 20 nm, but the spectrum was multimoded.

As an alternative to gratings, it is possible to use an electro-optically tunable birefringent filter or a tunable acousto-optic filter as the wavelength-selective element. A 7-nm tuning range with a linewidth of under 60 kHz has been reported for the birefringent filter case [10], and 83 nm has been reported for the acousto-optic filter case [11].

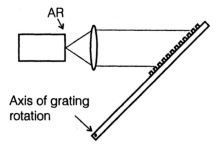

AR

Axis of grating
rotation

Figure 8.2   Grating external cavity where the axis for the grating rotation is offset.

The ultimate limit to the tuning range is set by the width of the gain curve (see the start of Section 7.6). For more details of tunable external cavity lasers, refer to [12].

8.1.2   Continuous Tuning of External Cavity Lasers

Although the tuning properties for external grating cavity lasers are very impressive, it is important to note that none of the results quoted above is for *continuous* tuning (i.e., tuning without mode jumps). In addition to the condition expressed by (8.1), continuous tuning requires the cavity length to vary in proportion to the wavelength. This is in contrast to the configuration shown in Figure 8.1, where the cavity length is constant.

Several different schemes providing simultaneous translation and rotation of the diffraction grating have been proposed [13–17]. An example is shown in Figure 8.2.

The widest continuous tuning range reported is 82 nm around 1,540 nm, with a linewidth below 100 kHz [16].

8.1.3   Tunable Vertical Cavity Lasers

Since the late 1980s there has been a rapid development of vertical cavity surface emitting lasers (VCSEL). In these lasers, the lasing is perpendicular to the plane defined by the active layer. Instead of cleaved facets, the optical feedback is provided by Bragg reflectors consisting of layers with alternating high and low refractive indices. Because of the very short cavity length, very high ($\geq$ 99%) reflectives are required, and the reflectors typically have 20 to 30 layer pairs. Due to the short cavity length, the modespacing is large compared with the width of the gain curve, and, if the resonant wavelength is close to the gain peak, single-longitudinal-mode operation occurs. It should be noted, however, that if the diameter of the active region is large, multitransverse-mode operation may occur.

One of the particular advantages of VCSELs is that the spot size can be made compatible with that of a single-mode optical fiber, making the coupling from laser to fiber easier and more efficient. The VCSEL structure also makes it possible to fabricate very-high-density two-dimensional laser arrays. Most VCSELs are fabricated using the AlGaAs material system, with one or more strained InGaAs quantum wells as the active

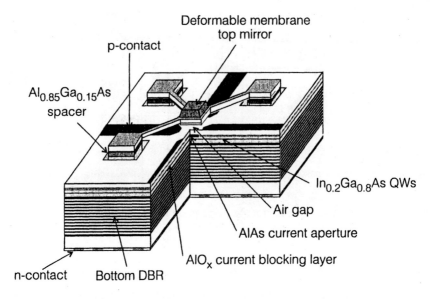

Figure 8.3   VCSEL with micromachined reflector membrane. (Reprinted with permission from *Applied Physics Letters*, Vol. 72, pp. 10–12, ©1998 American Institute of Physics.)

material; for these lasers, the wavelength is usually close to 1 μm. For more details on VCSELs, refer to [18].

The simplest method for tuning VCSELs is the use of the temperature dependence of the refractive index of the Bragg reflector. By adding an extra contact, thermal tuning can be achieved by resistive heating. The first publications reported tuning ranges of about 2 nm [19, 20]. A continuous tuning range of 10.1 nm has been achieved using thin-film heaters [21]. We note that the Bragg wavelength has a much smaller temperature coefficient than the gain peak, and the mismatch between the Bragg wavelength and the gain peak will limit the thermal tuning range (see also Section 3.5.2).

Two groups have reported tunable VCSELs with micromachined reflectors. In the first approach, a deformable membrane mirror is used [22]. This structure is designed to have an air-gap of about $3\lambda/4$. When a voltage is applied to the membrane, the resulting electrostatic force reduces the air gap thickness, and, consequently, the resonant wavelength will be reduced. Subsequent improvements in design and fabrication have resulted in improved performance. A tuning range of 19 nm with a threshold current of 0.34 mA is reported in [23], and 30-nm tuning (23-nm with single-mode operation) is reported in [24]. The structure is shown in Figure 8.3.

An alternative approach is described in [25]; see Figure 8.4. The operating principle is very similar to that of the previous example: the optical cavity length is changed by applying a voltage that deflects the cantilever electrostatically. In [26], a tuning range of 19.1 nm is reported for this structure, with a threshold current below 0.5 mA and a power of 0.9 mW over 7 nm of the tuning range. In a modified structure [27], a tuning range of 20 nm is achieved, with the light emitted from the top rather than through the substrate. This tuning range has been further extended to 31.6 nm [28].

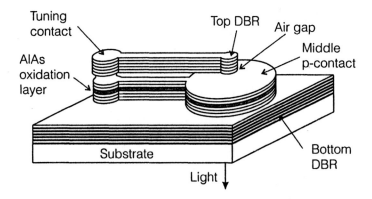

Figure 8.4   VCSEL with DBR mirror on a cantilever. (Reprinted with permission from *Electronics Letters*, Vol. 32, pp. 1888–1889, ©1996 IEE.)

8.2   DIODE LASER ARRAYS AND MULTIWAVELENGTH SOURCES

Laser arrays, where each laser in the array operates at a particular wavelength (or wavelength range), are an alternative to tunable lasers. In their simplest form, these arrays have separate outputs for each array element. More sophisticated structures incorporate a combiner element, which makes it possible to couple the output to a single optical fiber without the use of complicated external coupling optics. If each laser in the array can be tuned by an amount exceeding the wavelength difference between the array elements, a very wide total wavelength range can be achieved.

This section reviews various diode laser array structures. We make a distinction between laser arrays with combiners designed for operation at a single wavelength at the time, and multiwavelength lasers that can, at least in principle, operate simultaneously at several wavelengths.

8.2.1   Simple Diode Laser Arrays

The Bragg wavelength for a DFB laser can be adjusted by varying the structural parameters as discussed in Section 3.5.1. The most obvious parameter to change is the grating period; an example is described in [29]. An array with five DFB lasers with a 125-μm separation is fabricated, and the grating period difference is 0.94 nm, giving a 5.0 ± 0.5 nm difference in lasing wavelength.

Arrays with up to 20 elements have been fabricated. In [30], grating period differences of 0.10 nm and 0.15 nm are used, giving lasing wavelength differences of 0.66 nm and 1.0 nm, respectively. In the array described in [31], a grating period difference of 0.5 nm is used, and the difference in lasing wavelength is about 3 nm. We notice that the relation between grating period and lasing wavelength is consistent with (3.72) if we assume the effective refractive index to be about 3.3 and the group index to be about 3.7.

Instead of varying the grating period in an array, it is, of course, possible to vary one or more of the other structural parameters. A 16-element array with varying stripe width is described in [32]. When the width is varied from 1.6 μm to 5.0 μm, the lasing wavelength increases by about 8 nm. The width dependence is broadly in line with the prediction from (3.71). In this example, fine adjustment of the wavelength for each element is accomplished by using individual thin-film heating elements.

In the three array examples discussed above, the variation in lasing wavelength results in a varying degree of detuning from the gain-peak, resulting in nonuniform characteristics of the array elements. This problem can be overcome by using selective-area growth techniques, which leads to different compositions and thicknesses of the active layers. In [33], a 40-element array with a 75-nm wavelength span is described; the threshold currents for the array elements vary by only a few milliamperes around an average of 8.9 mA.

Some applications require a high degree of uniformity of the array's wavelength spacing. Results reported on this issue include a six-element array with a 1.61-nm (200-GHz) nominal wavelength spacing and a 0.18-nm standard deviation [34], and a six-element array with a 0.11-nm standard deviation from a 2-nm spacing [35].

8.2.2   Arrays Integrated With Combiners

In [36], an array of three DBR lasers is integrated with a passive waveguide combiner and an amplifier that compensates for the combiner loss. The advantage over a simple array is that output from all array elements is available from a single-output waveguide. This configuration allows operation over a wide wavelength range by staggering the tuning ranges from the individual DBR lasers.

A more advanced structure is shown in Figure 8.5. Here six DFB lasers are integrated with a passive 6 × 1 combiner, an amplifier, and a modulator [37]; detectors are placed at the back of the lasers for power monitoring.

For this structure, the wavelength spacing was designed to be 200 GHz (1.6 nm). Because only one laser is operating at a time, with the signal being imposed by the modulator, the elements in the array can be closely spaced (80 μm). The total device size is 0.5 mm × 3.5 mm.

An array structure with 21 DFB lasers integrated with a 25 × 25 star coupler and an output amplifier is described in [38]. Eighteen of the lasers were working with a wavelength spacing averaging 3.7 nm due to a 0.625-nm change in grating period between elements. The chip area is 1 mm × 4 mm. Instead of having all the lasers operating at different wavelengths, the array can be designed for redundancy with two lasers per wavelength, and to compensate for fabrication tolerances, additional lasers can be added to increase the chance of covering the desired system wavelengths. Details for a 20-laser array aimed at eight specific wavelengths are given in [39]. This laser array is designed for simultaneous operation at several wavelengths, with the lasers being directly modulated. The electrical crosstalk was found to be low, but cross-gain modulation in the output amplifier may be a problem.

A different approach is reported in [40]. Here, 16 DBR lasers are integrated with a star coupler and an output amplifier. Instead of relying on direct modulation, each laser is integrated with an electroabsorption modulator.

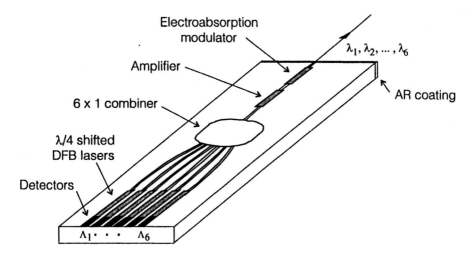

Figure 8.5   Six-element laser array integrated with an amplifier and a modulator. (Reprinted with permission from *Electronics Letters*, Vol. 31, pp. 1835–1836, ©1995 IEE.)

8.2.3   Multistripe Grating Cavities

A laser array with an external grating reflector can be used as a multiwavelength source; the principle of this structure is shown in Figure 8.6.

Lasing is achieved by turning on one of the reflector guides and the output amplifier; the lasing wavelength is determined by the grating and the device geometry. Simultaneous lasing at several wavelengths can be achieved by turning on several reflector guides. The design of multichannel grating cavity (MGC) lasers is discussed in [41], and some experimental results are reported in [42]. An integrated version working at two wavelengths with a 21-nm separation is reported in [43].

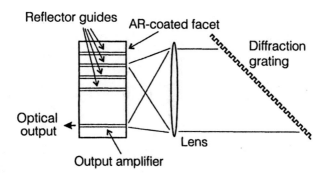

Figure 8.6   Multichannel grating cavity (MGC) laser. (Reprinted with permission from *IEEE Journal of Lightwave Technology*, Vol. 9, pp. 893–899, ©1991 IEEE.)

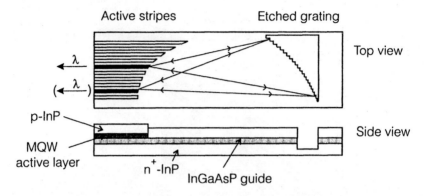

Figure 8.7   Multistripe array grating integrated cavity (MAGIC) laser. (Reprinted with permission from *Applied Physics Letters*, Vol. 61, pp. 2750–2752, ©1992 American Institute of Physics.)

A slightly different implementation of the same idea is the multistripe array grating integrated cavity (MAGIC) laser which is shown in Figure 8.7.

The results reported for this laser in [44] show operation at 15 wavelengths with a 2-nm separation and less than 0.06-nm standard deviation from a linear wavelength spacing. Design details for this structure are described in [45], and simultaneous operation in up to four different wavelengths is demonstrated in [46].

8.2.4   Phased Arrays

A different approach to multiwavelength lasers is shown in Figure 8.8 [47].

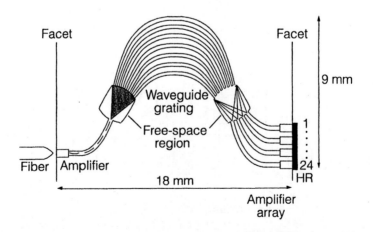

Figure 8.8   Phased array multi wavelength laser. (Reprinted with permission from *IEEE Photonics Technology Letters*, Vol. 8, 1996, pp. 870–872, ©1996 IEEE.)

The different lengths of the waveguides in the array causes a wavelength-dependent phase change, and hence different wavelengths are focused on different output waveguides on the right-hand side of the structure. Consequently, different wavelengths are controlled by different amplifiers. For this device, 18 lasers were working, and the channel spacing was 103 GHz (0.8 nm), close to the design value of 100 GHz. Each wavelength channel could be modulated at 1.24 Gbit/s.

In [48], a higher refractive index contrast design is used, leading to a reduced device size. A size of 3.5 mm × 2.5 mm is reported for a nine-channel device with a 400-GHz spacing. Simultaneous CW operation of four channels was reported.

An improved and more compact (15 mm × 4 mm) version of the device from [47] is reported in [49]. In this device, there are 16 channels with a 200-GHz (1.6-nm) spacing. The channels can each be tuned thermally by 275 GHz (2.2 nm); during thermal tuning the channel spacing remains unchanged. Simultaneous modulation of several channels is possible. For a modulation rate of 622 Mbit/s there is a 2-dB penalty due to electrical crosstalk, while at 310 Mbit/s, no crosstalk penalty occurs.

The phased-array lasers discussed above have rather long cavities, and consequently a small spacing of the longitudinal modes. As they have no frequency-selective element (i.e., a grating), they might be expected to operate simultaneously in several longitudinal modes. Experimentally, this does not seem to be the case, and it is thought that nonlinear wave mixing, helped by the small mode spacing, may provide single-mode stabilization [50]. A more detailed stability analysis is reported in [51].

8.3   RELATED SEMICONDUCTOR COMPONENTS

A number of semiconductor-based components may be integrated with tunable lasers, or perform functions that are of interest in some of the areas where tunable lasers are used. Some of these components and functions are discussed in this section. Within the scope of this review, it is only possible to provide very brief descriptions; consult the references for more detailed information. The June 1996 issue of the *IEEE Journal of Lightwave Technology*, for example, contains a number of relevant review papers.

8.3.1   Electroabsorption Modulators

The main spectral feature of a semiconductor is the sharp absorption edge at the photon energy corresponding to the bandgap energy. For photon energies below this edge, the semiconductor is nearly transparent, whereas for photon energies above the edge, it is highly absorbing. If the material consists of one or more quantum wells, the absorption edge can be shifted to lower energies by applying an electric field perpendicular to the wells, resulting in a range of photon energies where the absorption increases as illustrated in Figure 8.9. This so-called quantum confined Stark effect (QCSE, c.f., Section 4.5.2) makes it possible to fabricate waveguide modulators which can provide high speed modulation with a high extinction ratio using a modest modulating voltage [52].

If a diode laser is modulated directly, both the amplitude and the optical frequency vary as a result of the nonzero value of the α_H factor (see Section 2.1). For a

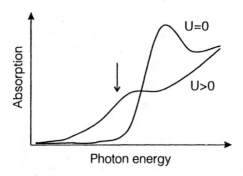

Figure 8.9   Schematic diagram of the absorption curve for a quantum well structure with ($U > 0$) and without ($U = 0$) an applied voltage. The arrow indicates a suitable operating point.

pulse of duration Δt, the resulting spectral width Δf_{opt} can be expressed in terms of a time-bandwidth product [53]:

$$\Delta t \Delta f_{\text{opt}} = \frac{2 \ln 2}{\pi} \sqrt{1 + \alpha_H^2} \tag{8.2}$$

A large value of α_H gives rise to a significant spectral broadening, denoted as *chirp*, which can severely limit the transmission distance for high-data-rate optical signals (e.g., 10 Gbit/s and higher) in the presence of fiber dispersion. A particular advantage of the quantum well electroabsorption modulator is reduced chirp.

Various schemes have been proposed for monolithic integration of a single-frequency laser (DFB or DBR) and an electroabsorption modulator. One technique is the use of selective-area growth as shown in Figure 8.10. The thickness and composition of quantum wells grown in a gap between SiO_2 masks depend on the gap and mask widths. This makes it possible to form a modulator section with a quantum well region with a higher absorption edge energy than the photon energy of the laser. Without an applied voltage, the modulator section is transparent, but it becomes absorbing when a voltage is applied.

A further discussion of laser and modulator integration schemes can be found in [54].

Several examples of integration of a tunable laser with a modulator have been published. In [55], a DBR laser/modulator structure with a tuning range of about 4 nm is used for transmission over 674 km of fiber at a data rate of 2.5 Gbit/s. A combination of a DBR laser with a 6-nm tuning range and a modulator with a 16-GHz modulation bandwidth is described in [56]. Similar techniques have been used in the AlGaAs material system. An AlGaAs/InGaAs/GaAs DBR laser operating at a wavelength near 1 μm with a 7-nm tuning range integrated with a modulator is reported in [57].

Examples of integration of electroabsorption modulators with laser arrays are mentioned in Section 8.2.

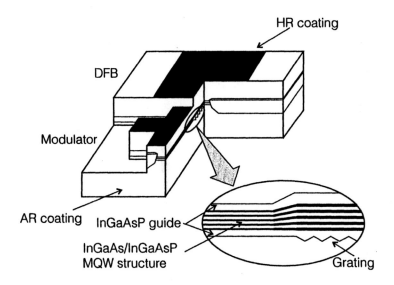

Figure 8.10   Schematic diagram of a DFB laser integrated with a modulator. (Reprinted with permission from *IEEE Journal of Quantum Electronics*, Vol. 29, pp. 2088–2096, ©1993 IEEE.)

8.3.2   Tunable Filters and Detectors

Tunable optical filters can, for example, be based on the use of tunable electro-optic polarization conversion in birefringent LiNbO$_3$ waveguides [58], or they can use surface acoustic waves to form an acousto-optical tunable filter, as discussed, for example, in [59] and references therein.

There are relatively few examples of semiconductor-based tunable filters. Such devices can, for example, be based on wavelength-dependent coupling between wave-guides [60]. The waveguide coupling can be grating assisted by using codirectional cou-pling [61]; this case was considered as a numerical example in Section 7.5.1. Special waveguide designs can also be used; for example, the antiresonant reflecting optical waveguide (ARROW) structure [62].

Absorbing layers can be integrated with semiconductor optical waveguides to form fast and efficient detectors [63]. By combining such detectors with a grating-coupled filter, it is possible to form tunable detectors. This approach has been demonstrated in both the GaAs and the InGaAsP material systems [64, 65]. The InGaAsP-based tunable detector described in [65] is integrated with a preamplifier, exhibiting a 30-nm tuning range and a 4-nm FWHM for the response.

8.3.3   Demultiplexers and Multiwavelength Detectors

The multiplexing function performed in the multiwavelength lasers described in Sec-tions 8.2.3 and 8.2.4 can also be used "in reverse" to give a demultiplexing function. Demultiplexing using a structure similar to the one from [43] is described in [66], and as

218 Tunable Laser Diodes

many as 78 channels spaced by 1 nm have been demultiplexed using a multistripe-array-grating integrated cavity [67].

By integration of photodiodes in the output waveguides, a multiwavelength detector array can be formed. This is reported in [68] for a structure similar to the one used in [67]. In this case, 65 channels with 0.7-nm passbands are operating with a 1-nm channel spacing. A somewhat modified design with eight channels spaced by 3.6-nm showed a detection bandwidth of 10 GHz [69].

Phased-array structures have also been used to form multiwavelength detectors. In [70], there are four channels with a 1.8-nm spacing and 0.7-nm-wide passbands. In [71], there are eight channels with a 200-GHz (1.6-nm) spacing and 0.7-nm-wide passbands, including an optical preamplifier at the input.

Other approaches include a structure with 42 channels with a 4-nm spacing [72], and a structure using an integrated aspheric lens and a tilted Bragg reflector [73].

The key issues in the design of multiwavelength detectors are crosstalk (both electrical and optical) and polarization sensitivity. For most applications, the state of polarization for the input optical signal is unknown and uncontrolled. Consequently, any polarization dependence in the detector structure may be detrimental to the performance.

8.3.4 Wavelength Converters

Wavelength conversion may be necessary for some applications, such as routing in a multiwavelength optical network. This function can be accomplished in a number of ways; "all-optical" methods are particularly interesting because they do not require detection and remodulation. Interested readers are referred to [74] for a general overview of wavelength conversion. Here we will concentrate on the use of cross-gain or cross-phase modulation of diode lasers and amplifiers. An alternative method is the use of four-wave mixing, discussed, for example, in [75] and references therein.

Wavelength conversion of a signal carried by the wavelength λ_{in} can be achieved by using the input signal to perform optical modulation of a DFB laser operating CW at λ_{out}. The input signal is amplified in the laser, leading to depletion of the carrier density in the laser. This in turn leads to both amplitude and frequency modulation of λ_{out}. Note that if amplitude modulation is used, the output signal is inverted relative to the input signal. In the case of a frequency-modulated signal, conversion to amplitude modulation can be performed using a Mach–Zehnder Interferometer (MZI). Details of conversion of signals with data rates up to 10 Gbit/s are reported in [76].

Using a tunable laser for the conversion process can change the output wavelength λ_{out}. Wavelength conversion of 2.5 Gbit/s signals over 18 nm has been achieved using a tunable DBR laser [77]. In [78], a SSG-DBR laser is used for conversion of 10 Gbit/s signals over a 90-nm wavelength range.

Wavelength conversion is also possible using a semiconductor optical amplifier (e.g., a laser structure with antireflection-coated facets). When both the input signal at λ_{in} and an external CW signal at λ_{out} are coupled into the amplifier "cross-gain modulation" occurs, and the input signal is transferred (and inverted) to λ_{out}.

"Cross phase modulation" can be achieved using an MZI structure with an amplifier in both arms. When an input signal at λ_{in} is present, the carrier density in one of the amplifiers is changed, thereby changing the phase relation for light at λ_{out} at the

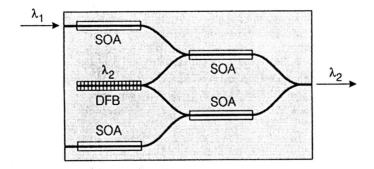

Figure 8.11   Wavelength converter based on an active MZI integrated with a CW DFB laser and pream-
plifiers. (SOA = semiconductor optical amplifier.) (Reprinted with permission from *IEEE
Photonics Technology Letters*, Vol. 9, pp. 1349–1351, ©1997 IEEE.)

output of the MZI. Both inverted and noninverted output signals are possible, depending
on the operating point of the interferometer. A review of wavelength conversion using
semiconductor optical amplifiers is given in [79].

Instead of using an external CW source, it is possible to integrate a laser with the
MZI; an example is shown in Figure 8.11.

In principle, it would be possible to integrate a tunable laser in the wavelength
converter structure, thus making it possible to transfer an incoming signal to any wavelength within the tuning range of the integrated laser.

8.4   NON-SEMICONDUCTOR TUNABLE LASERS

The majority of laser types are based on transitions between two well-defined energy levels. Consequently, the lasing wavelength is fixed and not readily tunable. Diode lasers, on
the other hand, rely on transitions between energy bands and are readily tunable because
of their wide gain curve. However, there are also other laser types that can be tuned over
a fairly wide spectral range. Tunable fiber lasers and tunable waveguide lasers are particularly interesting because they are compatible with many of the applications for which
diode lasers are normally used; for example, fiber optics. Many of the non-semiconductor
tunable lasers, however, require another laser for pumping.

8.4.1   Tunable Fiber Lasers

The advent of fiber amplifiers has had a major impact on the development of fiber-optic
systems. The best known example is the Erbium-doped silica-fiber amplifier (EDFA).
The EDFA is pumped by diode lasers operating at 980 or 1,480 nm and provides a gain
band from 1,530 to 1,565 nm, see [80] and [81] for more details. By combining a fiber
amplifier with suitable reflectors, it is possible to obtain lasing at wavelengths within the
gain band.

By using an external grating as a reflector, tunable lasing has been demonstrated for a variety of dopants and fiber materials [82–84].

Instead of using an external reflector in-fiber Bragg gratings can be formed by exposing a fiber to two interfering beams of UV laser light, similar to the way gratings are fabricated in diode lasers (see Section 3.5). Refer to [85] for a review of fiber gratings. Tuning of a Bragg grating fiber laser is possible by stretching or heating the fiber. A continuous tuning range of 32 nm, achieved by a 2.5% compression, has been reported [86].

In complete analogy with the approach described in Section 7.3, it is possible to use gratings with modified reflection characteristics, such as sampled gratings. Tuning over a 16.7-nm range with a strain of only 0.14% has been achieved [87]. In this case, the two sampled gratings had reflection peak separations of 1.85 and 2.05 nm, respectively, giving a tuning enhancement by about a factor of 10.

8.4.2   Tunable Waveguide Lasers

By doping waveguides fabricated in $LiNbO_3$ with Erbium, amplifiers and lasers for the 1,530- to 1,610-nm wavelength range can be made [88]. By combining this with an acousto-optical tunable filter, a tunable waveguide laser can be formed. The principle of the acousto-optical tunable filter is that a surface acoustic wave provides a narrowband mode coupling. The coupling wavelength can be tuned by varying the frequency of the acoustic wave, as described in more detail in [89]. The reported tuning range is 31 nm, with a wavelength variation of 8.6 nm per 1 MHz variation in the acoustic frequency, and the acoustic frequency is in the 170 MHz range.

8.4.3   Other Tunable Lasers

Other types of tunable lasers are less compatible with fiber optics and other applications where diode lasers are of interest. Some examples are mentioned below for completeness; for more details see [90].

Solid-state and color center lasers: Solid-state lasers consist of crystals doped with transition metals (e.g., Cr or Ti) or Lanthanides (e.g., Nd or Er). Ruby (Al_2O_3 doped with Cr) was the first material in which lasing was demonstrated in 1960, at the 694-nm wavelength. Another well-known example is the Nd:YAG laser working at 1,064 nm. The energy levels involved in the lasing transition are split, forming a manifold and making tuning possible. The tuning range is widest for the transition metal lasers, but wavelength and tuning range vary considerably from system to system. Color centers in crystals such as LiF can form the basis for widely tunable lasers. Operation in both the visible and the near-infrared wavelength regions is also possible [91].

Dye lasers: A number of organic dye molecules, usually in a liquid, can be used for lasers. The energy levels are split in numerous rotational and vibrational states, making tuning possible. The best known example is Rhodamine 6G, which can be tuned in the visible wavelength range from 570 to 610 nm.

Eximer lasers: These are pulsed gas lasers (ArF, KrF, XeCl, XeF) operating in the UV region at wavelengths from about 190 nm to about 350 nm, with tuning ranges of a few nanometers. Pumping is possible by using an electron beam. A special case is one of the transitions of the XeF laser, which is tunable over about 50 nm around a wavelength of about 500 nm.

Free-electron lasers: In this laser type, the lasing transition is between states in a continuum, making extremely wide tuning (usually in the infrared and far infrared) possible. The main drawback is that an accelerator is required to generate a beam of electrons moving at relativistic speeds. Only a very limited number of free-electron laser facilities are therefore available worldwide.

REFERENCES

[1] Tkach, R. W., and Chraplyvy, A. R., "Regimes of feedback effects in 1.5 μm distributed feedback lasers," *IEEE Journal of Lightwave Technology*, Vol. 4, 1986, pp. 1655–1661.

[2] Petermann, K., "External optical feedback phenomena in semiconductor lasers," *IEEE Journal of Selected Topics in Quantum Electronics*, Vol. 1, 1995, pp. 480–489.

[3] Mellis, J., Al-Chalabi, S. A., Cameron, K. H., Wyatt, R., J. C. Regnault, W. J. Devlin, and Brain, M. C., "Miniature packaged external-cavity semiconductor laser with 50 GHz continuous electrical tuning range," *Electronics Letters*, Vol. 24, 1988, pp. 988–989.

[4] Mehuys, D., Welch, D., and Scifres, D., "1W CW, diffraction-limited, tunable external-cavity semiconductor laser," *Electronics Letters*, Vol. 28, 1992, pp. 1254–1255.

[5] Wyatt, R., and Devlin, W. J., "10 kHz linewidth 1.5 μm InGaAsP external cavity laser with 55 nm tuning range," *Electronics Letters*, Vol. 19, 1983, pp. 110–112.

[6] Mehuys, D., Mittelstein, M., Yariv, A., Sarfaty, R., and Ungar, J. E., "Optimised Fabry-Perot (AlGa)As quantum-well lasers tunable over 105 nm," *Electronics Letters*, Vol. 25, 1989, pp. 143–145.

[7] Bagley, M., Wyatt, R., Elton, D. J., Wickes, H. J., Spurdens, P. C., Seltzer, C. P., Cooper, D. M., and Devlin, W. J., "242 nm continuous tuning from a GRIN-SC-MQW-BH InGaAsP laser in an extended cavity," *Electronics Letters*, Vol. 26, 1990, pp. 267–269.

[8] Tabuchi, H., and Ishikawa, H., "External grating tunable MQW laser with wide tuning range of 240 nm," *Electronics Letters*, Vol. 26, 1990, pp. 742–743.

[9] Uenishi, Y., Honma, K., and Nagaoka, S., "Tunable laser diode using a nickel micromachined external mirror," *Electronics Letters*, Vol. 32, 1996, pp. 1207–1208.

[10] Heismann, F., Alferness, R. C., Buhl, L. L., Eisenstein, G., Korotky, S. K., Veselka, J. J., Stulz, L. W., and Burrus, C. A., "Narrow-linewidth, electro-optically tunable InGaAsP-Ti:LiNbO₃ extended cavity laser," *Applied Physics Letters*, Vol. 51, 1987, pp. 164–166.

[11] Coquin, G., Cheung, K.-W., and Choy, M. M., "Single- and multiple-wavelength operation of acoustooptically tuned semiconductor lasers at 1.3 μm," *IEEE Journal of Quantum Electronics*, Vol. 25, 1989, pp. 1575–1579.

[12] Zorabedian, P., *Tunable external-cavity semiconductor lasers, In: Tunable lasers handbook*, San Diego, CA, Academic Press, 1995.

[13] Favre, F., Le Guen, D., Simon, J. C., and Landousies, B., "External cavity semiconductor laser with 15 nm continuous tuning range," *Electronics Letters*, Vol. 22, 1986, pp. 795–796.

[14] Schremer, A. T., and Tang, C. L., "External-cavity semiconductor laser with 1000 GHz continuous piezoelectric tuning range," *IEEE Photonics Technology Letters*, Vol. 2, 1990, pp. 3–5.

[15] Nilsson, O., and Goobar, E., "Continuously tunable external-cavity laser," *16th European Conference on Optical Communication (ECOC '90)*, p. TuP7, Amsterdam, The Netherlands, 1990.

[16] Favre, F., and Le Guen, D., "82 nm of continuous tunability for an external cavity semiconductor laser," *Electronics Letters*, Vol. 27, 1991, pp. 183–184.

[17] Trutna, W. R., and Stokes, L. F., "Continuously tuned external cavity semiconductor lasers," *IEEE Journal of Lightwave Technology*, Vol. 11, 1993, pp. 1279–1286.

[18] Sale, T. E., *Vertical cavity surface emitting lasers*, Chichester, U.K., Wiley, 1995.

[19] Chang-Hasnain, C. J., Harbison, J. P., Zah, C. E., Florez, L. T., and Andreadakis, N. C., "Continuous wavelength tuning of two-electrode vertical cavity surface emitting lasers," *Electronics Letters*, Vol. 27, 1991, pp. 1002–1003.

[20] Wipiejewski, T., Panzlaff, K., Zeeb, E., and Ebeling, K. J., "Tunable extremely low threshold vertical-cavity laser diodes," *IEEE Photonics Technology Letters*, Vol. 5, 1993, pp. 889–892.

[21] Fan, L., Wu, M. C., Lee, H. C., and Grodzinski, P., "10.1 nm range continuous wavelength-tunable vertical-cavity surface-emitting lasers," *Electronics Letters*, Vol. 30, 1994, pp. 1409–1410.

[22] Larson, M. C., and Harris, J. S., "Wide and continuous wavelength tuning in a vertical-cavity surface-emitting laser using a micromachined deformable-membrane mirror," *Applied Physics Letters*, Vol. 68, 1996, pp. 891–893.

[23] Sugihwo, F., Larson, M. C., and Harris, J. S., "Low threshold continuously tunable vertical-cavity surface-emitting lasers with 19.1 nm wavelength range," *Applied Physics Letters*, Vol. 70, 1997, pp. 547–549.

[24] Sugihwo, F., Larson, M. C., and Harris, J. S., "Simultaneous optimization of membrane reflectance and tuning voltage for tunable vertical cavity lasers," *Applied Physics Letters*, Vol. 72, 1998, pp. 10–12.

[25] Wu, M. S., Vail, E. C., Li, G. S., Yuen, W., and Chang-Hasnain, C. J., "Tunable micromachined vertical cavity surface emitting laser," *Electronics Letters*, Vol. 31, 1995, pp. 1671–1672.

[26] Vail, E. C., Li, G. S., Yuen, W., and Chang-Hasnain, C. J., "High performance micromechanical tunable vertical cavity surface emitting lasers," *Electronics Letters*, Vol. 32, 1996, pp. 1888–1889.

[27] Li, M. Y., Yuen, W., Li, G. S., and Chang-Hasnain, C. J., "High performance continuously tunable top-emitting vertical cavity laser with 20 nm wavelength range," *Electronics Letters*, Vol. 33, 1997, pp. 1051–1052.

[28] Li, M. Y., Yuen, W., Li, G. S., and Chang-Hasnain, C. J., "Top-emitting micromechanical VCSEL with a 31.6 nm tuning range," *IEEE Photonics Technology Letters*, Vol. 10, 1998, pp. 18–20.

[29] Okuda, H., Hirayama, Y., Furuyama, H., Kinoshita, J.-I., and Nakamura, M., "Five-wavelength integrated DFB laser arrays with quarter-wave-shifted structures," *IEEE Journal of Quantum Electronics*, Vol. 23, 1987, pp. 843–848.

[30] Nakao, M., Sato, K., Nishida, T., and Tamamura, T, "Distributed feedback laser arrays fabricated by synchrotron orbital radiation lithography," *IEEE Journal on Selected Areas in Communications*, Vol. 8, 1990, pp. 1178–1182.

[31] Zah, C. E., Pathak, B., Favire, F., Bhat, R., Caneau, C., Lin, P. S. D., Gozdz, A. S., Andreadakis, N. C., Koza, M. A., and Lee, T. P., "1.5 μm tensile-strained single quantum well 20-wavelength distributed feedback laser arrays," *Electronics Letters*, Vol. 28, 1992, pp. 1585–1587.

[32] Li, G. P., Makino, T., Saragan, A., and Huang, W., "16-wavelength gain-coupled DFB laser array with fine tunability," *IEEE Photonics Technology Letters*, Vol. 8, 1996, pp. 22–24.

[33] Kudo, K., Yamazaki, H., Sasaki, T., and Yamaguchi, M., "Wide-wavelength range detuning-adjusted DFB-LD's of different wavelengths fabricated on a wafer," *IEEE Photonics Technology Letters*, Vol. 9, 1997, pp. 1313–1315.

[34] Young, M. G., Koch, T. L., Koren, U., Tennant, D. M., Miller, B. I., Chien, M., and Feder, K., "Wavelength uniformity in $\lambda/4$ shifted DFB laser array WDM transmitters," *Electronics Letters*, Vol. 31, 1995, pp. 1750–1752.

[35] Talneau, A., Bouadma, N., Slempkes, S., Ougazzaden, A., and Hansmann, S., "Accurate wavelength spacing from absorption-coupled DFB laser arrays," *IEEE Photonics Technology Letters*, Vol. 9, 1997, pp. 1316–1318.

[36] Koren, U., Koch, T. L., Miller, B. I., Eisenstein, G., and Bosworth, R. H., "Wavelength division multiplexing light source with integrated quantum well tunable lasers and optical amplifiers," *Applied Physics Letters*, Vol. 54, 1989, pp. 2056–2058.

[37] Young, M. G., Koren, U., Miller, B. I., Chien, M., Koch, T. L., Tennant, D. M., Feder, K., Dreyer, K., and Raybon, G., "Six wavelength laser array with integrated amplifier and modulator," *Electronics Letters*, Vol. 31, 1995, pp. 1835–1836.

[38] Zah, C. E., Favire, F., Pathak, B., Bhat, R., Caneau, C., Lin, P. S. D., Gozdz, A. S., Andreadakis, N. C., Koza, M. A., and Lee, T. P., "Monolithic integration of multiwavelength compressive-strained multiquantum-well distributed-feedback laser array with star coupler and optical amplifiers," *Electronics Letters*, Vol. 28, 1992, pp. 2361–2362.

[39] Zah, C.-E., Amersfoort, M. R., Pathak, B. N., Favire, F. J., Lin, P. S. D., Andreadakis, N. C., Rajhel, A. W., Bhat, R., Caneau, C., Koza, M. A., and Gamelin, J., "Multiwavelength DFB laser arrays with integrated combiner and optical amplifier for WDM optical networks," *IEEE Journal of Selected Topics in Quantum Electronics*, Vol. 3, 1997, pp. 584–597.

[40] Young, M. G., Koren, U., Miller, B. I., Newkirk, M. A., Chien, M., Zirngibl, M., Dragone, C., Tell, B., Presby, H. M., and Raybon, G., "A 16 × 1 wavelength division multiplexer with integrated distributed Bragg reflector lasers and electroabsorption modulators," *IEEE Photonics Technology Letters*, Vol. 5, 1993, pp. 908–910.

[41] White, I. H., "A multichannel grating cavity laser for wavelength division multiplexing applications," *IEEE Journal of Lightwave Technology*, Vol. 9, 1991, pp. 893–899.

[42] Nyairo, K. O., White, I. H., Kirkby, P. A., and Armistead, C. J., "Multichannel grating cavity (MGC) laser transmitter for wavelength division multiplexing applications," *IEE Proceedings, Part J*, Vol. 138, 1991, pp. 337–342.

[43] Asghari, M., Zhu, B., White, I. H., Seltzer, C. P., Nice, C., Henning, I. D., Burness, A. L., and Thompson, G. H. B., "Demonstration of an integrated multichannel grating cavity laser for WDM applications," *Electronics Letters*, Vol. 30, 1994, pp. 1674–1675.

[44] Soole, J. B. D., Poguntke, K. R., Scherer, A., LeBlanc, H. P., Chang-Hasnain, C., Hayes, J. R., Caneau, C., Bhat, R., and Koza, M. A., "Wavelength-selectable laser emission from a multistripe array grating integrated cavity laser," *Applied Physics Letters*, Vol. 61, 1992, pp. 2750–2752.

[45] Poguntke, K. R., and Soole, J. B. D., "Design of a multistripe array grating integrated cavity (MAGIC) laser," *IEEE Journal of Lightwave Technology*, Vol. 11, 1993, pp. 2191–2200.

[46] Poguntke, K. R., Soole, J. B. D., Scherer, A., LeBlanc, H. P., Caneau, C., Bhat, R., and Koza, M. A., "Simultaneous multiple wavelength operation of a multistripe array grating integrated cavity laser," *Applied Physics Letters*, Vol. 62, 1993, pp. 2024–2026.

[47] Zirngibl, M., Joyner, C. H., Doerr, C. R., Stulz, L. W., and Presby, H. M., "An 18-channel multifrequency laser," *IEEE Photonics Technology Letters*, Vol. 8, 1996, pp. 870–872.

[48] Staring, A. A. M., Spiekman, L. H., Binsma, J. J. M., Jansen, E. J., van Dongen, T., Thijs, P. J. A., Smit, M. K., and Verbeek, B. H., "A compact 9-channel multiwavelength laser," *IEEE Photonics Technology Letters*, Vol. 8, 1996, pp. 1139–1141.

[49] Monnard, R., Doerr, C. R., Joyner, C. H., Zirngibl, M., and Stulz, L. W., "Direct modulation of a multifrequency laser up to 16 × 622 Mb/s," *IEEE Photonics Technology Letters*, Vol. 9, 1997, pp. 815–817.

[50] Doerr, C. R., Zirngibl, M., and Joyner, C. H., "Single longitudinal-mode stability via wave mixing in long-cavity semiconductor lasers," *IEEE Photonics Technology Letters*, Vol. 7, 1995, pp. 962–964.

[51] Doerr, C. R., "Theoretical stability analysis of single-mode operation in uncontrolled mode-selection semiconductor lasers," *IEEE Photonics Technology Letters*, Vol. 9, 1997, pp. 1457–1459.

[52] Wood, T. H., "Multiple quantum well MQW waveguide modulators," *IEEE Journal of Lightwave Technology*, Vol. 6, 1988, pp. 743–757.

[53] Osiński, M., and Buus, J., "Linewidth broadening factor in semiconductor lasers—an overview," *IEEE Journal of Quantum Electronics*, Vol. 23, 1987, pp. 9–29.

[54] Ramdane, A., Devaux, F., Souli, N., Delprat, D., and Ougazzaden, A., "Monolithic integration of multiple-quantum-well lasers and modulators for high-speed transmission," *IEEE Journal of Selected Topics in Quantum Electronics*, Vol. 2, 1996, pp. 326–335.

[55] Reichmann, K. C., Magill, P. D., Koren, U., Miller, B. I., Young, M., Newkirk, M., and Chien, M. D., "2.5 Gb/s transmission over 674 km at multiple wavelengths using a tunable DBR laser with an integrated electroabsorption modulator," *IEEE Photonics Technology Letters*, Vol. 5, 1993, pp. 1098–1100.

[56] Delprat, D., Ramdane, A., Silvestre, L., Ougazzaden, A., Delorme, F., and Slempkes, S., "20-Gb/s integrated DBR laser-EA modulator by selective area growth for 1.55-μm WDM applications," *IEEE Photonics Technology Letters*, Vol. 9, 1997, pp. 898–900.

[57] Lammert, R. M., Smith, G. M., Hughes, J. S., Osowski, M. L., Jones, A. M., and Coleman, J. J., "MQW wavelength-tunable DBR lasers with monolithically integrated external cavity electroabsorption modulators with low-driving-voltages fabricated by selective-area MOCVD," *IEEE Photonics Technology Letters*, Vol. 8, 1996, pp. 797–799.

[58] Heismann, F., and Alferness, R. C., "Wavelength-tunable electrooptic polarization conversion in birefringent waveguides," *IEEE Journal of Quantum Electronics*, Vol. 24, 1988, pp. 83–93.

[59] Smith, D. A., Chakravarthy, R. S., Bao, Z., Baran, J. E., Jackel, J. L., d'Alessandro, A., Fritz, D. J., Huang, S. H., Zou, X. Y., Hwang, S.-M., Willner, A. E., and Li, K. D., "Evolution of the acousto-optic wavelength routing switch," *IEEE Journal of Lightwave Technology*, Vol. 14, 1996, pp. 1005–1019.

[60] Broberg, B., Lindgren, S., Öberg, M. G., and Jiang, H., "A novel integrated optics wavelength filter in InGaAsP-InP," *IEEE Journal of Lightwave Technology*, Vol. 4, 1986, pp. 196–203.

[61] Alferness, R. C., Koch, T. L., Buhl, L. L., Storz, F., Heismann, F., and Martyak, M. J. R., "Grating-assisted InGaAsP/InP vertical codirectional coupler filter," *Applied Physics Letters*, Vol. 55, 1989, pp. 2011–2013.

[62] Koch, T. L., Burkhardt, E. G., Storz, F. G., Bridges, T. J., and Sizer, T., "Vertically grating-coupled ARROW structures for III-V integrated optics," *IEEE Journal of Quantum Electronics*, Vol. 23, 1987, pp. 889–897.

[63] Soole, J. B. D., Silberberg, Y., Scherer, A., LeBlanc, H. P., Andreadakis, N. C., Caneau, C., Schumacher, H., and Erben, U., "Fast high-efficiency integrated waveguide photodetectors using novel vertical/butt coupling geometry," *Applied Physics Letters*, Vol. 61, 1992, pp. 13–15.

[64] Sakata, H., Takeuchi, S., and Hiroki, T., "Codirectional grating-coupled filter for wavelength selective photodetection," *Electronics Letters*, Vol. 28, 1992, pp. 749–751.

[65] Jan, Y.-H., Heimbuch, M. E., Coldren, L. A., and DenBaars, S. P., "InP/InGaAsP grating-assisted codirectional coupler tunable receiver with a 30 nm wavelength tuning range," *Electronics Letters*, Vol. 32, 1996, pp. 1697–1699.

[66] Ojha, S. M., Thompson, G. H. B., Cureton, C. G., Rogers, C. B., Clements, S. J., Asghari, M., and White, I. H., "Demonstration of low loss integrated InP/InGaAsP demultiplexer device with low polarisation sensitivity," *Electronics Letters*, Vol. 29, 1993, pp. 805–807.

[67] Soole, J. B. D., Scherer, A., LeBlanc, H. P., Andreadakis, N. C., Bhat, R., and Koza, M. A., "Monolithic InP/InGaAsP/InP grating spectrometer for the 1.48–1.56 μm wavelength range," *Applied Physics Letters*, Vol. 58, 1991, pp. 1949–1951.

[68] Soole, J. B. D., Scherer, A., Silberberg, Y., LeBlanc, H. P., Andreadakis, N. C., Caneau, C., and Poguntke, K. R., "Integrated grating demultiplexer and *pin* array for high-density wavelength division multiplexed detection at 1.5 μm," *Electronics Letters*, Vol. 29, 1993, pp. 559–561.

[69] Soole, J. B. D., LeBlanc, H. P., Andreadakis, N. C., Caneau, C., Bhat, R., and Koza, M. A., "High speed monolithic WDM detector for 1.5 μm fibre band," *Electronics Letters*, Vol. 31, 1995, pp. 1276–1277.

[70] Amersfoort, M. R., de Boer, C. R., Verbeek, B. H., Demeester, P., Looyen, A., and van der Tol, J. J. G. M., "Low-loss phased-array based 4-channel wavelength demultiplexer integrated with photodetectors," *IEEE Photonics Technology Letters*, Vol. 6, 1994, pp. 60–62.

[71] Zirngibl, M., Joyner, C. H., and Stulz, L. W., "WDM receiver by monolithic integration of an optical preamplifier, waveguide grating router and photodiode array," *Electronics Letters*, Vol. 31, 1995, pp. 581–582.

[72] Cremer, C., Emeis, N., Schier, M., Heise, G., Ebbinghaus, G., and Stoll, L., "Grating spectrograph integrated with photodiode array in InGaAsP/InGaAs/InP," *IEEE Photonics Technology Letters*, Vol. 4, 1992, pp. 108–110.

[73] Verdiell, J.-M., Koch, T. L., Miller, B. I., Young, M. G., Koren, U., Storz, F., and Brown-Goebeler, K. F., "A WDM receiver photonic integrated circuit with net on-chip gain," *IEEE Photonics Technology Letters*, Vol. 6, 1994, pp. 960–962.

[74] Yoo, S. J. B., "Wavelength conversion technologies for WDM network applications," *IEEE Journal of Lightwave Technology*, Vol. 14, 1996, pp. 955–966.

[75] Minch, J. R., Chang, C.-S., and Chuangi, S.-L., "Wavelength conversion in distributed-feedback lasers," *IEEE Journal of Selected Topics in Quantum Electronics*, Vol. 3, 1997, pp. 569–576.

[76] Mikkelsen, B., Pedersen, R. J. S., Duurhus, T., Braagaard, C., Joergensen, C., and Stubkjaer, K. E., "Wavelength conversion of high speed data signals," *Electronics Letters*, Vol. 29, 1993, pp. 1716–1718.

[77] Duurhus, T., Pedersen, R. J. S., Mikkelsen, B., Stubkjaer, K. E., Öberg, M., and Nilsson, S., "Optical wavelength conversion over 18 nm at 2.5 Gb/s by DBR-laser," *IEEE Photonics Technology Letters*, Vol. 5, 1993, pp. 86–88.

[78] Yasaka, H., Ishii, H., Takahata, K., Oe, K., Yoshikuni, Y., and Tsuchiya, H., "Broad-range wavelength conversion of 10 Gbit/s signal using a superstructure grating distributed Bragg reflector laser," *Electronics Letters*, Vol. 30, 1994, pp. 133–134.

[79] Duurhus, T., Mikkelsen, B., Joergensen, C., Danielsen, S. L., and Stubkjaer, K. E., "All-optical wavelength conversion by semiconductor optical amplifiers," *IEEE Journal of Lightwave Technology*, Vol. 14, 1996, pp. 942–954.

[80] Desurvire, E., *Erbium-doped fiber amplifiers: Principles and applications*, Chichester, U.K., Wiley, 1994.

[81] Bjarklev, A., *Optical fiber amplifiers: Design and system applications*, Norwood, MA, Artech House, 1993.

[82] Reekie, L., Mears, R. J., Poole, S. B., and Payne, D. N., "Tunable single-mode fiber lasers," *IEEE Journal of Lightwave Technology*, Vol. 4, 1986, pp. 956–960.

[83] Allain, J. Y., Monerie, M., and Poignant, H., "Tunable CW lasing around 0.82, 1.48, 1.88 and 2.35 μm in Thulium-doped Fluorozirconate fibre," *Electronics Letters*, Vol. 25, 1989, pp. 1660–1662.

[84] Shi, Y., Poulsen, C. V., Sejka, M., Ibsen, M., and Poulsen, O., "Tunable Pr^{3+}-doped silica-based fibre laser," *Electronics Letters*, Vol. 29, 1993, pp. 1426–1427.

[85] Bennion, I., Williams, J. A. R., Zhang, L., Sugden, K., and Doran, N. J., "UV-written in-fibre Bragg gratings," *Optical and Quantum Electronics*, Vol. 28, 1996, pp. 93–135.

[86] Ball, G. A., and Morey, W. W., "Compression-tuned single-frequency Bragg grating fiber laser," *Optics Letters*, Vol. 23, 1994, pp. 1979–1981.

[87] Ibsen, M., Eggleton, B. J., Sceats, M. G., and Ouellette, F., "Broadly tunable DBR fibre laser using sampled fibre Bragg gratings," *Electronics Letters*, Vol. 31, 1995, pp. 37–38.

[88] Baumann, I., Bosso, S., Brinkmann, R., Corsini, R., Dinard, M., Greiner, A., Schäfer, K., Söchtig, J., Sohler, W., Suche, H., and Wessel, R., "Er-doped integrated optical devices in $LiNbO_3$," *IEEE Journal of Selected Topics in Quantum Electronics*, Vol. 2, 1996, pp. 355–366.

[89] Schäfer, K., Baumann, I., Sohler, W., Suche, H., and Westenhöfer, S., "Diode-pumped and packaged acoustooptically tunable Ti:Er:LiNbO3 waveguide laser of wide tuning range," *IEEE Journal of Quantum Electronics*, Vol. 33, 1997, pp. 1636–1641.

[90] Duarte, F. J. (ed.), *Tunable lasers handbook*, San Diego, CA, Academic Press, 1995.

[91] Mirov, S. B., and Basiev, T., "Progress in colour center lasers," *IEEE Journal of Selected Topics in Quantum Electronics*, Vol. 1, 1995, pp. 22–30.

Chapter 9

Practical Issues and Applications

In the previous chapters, we mainly considered the physical basis for tunable lasers, the predicted performance, and the reported results. In this chapter, we turn our attention to issues of a more practical nature, as well as to the description of the role and advantages of tunable lasers for various applications. This discussion of applications is intended to provide an overview only; for further details of the applications discussed refer to specialist literature.

9.1 PRACTICAL ISSUES

In general, tunable lasers are more complicated than standard diode lasers. Consequently there are additional practical issues that need to be addressed, and some of the issues that are also relevant for conventional lasers become more complicated. Here we will concentrate on issues that are particularly important for tunable lasers.

9.1.1 Characterization and Wavelength Control

For a conventional diode laser, with one contact on the n-side and one on the p-side, the light current characteristic, which shows the output (optical) power as a function of the drive current, gives a lot of information of practical interest: Threshold current, slope efficiency, power at the maximum drive current and linearity. For single-frequency lasers, the measurement of the spectrum at various drive currents gives information about the lasing wavelength and the spectral purity, usually expressed in terms of the *SSR*.

The main property of interest for a tunable laser is the lasing wavelength as a function of the drive conditions. Even moderate tuning, however, requires more than one drive current; and the spectral measurements have to be carried out for a number of combinations of drive currents. As an example, we show in Figure 9.1 the wavelength of a three-section DBR laser. Notice the qualitative agreement with Figure 5.6.

In a sampled grating (SG) DBR laser, there are four drive currents (front and rear sampled grating, phase section, and active section, c.f., Section 7.3). In Figure 9.2, we

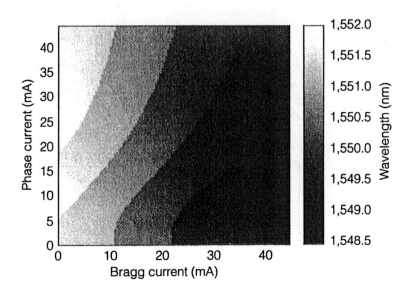

Figure 9.1   Lasing wavelength for a three-section DBR laser as a function of the Bragg and phase currents. The discontinuities indicate mode jumps. (Reprinted with permission from IMC.)

show the lasing wavelength as a function of the front and rear tuning currents; in this case, the phase control contact is not used.

If we assume that a spectral measurement takes about 10 seconds, then a high-resolution spectral characterization of a laser with two control currents takes about 30 hours if 100 values are used for each current. This clearly shows that a complete high-resolution spectral characterization of a tunable laser with three or more control currents becomes unpractical. Even for lasers with just two control currents, the characterization has to be automated. Figure 9.3 shows an example of a setup for automated measurement of spectrum, power, and linewidth. Additional measurements are required to quantify relative intensity noise and modulation properties.

To reduce the characterization time, it is necessary to reduce the resolution, to reduce the number of spectral measurements, or to concentrate on the regions of interest where the laser is used. Another option is to identify a limited number of characteristics that will allow the complete laser behavior to be found by interpolation. Such characteristics would also be helpful for monitoring of the long-time laser stability: if they remain unchanged, there are no major changes in the laser behavior; if they have changed, the changes to the laser behavior can be derived from the changes of the characteristics.

Considering again an SG-DBR laser, Figure 9.4 shows the optical power as a function of the front and rear tuning currents with a constant current to the active section and with no phase control current.

As reported in [1], the power variation for an SSG-DBR laser shows characteristic saddle points (as explained in Section 7.3, the SG-DBR laser can be considered a special case of the SSG-DBR laser). The reason for the existence of these saddle points

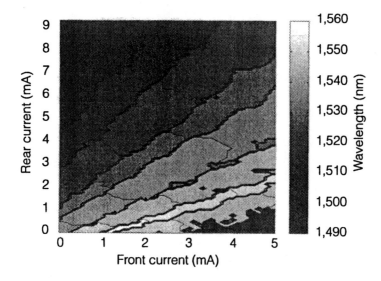

Figure 9.2   Lasing wavelength for an SG-DBR laser as a function of the front and rear tuning currents. (Reprinted with permission from GEC-Marconi Materials Technology Limited.)

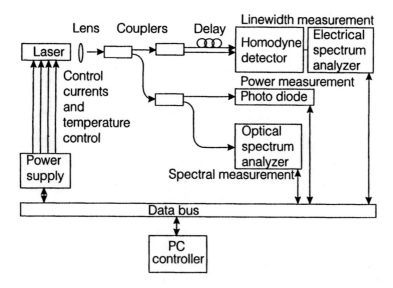

Figure 9.3   Laser characterization setup.

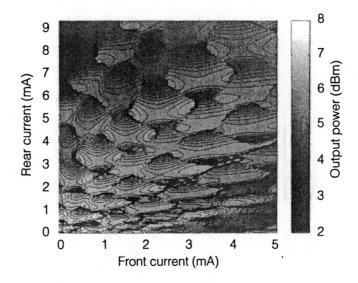

Figure 9.4   Output power from an SG-DBR laser as a function of the front and rear tuning currents. This power measurement is carried out for the same laser, and under the same conditions as the spectral measurement shown in Figure 9.2. (Reprinted with permission from GEC-Marconi Materials Technology Limited.)

is explained as follows: The front end optical power has a maximum (with respect to variations in the rear section tuning current) when the phase condition is satisfied at a wavelength coinciding with a rear section reflection peak because this coincidence gives the highest front-end efficiency. Likewise, the front-end optical power has a minimum (with respect to variations in the front-section tuning current) when the phase condition is satisfied at a wavelength coinciding with a front section reflection peak because this coincidence gives the lowest front-end efficiency. The positions of the saddle points, in terms of wavelength, depend on, and can be controlled by, the current to the phase section. The saddle points are clearly visible in Figure 9.4. The *SSR* has maxima of well over 40 dB in the regions around the saddle points.

As pointed out in [1], these saddle points have important implications for wavelength control and stabilization of SG-DBR lasers. At a saddle point, the lasing wavelength coincides with reflection peaks for both the front and rear reflectors; consequently, a high *SSR* is achieved. Two simple control circuits for the front and rear tuning currents ensure that the laser is kept at the saddle point. The phase control current is set to ensure that the saddle point coincides with the required wavelength, and operation at this wavelength is maintained using an optical filter and a separate control circuit for the phase current.

Use of the saddle points, or some other similar feature, may also lead to an important simplification and time-saving in the characterization of tunable lasers. The reason is that the saddle points can be found directly from power measurements that are much faster than spectral measurements. A possible strategy could be as follows: First the saddle points are found in terms of front and rear section currents; next, the wavelength for

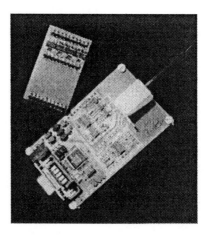

Figure 9.5   Circuitboard containing a laser module and drive electronics. The size of the board is 49 mm
by 83 mm. Data on tuning properties are stored electronically. (Reprinted with permission
from IMC/Altitun.)

each saddle point is found; and finally, the dependence of the wavelengths at the saddle
points on the phase section current is determined.

For practical applications, the user of the laser needs information about the current
settings required to achieve given wavelength and power combinations. For lasers with
three or more control currents, it is clearly impractical to use complete high-resolution
lookup tables. Instead, a reduced set of data or interpolation parameters can be stored in
a memory chip that is delivered with the laser. Ultimately all necessary drive hardware
and software can be contained on a small circuitboard that is delivered with the laser. In
this case, the user only needs to send a simple command to the board containing information about the wavelength and power required from the laser. An example is shown in
Figure 9.5.

It may also be possible to adjust the stored data based on periodic re-
measurement. The software for these measurements could be stored with the original
data. In this way, any long-term changes in the laser properties can be compensated.

9.1.2   Ageing and Reliability

A substantial amount of work has been carried out on semiconductor laser degradation
and lifetime [2]. Laser failure can be defined in a number of different ways; for example
as a given rise in the threshold current or as failure to supply a given amount of optical
power at a given current. The lifetime is given as the mean time to failure (MTTF) for
an ensemble of devices. As the lifetime at room temperature is typically in the order
of 10^5 to 10^6 hours, it is clearly not possible to measure it directly. Instead, lasers are
operated at elevated temperatures, and the expected lifetime at room temperature is found
by extrapolation. To improve the reliability of lasers supplied to customers, it is common
for manufacturers to perform various burn-in and screening procedures.

For single-frequency or tunable lasers, the stability of the spectral properties is an important practical issue, but there is so far very limited experimental data available. A set of DFB lasers operated continuously at room temperature for several years was reported to show a wavelength drift of about –0.01 nm/year [3]. The slight decrease in wavelength is associated with a slight increase in the threshold current from ageing.

In a separate study [4], a large number of lasers were operated at increased temperatures (50 °C, 70 °C, and 90 °C), over periods estimated to correspond to up to 25 years at room temperature. About 90% of the lasers showed wavelength shifts of less than 0.1 nm.

A study of tunable two-section DBR lasers showed significant changes from ageing [5]. In particular, the tuning efficiency (the wavelength change obtained for a given change in tuning current) decreased. The proposed explanation was the development of defects in the tuning section. This increases the nonradiative recombination rate. A similar degradation in the active region increases the threshold current, but not the carrier density at threshold. Consequently, the impact on wavelength is limited. Tunable DBR lasers using temperature tuning may not suffer from the same degradation problem.

Later results for three-section tunable DBR lasers show no degradation in the spectral properties after several thousand hours' operation at 60 °C [6].

9.2   OPTICAL COMMUNICATION

The development of high-performance single-frequency diode lasers has, to a large degree, been spurred on by the rapid growth in the use of fiber optical communication. Today this is one of the most important areas for the application of these lasers. The development of more and more sophisticated diode lasers has, on the other hand, made new concepts in optical communication practical.

In addition to the usual advantages quoted for diode lasers, the use of InGaAsP material has made it possible to fabricate lasers operating at wavelengths around 1,300 nm where the dispersion in standard fibers vanishes, and around 1,550 nm, where the fiber loss has its minimum. This latter wavelength region also coincides with the gain band for EDFAs.

The emergence of wavelength division multiplexing (WDM) and coherent detection techniques is leading to increased capacity and flexibility of optical networks. Tunable lasers are particularly interesting for applications in these areas.

9.2.1   Wavelength Standards

The increased use of WDM has lead to the need for wavelength standards to ensure compatibility of equipment from different manufacturers. The ITU draft recommendation G.msc "Optical Interfaces for Multichannel Systems With Optical Amplifiers" defines a grid expressed in frequency rather than wavelength. The anchor point is 193.1 THz (corresponding to 1,552.52 nm), and the frequency grid unit is 100 GHz (about 0.8 nm). For WDM systems, frequency spacings equal to an integer multiple of 100 GHz are allowed as well as a nonuniform frequency spacing as long as all the frequencies used belong to the standard grid.

The frequency accuracy is specified as 10% of the frequency spacing. For a 100-GHz spacing, this translates to a wavelength accuracy of 0.08 nm. Consequently, the laser temperature must be stabilized to better than 1 °K because the temperature coefficient of the wavelength is usually about 0.1 nm/K. To maintain the correct wavelength for a fixed-wavelength laser (such as a DFB laser), the thermal tunability can be used. If a filter with a well-defined, and thermally stable, passband is used, it is a relatively simple matter to construct a control circuit that will ensure the laser always operates with the desired wavelength accuracy.

In a system with a large number of equally spaced channels, there is a potential crosstalk problem due to four-wave mixing in the transmission fiber. This is a nonlinear process whereby a "new" frequency f_{ijk} is generated according to

$$f_{ijk} = f_i + f_j - f_k \tag{9.1}$$

where f_i, f_j, and f_k are "original" frequencies. In a system with N ($N \gg 1$) equally spaced frequencies, the number of four-wave mixing products is proportional to N^3. Consequently, the number of mixing products coinciding with a given channel increases as N^2. The problems caused by four-wave mixing may be reduced by using a nonuniform frequency spacing.

9.2.2 Point-to-Point Links

Single-mode optical fibers are characterized by their low loss and enormous bandwidth. The minimal loss is below 0.2 dB/km and occurs for wavelengths around 1,550 nm. Allowing a loss of up to 1 dB/km, the bandwidth is in the order of 100 THz. Transmission distances can be increased by the use of EDFAs, which provide gain in the wavelength region from about 1,530 nm to about 1,565 nm (corresponding to a bandwidth of 4.4 THz).

The highest data rate currently in use is 10 Gbit/s, which is several orders of magnitude less than the available fiber bandwidth. Time-division multiplexing (TDM) can be used to generate higher data rates (over 100 Gbit/s has been demonstrated). Increasing data rates, however, leads to restrictions on the transmission distance from fiber dispersion. For a fiber with dispersion D, usually expressed in the unit ps/(km· nm), a transmission distance L, a spectral width $\Delta\lambda$, and a data rate f, the dispersion limit can be expressed as

$$DL\Delta\lambda \leq \frac{1}{4f} \tag{9.2}$$

By translating the spectral width to an optical frequency width Δf_{opt}, taking the pulsewidth as the reciprocal of the data rate, and using (8.2) to relate Δf_{opt} to the pulsewidth, we have

$$Lf^2 \leq \frac{c}{1.76\lambda^2 \sqrt{1 + \alpha_H^2 D}} \tag{9.3}$$

where c is the speed of light and λ is the wavelength.

Numerical Example: For a 2.5-Gbit/s data rate at 1,550-nm wavelength with chirp-free modulation ($\alpha_H = 0$), and a $D = 17$ ps/(km· nm) fiber dispersion, the dispersion limit is about 670 km. This is reduced to about 130 km for $\alpha_H = 5$ and to about 40 km for a 10 Gbit/s data rate with $\alpha_H = 0$.

Unless some form of dispersion compensation is used, dispersion is the dominating factor limiting the transmission distance, in particular at high data rates. According to (9.3), a doubling of the date rate leads to a reduction in the distance by a factor of 4.

A possible solution to this problem is the use of WDM. Several optical signals with a moderate data rate, each carried by a particular wavelength, are multiplexed at the transmitter end, transmitted over a single fiber and demultiplexed at the receiver end. By using WDM, a better utilization of the available fiber bandwidth is achieved. WDM is also of interest for upgrading of existing links to a higher capacity.

There are several alternative options for the transmitters in a WDM point-to-point system: The simplest solution is to use several fixed-wavelength single-frequency lasers. However, this will require preselection of lasers to ensure that each transmitter operates at the appropriate wavelength. Multiwavelength lasers (see Section 8.2) are particularly interesting because the multiplexing function can be monolithically integrated with the lasers.

Use of tunable lasers is also a possibility. No preselection is necessary if the tuning range covers the wavelength range of interest. This also means that it will not be necessary to keep a stock of spare lasers for each wavelength used, because the wavelength of the tunable laser can be set at the time of installation [7]. Tunable lasers are likely to become more attractive as the number of wavelengths increases.

An interesting option is the combination of a set of fixed-wavelength transmitters, one for each wavelength used in the link, with a single tunable laser connected to the same multiplexer. The tunable laser acts as a flexible backup transmitter, capable of taking over immediately if any of the fixed wavelength lasers fail.

Systems with 8, 16, 32, or 40 wavelength channels, operating at 2.5 Gbit/s per channel, are now commercially available from several vendors, including Ciena, Lucent, Pirelli, Nortel, Ericsson, and Alcatel. An example is the 40-channel system announced by Ciena in early 1998. This system is using a uniform 100-GHz (0.8 nm) channel separation, thus giving a total capacity of 100-Gbit/s within a 32-nm band.

9.2.3 Fixed-Wavelength Networks

A fully connected network with N nodes requires $N(N - 1)/2$ links. Using a number of different wavelengths can reduce the number of links. If the actual number of links in the network is L, we define the *connectivity* as

$$\alpha = \frac{2L}{N(N - 1)} \qquad (9.4)$$

We assume that the traffic between all pairs of nodes is the same, and all node pairs are assigned a physical path (which may pass through other nodes) and a specific wavelength. If the network is not fully connected (i.e., $\alpha < 1$), more than one wavelength is required. In [8], a number of network topologies are studied, and an empirical result is found for the minimal number of wavelengths required (For some particular topologies the required number of wavelength can be significantly higher.):

$$N_{\lambda,\min} = \frac{3}{\alpha} - 2 \qquad (9.5)$$

Use of WDM clearly facilitates a tradeoff between the number of fiber links (i.e., the cost and complexity of the physical network) and the number of wavelengths used (i.e., the cost and complexity of the transmitters and receivers).

The transmitter requirements for a fixed-wavelength network are rather similar to those for a point-to-point WDM link. At each node in the network, optical sources are required for a number of specific wavelengths. As for the simple WDM link, this can be provided by using a number of preselected fixed-wavelength lasers, by using one or more multiwavelength lasers, by using a number of tunable lasers, or by using fixed-wavelength lasers with a tunable laser as backup.

9.2.4   Reconfigurable Networks

The use of multiwavelengths on each fiber in a network adds an extra switching dimension to space and time switching. This allows the construction of flexible networks where wavelengths are allocated according to traffic demand, signals can be routed according to their wavelength and rerouted in case of failure, and the same wavelength can be used in different parts of the network. Refer to [9–11] for reviews of optical networks.

The connection between a pair of nodes (i,j) is facilitated by a number of *cross-connects*, which the signal passes on its way from node i to node j. At each cross-connect, there are several incoming and outgoing fibers, and each fiber carries a number of wavelengths. The crossconnect includes demultiplexers to separate the wavelengths on each fiber, space switches to route the signals to the appropriate output fiber, and multiplexers to combine the signals going into the same output fiber.

To ensure that wavelength blocking does not occur, wavelength conversion (possibly tunable) may have to be used at the crossconnects. Alternatively, tunable transmitters may be used at the edge of the network. See [12] for a discussion of wavelength requirements and wavelength allocation in networks with and without wavelength conversion.

Examples of lasers used in experimental optical networks:

Lambdanet: Eighteen fixed-wavelength DFB lasers with 2-nm spacing combined in a star coupler [13].

Rainbow: Fixed-wavelength transmitters with tunable filter receivers (broadcast and select) [14].

ONTC: Laser array with four wavelengths spaced by 4 nm [15].

MONET: Four- and eight-wavelength arrays, and wavelength-selectable lasers [16]. The channel spacing is 200 GHz (1.6 nm) [17].

With the increased performance and availability of widely tunable lasers, it is expected that these lasers will find their way into future optical networks.

9.2.5 WDM Packet Switching

In a packet-switched system, blocks of data are sent from a number of transmitters to a number of receivers. A particular example is the asynchronous transfer mode (ATM) [18]. The original data, which do not have to have a given data rate, are broken into 53-byte packets referred to as *cells*. Each cell has a header that contains address information. The packets from a transmitter, which may have different origins and different original data rates, can be carried on the synchronous digital hierarchy at one of the standard data rates: 155 Mbit/s (OC-3/STM-1), 622 Mbit/s (OC-12/STM4), 2.488 Gbit/s(OC-48/STM16), and so forth.

An interesting option is the optical switching of packets [19]. Packets are carried on different wavelengths, and wavelength conversion is used for routing and contention resolution. (If two packets on the same wavelength have the same destination, the wavelength of one packet is converted.) A traffic analysis has shown that the use of tunable-wavelength conversion significantly reduces the switch complexity [20].

A demonstration of the use of a widely tunable laser combined with a semiconductor optical amplifier to achieve tunable-wavelength conversion is reported in [21]. In this example, wavelength conversion is achieved over 40 nm with a switching time of 2 ns.

9.2.6 Coherent Systems

Conventional optical communications systems are based on direct detection of intensity-modulated signals. In such systems, the receiver sensitivity (received power required to obtain a given bit error rate) is limited by thermal noise in the detector rather than by the fundamental (quantum) shot noise in the signal. The development of lasers with a sufficiently narrow linewidth makes it possible to use coherent detection techniques (see [22] and [23] for details); this is in complete analogy with standard radio frequency techniques.

In a coherent receiver, the incoming (low-power) optical signal of frequency ν_S is mixed with the light from a (high-power) local oscillator (L.O.) laser of frequency ν_{LO}. The signal power detected at the intermediate frequency $\nu_{if} = \nu_S - \nu_{LO}$ is proportional to the product of the signal power and the local oscillator power. The noise is proportional to the sum of the signal power, the L.O. power and the noise equivalent power of the detector. If the L.O. power is sufficiently high, the signal-to-noise ratio is simply equal to the number of "signal photons" detected during a bit period, and the receiver sensitivity is limited by the shot noise in the signal.

A number of different modulation formats are possible, including amplitude-shift keying (ASK), frequency-shift keying (FSK), phase-shift keying (PSK), and differential-phase-shift keying (DPSK) [24]. The different formats lead to different receiver sensitivities, and the requirements on laser linewidth differ. As a rule, the more sensitive systems require narrower laser linewidths. For a DPSK system, the laser linewidth should be about or less than 0.3% of the data rate [25] (assuming that the linewidth of the transmitter and receiver lasers are identical). This means that in a system operating at a data rate of 2.5 Gbit/s, the laser linewidths of the signal and L.O. lasers should be less than 10 MHz.

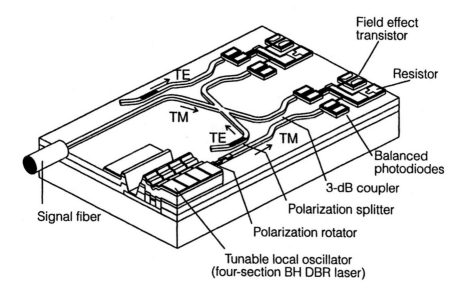

Field effect
transistor

Resistor

Balanced
photodiodes

3-dB coupler

Polarization splitter

Polarization rotator

Tunable local oscillator
(four-section BH DBR laser)

Signal fiber

Figure 9.6   Fully integrated polarization-diversity heterodyne receiver. (Reprinted with permission from *Optical and Quantum Electronics*, Vol. 28, pp. 566–573, ©1996 Chapman & Hall.)

In addition to being more sensitive than conventional systems, coherent systems also offer a better bandwidth use. Different channels can be packed more closely because the filtering process in the receiver takes place in the electrical domain rather than in the optical domain.

By using a tunable L.O. laser, channel selection can be performed by tuning, in analogy with a radio receiver. For details about such coherent multichannel systems, see [26]. Note that there is a tradeoff between the tuning range and the linewidth requirement (see Chapter 6).

By integrating L.O. laser with a directional coupler and waveguide detectors, a monolithic heterodyne receiver can be formed [27]. A diagram of the most ambitious opto-electronic integrated circuit demonstrated to date is shown in Figure 9.6 [28]. The chip size is 9 mm × 0.6 mm. The fabrication includes 23 lithographic steps and 7 epitaxial growth steps. The tuning range for the integrated L.O. laser is about 5.5 nm, corresponding to over 600 GHz.

9.2.7   Tunable Lasers versus Laser Arrays

For a number of systems, tunable lasers, laser arrays, or multiwavelength lasers perform interchangeable operations. The choice of laser type of course depends strongly on the particular application and involves a number of tradeoffs. Some of the key factors influencing the choice are discussed below.

Fixed-wavelength operation: The simplest solution is to use a number of fixed-wavelength single-frequency (e.g., DFB) lasers. For this solution, tunable lasers may be of interest as a flexible backup, in particular if the number of wavelengths is high. Multiwavelength lasers are of particular interest for transmitters required to operate simultaneously at several fixed wavelengths. However, if only a few wavelengths out of a large number of possible wavelengths are used at any one time, use of a few tunable lasers is an alternative.

Number of wavelengths used: In general, if the number of possible wavelengths is large, a single array, or the use of a high number of fixed-wavelength lasers, is unattractive because of the loss associated with the combiner.

Wavelength coverage: Widely tunable lasers are of interest if only a single wavelength at a time is required from within a large set of wavelengths.

Tuning speed: The ability to switch quickly between wavelengths may be required (e.g., for WDM packet switching). Laser arrays and electronically tuned lasers have comparable switching speeds; however, thermally tuned lasers may be too slow.

Complexity: In general, there is a tradeoff between the complexity of the laser structure (e.g., an array integrated with combiner, amplifier, and modulator), and the complexity of the required wavelength control for a widely tunable laser. This is also related to the long-term wavelength stability of widely tunable lasers, an issue that has not yet been settled.

9.3   OTHER APPLICATIONS

The development of narrow linewidth and wavelength-tunable laser diodes enables many new laser diode applications in measurement and sensing. This particularly holds for applications, where the coherent detection scheme is required. Among those, we will briefly discuss coherent light detection and ranging (LIDAR, optical radar) and reflectometry, for which continuously tunable laser diodes are required, gas monitoring and spectroscopy, optical spectrum and network analysis, and anemometry.

9.3.1   Optical Frequency-Modulated Continuous Wave Radar

Frequency-modulated continuous wave (FMCW) radar is a complementary technique to the more popular pulse-radar systems and offers significant advantages with respect to sensitivity and resolution in distance sensing [29, 30]. While the better sensitivity is due to the application of the heterodyne detection of the object signals, the maximal distance range is limited to about the coherence length, which is typically of the order 10 to 100 m corresponding to a spectral linewidth $\Delta\nu$ of 3 to 30 MHz.

The operation principle of an optical FMCW radar is illustrated in Figure 9.7 [29]. The optical power from a continuously tunable laser diode, the instantaneous frequency of which is periodically shifted by Δf via a sawtooth-like modulated tuning current, is sent simultaneously to the object and a reference mirror, and the reflected signals are then superimposed in a square law detector (PIN diode). To avoid deteriorations of the laser characteristics by the reflected signal, an optical isolator with isolation of typically at least 50 dB is used.

Because of the time-dependent instantaneous frequency and path difference R, the two signals exhibit different instantaneous frequencies when entering the PIN diode. This

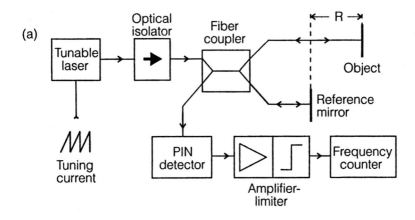

(a)

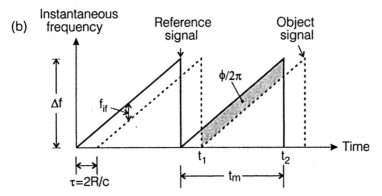

(b)

Figure 9.7   Optical FMCW radar system. Schematic setup using a fiber coupler for beam splitting (a) and instantaneous optical frequencies of reference and object signals at the PIN photodetector (b).

frequency difference f_{if}, which according to the analogy to the heterodyne detection is denoted as intermediate frequency, is extracted electronically from the PIN diode. After the subsequent amplifier-limiter, the intermediate frequency is determined in the frequency counter. The time dependence of the instantaneous frequencies at the PIN detector of an object signal and a reference signal is shown schematically in Figure 9.7(b). In case of a linear ramp of period t_m, the intermediate frequency f_{if} is proportional to the delay time $\tau = 2R/c$:

$$f_{if} = \Delta f \frac{\tau}{t_m} \tag{9.6}$$

In this way, the distance sensing is done by a frequency measurement, while in the case of the pulse radar, the delay time is measured directly. Since the value range of f_{if} can be almost arbitrarily defined by a proper choice of the period t_m, the FMCW radar may determine τ values in the picosecond range by simply performing a frequency measurement in the kilohertz regime and thus requires no high-speed electronics to determine delay times in the subpicosecond range. In practice, the frequency measurement is done by measuring the phase ϕ of the photodetector signal over a period $t_2 - t_1$, which should preferably extend over the entire repetition period of the frequency ramp ($t_2 - t_1 \to t_m$):

$$\phi = 2\pi \int_{t_1}^{t_2} f_{if}(t)\, dt = 2\pi \Delta f \tau \frac{t_2 - t_1}{t_m} \leq 2\pi \Delta f \tau \qquad (9.7)$$

It should be noted that ϕ corresponds to 2π times the shaded area in Figure 9.7(b) which for a constant $(t_2 - t_1)/t_m$-ratio is independent of t_m.

The phase measurement in turn is usually accomplished by counting the number of zero crossings N of the photodetector signal as

$$\phi = \pi(N - 1) \qquad (9.8)$$

N is independent of t_m for a constant $(t_2 - t_1)/t_m$-ratio. The frequency difference is then obtained as

$$f_{if} = \frac{N - 1}{2(t_2 - t_1)} \qquad (9.9)$$

where t_1 and t_2 are both chosen at a zero crossing, so that no discretization error occurs. The range R is given by

$$R = \frac{(N - 1)c}{4\Delta f} \frac{t_m}{t_2 - t_1} \qquad (9.10)$$

As the FMCW radar relies on a phase measurement, its resolution is limited by the phase noise of the laser diode [31, 32]. To estimate the one-shot (measuring over one period t_m) distance error for an FMCW optical radar, we write for the phase of the photodetector signal

$$\phi = \underbrace{2\pi \int_{t_1}^{t_2} f_{if}(t)\, dt}_{\phi_0} + \Delta\phi_a + \Delta\phi_t \qquad (9.11)$$

where ϕ_0, $\Delta\phi_a$, and $\Delta\phi_t$ denote the deterministic phase change due to the ramped emission frequency, the phase noise due to the spontaneous emission of the active region, and the IRSN phase noise from the tuning region, respectively. Because of the uncorrelated noise sources, the mean square of the phase error reads

$$< \Delta\phi^2 > = < (\phi - \phi_0)^2 > = < \Delta\phi_a^2 > + < \Delta\phi_t^2 > \qquad (9.12)$$

The mean square of the white spontaneous emission phase noise is proportional to the natural spectral linewidth (Schawlow-Townes-Henry linewidth; c.f., (3.82)) $\Delta\nu_{STH}$ and the delay time

$$< \Delta\phi_a^2 > = 2\pi \Delta\nu_{STH}\tau \qquad (9.13)$$

The noise contribution of the tuning region

$$\Delta \phi_t(t) = \phi_t(t) - \phi_t(t - \tau) \tag{9.14}$$

is obtained by considering the relation to the carrier density fluctuations in the tuning region as

$$\dot{\phi}_t(t) = \omega_e V_t \Delta N_t \tag{9.15}$$

where ω_e is the angular frequency change per electron-hole pair, V_t is the tuning region volume and ΔN_t is the (spatially averaged) carrier density fluctuation in the tuning region. This yields for the mean square phase difference

$$< \Delta \phi_t^2 > = (\omega_e V_t)^2 \int_{t-\tau}^{t} \int_{t-\tau}^{t} < \Delta N_t(\xi) \Delta N_t(\xi') > d\xi' \, d\xi \tag{9.16}$$

Taking the autocorrelation function of ΔN_t (6.11), we obtain

$$< \Delta \phi_t^2 > = \frac{I_t \tau_d}{e} \omega_e^2 \int_{t-\tau}^{t} \int_{t-\tau}^{t} \exp\left(-\frac{|\xi - \xi'|}{\tau_d}\right) d\xi' \, d\xi \tag{9.17}$$

which after integration yields

$$< \Delta \phi_t^2 > = \frac{2 I_t \tau_d^2 \omega_e^2}{e} \left(\tau + \tau_d \left[\exp\left(-\tau/\tau_d\right) - 1\right]\right) \tag{9.18}$$

where τ_d is the differential carrier lifetime (2.77). Noting that the linewidth contribution by the IRSN in the tuning region may be written as $\Delta \nu_t = 4\pi I_t (\omega_e \tau_d)^2 / e$ [33], we finally obtain [32]

$$< \Delta \phi_t^2 > = 2\pi \Delta \nu_t \left(\tau + \tau_d \left[\exp\left(-\tau/\tau_d\right) - 1\right]\right) \tag{9.19}$$

For large distances, where the delay time τ is large against the differential carrier lifetime in the tuning region τ_d, $< \Delta \phi_t^2 >$ asymptotically becomes proportional to τ in analogy with the $< \Delta \phi_a^2 >$ versus τ relationship (9.13):

$$< \Delta \phi_t^2 > = 2\pi \Delta \nu_t \tau \qquad \tau >> \tau_d \tag{9.20}$$

while for short distances, where τ is much smaller than τ_d, the mean square phase difference becomes proportional to the delay time squared:

$$< \Delta \phi_t^2 > = \pi \Delta \nu_t \frac{\tau^2}{\tau_d} \qquad \tau << \tau_d \tag{9.21}$$

In the latter case, therefore, the phase-noise contribution of the tuning region decreases more rapidly with decreasing distance than the contribution by the natural linewidth $\Delta \nu_{STH}$. This is a consequence of the bandpass-limited power spectrum of the carrier noise in the tuning region with cutoff frequency of $\sqrt{3}/(2\pi \tau_d)$, making the accuracy in the short-distance regime almost independent of the IRSN. The relative accuracy for a

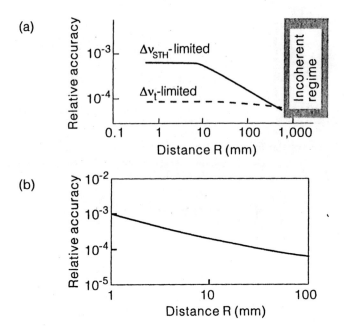

Figure 9.8   Contributions of $\Delta\nu_{STH}$ and $\Delta\nu_t$ on the relative accuracy versus distance for a typical tunable laser diode exploiting the plasma effect for tuning (a) and total relative accuracy (b). (Reprinted with permission from *Optical Engineering*, Vol. 34, pp. 896–903, ©1995 SPIE.)

one-shot measurement in the phase-noise-limited regime in the general case is thus given as

$$\frac{\Delta R}{R} = \frac{\sqrt{<\Delta\phi^2>}}{\phi_0} = \frac{1}{\Delta f}\sqrt{\frac{2\pi}{\tau}\left\{\Delta\nu_{STH} + \Delta\nu_t\left(1 + \frac{\tau_d}{\tau}[\exp(-\tau/\tau_d) - 1]\right)\right\}} \quad (9.22)$$

The effect of both linewidth contributions on the relative accuracy is shown schematically in Figure 9.8(a) and the experimentally achieved total relative accuracy [34] for a typical TTG laser is plotted versus the distance in Figure 9.8(b). As with other radar techniques, the accuracy can be significantly improved by repeated measurements and averaging, whereby the accuracy increases with the square root of the number of measurements.

Numerical Example: Assuming an object at distance $R = 1$ m (with respect to the reference mirror; c.f., Figure 9.7(a)), a frequency sweep of $\Delta f = 500$ GHz (corresponding to a 4-nm tuning range at a 1,550-nm wavelength), a natural linewidth of $\Delta\nu_{STH} = 5$ MHz, an IRSN linewidth broadening of $\Delta\nu_t = 20$ MHz, and a repetition period of $t_m = 0.01$ ms (100 Hz), we obtain $\tau = 6.67$ ns, $f_{if} = 330$ kHz, $N = 6,600$, and a one-shot relative accuracy of $\Delta R/R = 4.3 \cdot 10^{-5}$ ($\Delta R = 43$ μm). In the case of $R = 1$ cm, we have $\Delta R/R = 2.7 \cdot 10^{-4}$ ($\Delta R = 2.7$ μm).

Owing to the high distance resolution, the optical radar is also well suited for optical frequency-domain reflectometry in applications, where a high spatial resolution is

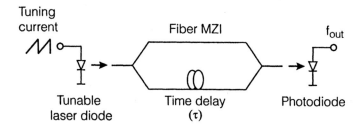

Figure 9.9   Schematic set-up for photoreceiver frequency response measurement by using the self-heterodyne technique with a tunable laser diode.

required. This is usually the case in fiber/integrated optic systems [35, 36]. With appropriately designed systems, a distance resolution around 100 μm has been reported [37].

9.3.2   Optical Components Characterization

The knowledge of the frequency response of photodiodes or photoreceivers is important for most device applications. Several measurement techniques have been proposed so far for the characterization of optical receivers. With the increasing bandwidth of the detectors, however, it becomes difficult to provide an optical source with a flat modulation characteristic. Here a measurement technique derived from the optical FMCW radar may be used [38], which requires no high-speed electronics for laser modulation because the modulated light signal is generated by self-heterodyning. The measurement setup is shown schematically in Figure 9.9. As with the laser radar, a continuously tunable laser diode is frequency modulated and the output is split into two differently long fibers, so that the two signals exhibit different instantaneous frequencies when being fed to the photodiode under test.

The interference of the two signals in the test device yields a beat frequency f_{out} equal to the difference of the instantaneous frequencies and thus acts as if the light signal would be AM modulated at frequency f_{out}. Because f_{out}, which is given by (9.6), may be freely adjusted by choosing the delay time difference between the two fibers τ accordingly, measurements up to the gigahertz regime are easily performed. Taking, for instance, $t_m = 1\,\mu$s, $\Delta f = 500\,$GHz, and $\tau = 50\,$ns (fiber length difference of 10 m) yields $f_{out} = 15\,$GHz.

Wavelength-tunable laser diodes have also been used for the alignment of polarization maintaining fibers, where an alignment accuracy of better than 0.2° has been achieved [39].

Various optical components may be characterized by means of coherent optical frequency-domain reflectometry [40] using tunable laser diodes. Among those are WDM filters [41], fiber amplifiers [42], and other fiber-optic network components [43].

Table 9.1
Absorption wavelengths of selected molecules (after [48]).

Molecule	Wavelength(s) (μm)
H_2O	1.365
HF	1.273, 1.331
CO_2	1.603, 2.004
CO	1.580
CH_4	1.651
NH_3	1.544
N_2O	1.954
HBr	1.341

9.3.3   Trace-Gas Sensing, Environmental Analysis, and Spectroscopy

Wavelength-tunable laser diodes are ideally suited as sources for gas-monitoring systems using absorption spectroscopy [44–46], provided absorption lines of sufficient strengths exist in the covered wavelength range. While most molecule resonances are in the mid-infrared, in many cases overtones in the near-infrared ($< 2\,\mu$m) are sufficiently strong. Consequently, state-of-the-art wavelength-tunable laser diodes in the 1,500-nm wavelength regime may be applied. However, with the emergence of antimonide-based devices [47] and by transferring the device concepts of the InGaAsP/InP tunable lasers to other material systems, an extension of the available wavelength regimes toward longer and shorter wavelengths than 1,500 nm will occur.

A list of selected molecules of practical importance is compiled in Table 9.1 [48] together with the absorption wavelengths. A fast and unambiguous gas analysis is feasible with continuously tunable laser diodes by scanning the relevant wavelength ranges. For most practical applications, the thermal tuning, using the striped heater technique, for example (c.f., Section 5.2.2), is sufficiently fast.

9.3.4   Optical Spectrum and Network Analysis

With the availability of wavelength-tunable laser diodes, advanced measurement techniques known from microwave electronics become feasible also in the optical domain. Among these are high-resolution spectrum analysis and optical network analysis. While the optical spectrum analysis offers highest resolution by exploiting the heterodyne technique with a continuously tunable device, impressive performance has been demonstrated with a discontinuously tunable three-section DBR laser with a tuning range of 13 nm [49].

The complete Jones matrix of a fiber Bragg grating has for the first time been determined with an optical network analyzer covering the complete wavelength range from 1,542 to 1,556 nm using three TTG lasers [50].

To use a widely tunable laser diode with a quasicontinuous tuning as source in a spectrometer, it is necessary to apply noncontinuous drive currents, set up in such a way that the output wavelength varies linearly with time with the optical power being

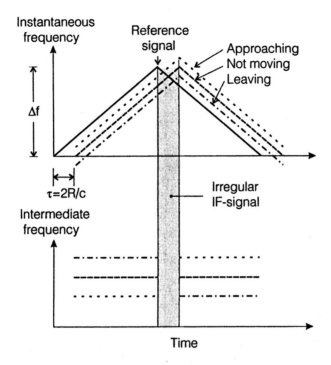

Figure 9.10   Schematic illustration of distance *and* velocity measurement by Doppler anemometer.

constant. Current discontinuities are necessary when the laser jumps from one longitudinal mode to another, and the duration of these resettings have to be small compared with the integration time.

9.3.5   Anemometry

Laser Doppler anemometry is a well-established technique for the determination of the velocity of moving objects [51, 52]. While Doppler anemometry is possible with many types of laser diodes, one usually only obtains the absolute velocity so that approaching and leaving objects cause the same signal. The application of wavelength-tunable devices, on the other hand, enables the convenient discrimination between these cases. This is illustrated in Figure 9.10. By using a triangle frequency modulation in an optical FMCW radar, the intermediate frequence f_{if} in the case of a nonmoving object is identical for the increasing and decreasing frequency slopes and is given by (9.6). For a moving object, on the other hand, the Doppler frequency shift is added to f_{if}, yielding different total frequency differences, whereby approaching and leaving objects may easily be distinguished.

REFERENCES

[1] Ishii, H., Kano, F., and Yoshikuni, Y., "Wavelength stabilisation of a superstructure grating DBR laser for WDM networks," *23rd European Conference on Optical Communication (ECOC'97)*, pp. 103–106 (volume 1), Edinburgh, U.K., 1997.

[2] Fukuda, M., *Reliability and degradation of semiconductor lasers and LEDs*, Norwood, MA, Artech House, 1991.

[3] Vodhanel, R. S., Krain, M., Wagner, R. E., and Sessa, W. B., "Long-term wavelength drift of the order of -0.01nm/yr for 15 free-running DFB laser modules," *Optical Fiber Communications (OFC'94)*, pp. 103–104, San Jose, CA, 1994.

[4] Chung, Y. C., and Jeong, J., "Ageing-induced wavelength shifths in 1.5-μm DFB lasers," *Optical Fiber Communications (OFC'94)*, pp. 104–105, San Jose, CA, 1994.

[5] Woodward, S. L., Parayanthal, P., and Koren, U., "The effects of ageing on the Bragg section of a DBR laser," *IEEE Photonics Technology Letters*, Vol. 5, 1993, pp. 750–752.

[6] Delorme, F., Alibert, G., Boulet, P., Grosmaire, S., Slempkes, S., and Ougazzaden, A., "High reliability of high-power and widely tunable 1.55 μm distributed Bragg reflector lasers for WDM applications," *IEEE Journal of Selected Topics in Quantum Electronics*, Vol. 3, 1997, pp. 607–614.

[7] Farrell, T., Anderson, L., Renlund, M., Dunne, J., McDonald, D., Broberg, B., Davis, M., and O'Dowd, R., "Low cost wavelength and power settable source for deployment in WDM networks," *23rd European Conference on Optical Communication (ECOC'97)*, pp. 155–158 (volume 2), Edinburgh, U.K., 1997.

[8] Baroni, S., and Bayvel, P., "Wavelength requirements in arbitrarily connected wavelength-routed optical networks," *IEEE Journal of Lightwave Technology*, Vol. 15, 1997, pp. 242–251.

[9] Brackett, C. A., "Dense wavelength division multiplexing networks: Principles and applications," *IEEE Journal on Selected Areas in Communications*, Vol. 8, 1990, pp. 948–964.

[10] Brackett, C. A., Acampora, A. S., Sweitzer, J., Tangonan, G., Smith, M. T., Lennon, W., K, C. Wang, and Hobbs, R. H., "A scalable multiwavelength multihop optical network: A proposal for research on all-optical networks," *IEEE Journal of Lightwave Technology*, Vol. 11, 1993, pp. 736–753.

[11] Green, P. E., "Optical netwoking update," *IEEE Journal on Selected Areas in Communications*, Vol. 14, 1996, pp. 764–779.

[12] Wauters, N., and Demeester, P., "Design of the optical path layer in multiwavelength cross-connected networks," *IEEE Journal on Selected Areas in Communications*, Vol. 14, 1996, pp. 881–892.

[13] Goodman, M. S., Kobrinski, H., Vecchi, M. P., Bulley, R. M., and Gimlett, J. L., "The LAMBDANET multiwavelength network: Architecture, applications and demonstrations," *IEEE Journal on Selected Areas in Communications*, Vol. 8, 1990, pp. 995–1004.

[14] Janniello, F. J., Ramaswami, R., and Steinberg, D. G., "A prototype circuit-switched multi-wavelength optical metropolitan-area network," *IEEE Journal of Lightwave Technology*, Vol. 11, 1993, pp. 777–782.

[15] Chang, G.-K., Ellinas, G., Gamelin, J. K., Iqbal, M. Z., and Brackett, C. A., "Multiwavelength reconfigurable WDM/ATM/SONET network testbed," *IEEE Journal of Lightwave Technology*, Vol. 14, 1996, pp. 1320–1340.

[16] Young, M. G., Koch, T. L., Koren, U., Tennant, D. M., Miller, B. I., Chien, M., and Feder, K., "Wavelength uniformity in λ/4 shifted DFB laser array WDM transmitters," *Electronics Letters*, Vol. 31, 1995, pp. 1750–1752.

[17] Wagner, R. E., Alferness, R. C., Saleh, A. A. M., and Goodman, M. S., "MONET: Multiwavelength optical networking," *IEEE Journal of Lightwave Technology*, Vol. 14, 1996, pp. 1349–1355.

[18] dePrycker, M., *Asynchronous Transfer Mode: Solution for B-ISDN*, Englewood Cliffs, NJ, Prentice Hall, 1995.

[19] Masetti, F., Benoit, J., Brillouet, F., Gabriagues, J. M., Jourdan, A., Renaud, M., Böttle, D., Eilenberger, G., Wünstel, K., Schilling, M., Chiaroni, D., Gavignet, P., Jacob, J. B., Bendelli, G., Cinato, P., Gambini, P., Puelo, M., Martinson, T., Vogel, P., Duurhus, T., Joergensen, C., Stubkjaer, K., Baets, R., Daele, P. Van, Bouley, J. C., Lefevre, R., Bachmann, M., Hunziker, W., Melchior, H., McGuire, A., Ratovelomanana, F., and Vodjdani, N., "High speed, high capacity ATM optical switches for future telecommunication transport networks," *IEEE Journal on Selected Areas in Communications*, Vol. 14, 1996, pp. 979–998.

[20] Danielsen, S. L., Mikkelsen, B., Joergensen, C., Duurhus, T., and Stubkjaer, K. E., "WDM packet switch architectures and analysis of the influence of tunable wavelength converters on the performance," *IEEE Journal of Lightwave Technology*, Vol. 15, 1997, pp. 219–227.

[21] Schell, M., Vaughn, M. D., Wang, A., Blumenthal, D. J., Rigole, P.-J., and Nilsson, S., "Experimental demonstration of an all-optical routing node for multihop wavelength routed networks," *IEEE Photonics Technology Letters*, Vol. 8, 1996, pp. 1391–1393.

[22] Jacobsen, G., *Noise in digital optical transmission systems*, Norwood, MA, Artech House, 1994.

[23] Hooijmans, P., *Coherent optical system design*, Chichester, U.K., Wiley, 1994.

[24] Stein, S., and Jones, J. J., *Modern communication principles*, New York, NY, McGraw Hill, 1967.

[25] Kazovsky, L. G., "Impact of laser phase noise on optical heterodyne communication systems," *Journal of Optical Communications*, Vol. 7, 1986, pp. 66–78.

[26] Khoe, G.-D., Heydt, G., Borges, I., Demeester, P., Ebberg, A., Labrujere, A., and Rawsthorne, J., "Coherent multicarrier technology for implementation in the customer accesss," *IEEE Journal of Lightwave Technology*, Vol. 11, 1993, pp. 695–714.

[27] Koch, T. L., Koren, U., Gnall, R. P., Choa, F. S., Hernandez-Gil, F., Burrus, C. A., Young, M. G., Oron, M., and Miller, B. I., "GaInAs/GaInAsP multiple-quantum-well integrated heterodyne receiver," *Electronics Letters*, Vol. 25, 1989, pp. 1621–1623.

[28] Kaiser, R., Trommer, D., Heidrich, H., Fidorra, F., and Hamacher, M., "Heterodyne receiver PICs as the first monolithically integrated tunable receivers for OFDM system applications," *Optical and Quantum Electronics*, Vol. 28, 1996, pp. 565–573.

[29] Burrows, E. C., and Liou, K.-Y., "High resolution laser lidar utilising two-section distributed feedback semiconductor laser as a coherent source," *Electronics Letters*, Vol. 26, 1990, pp. 577–579.

[30] Strzelecki, E. M., Cohen, D. A., and Coldren, L. A., "Investigation of tunable single frequency diode lasers for sensor applications," *IEEE Journal of Lightwave Technology*, Vol. 6, 1988, pp. 1610–1618.

[31] Economou, G., Youngquist, R. C., and Davies, D. E. N., "Limitations and noise in interferometric systems using frequency ramped single-mode diode lasers," *IEEE Journal of Lightwave Technology*, Vol. 4, 1986, pp. 1601–1608.

[32] Amann, M.-C., "Phase noise limited resolution of coherent LIDAR using widely tunable laser diodes," *Electronics Letters*, Vol. 28, 1992, pp. 1694–1696.

[33] Amann, M.-C., and Schimpe, R., "Excess linewidth broadening in wavelength-tunable laser diodes," *Electronics Letters*, Vol. 26, 1990, pp. 279–280.

[34] Dieckmann, A., and Amann, M.-C., "Phase-noise-limited accuracy of distance measurements in a frequency-modulated continuous-wave LIDAR with a tunable twin-guide laser diode," *Optical Engineering*, Vol. 34, 1995, pp. 896–903.

[35] Uttam, D., and Culshaw, B., "Precision time domain reflectometry in optical fiber systems using a frequency modulated continuous wave ranging technique," *IEEE Journal of Lightwave Technology*, Vol. 3, 1985, pp. 971–977.

[36] Lee, C. W., Peng, E. T., and Su, C. B., "Optical homodyne frequency domain reflectometer using an external cavity semiconductor laser," *IEEE Photonics Technology Letters*, Vol. 7, 1995, pp. 664–666.

[37] Kingsley, S. A., and Davies, D. E. N., *OFDR diagnostics for fiber/integrated optic systems and high resolution distributed fiber optic sensing*, pp. 265–275, SPIE, 1985.

[38] Wang, J., Krüger, U., Schwarz, B., and Petermann, K., "Measurement of frequency response of photoreceivers using self-homodyne method," *Electronics Letters*, Vol. 25, 1989, pp. 722–723.

[39] Ebberg, A., and Nòe, R., "Novel high precision alignment technique for polarisation maintaining fibres using a frequency modulated tunable laser," *Electronics Letters*, Vol. 26, 1990, pp. 2009–2010.

[40] Von der Weid, J. P., Passy, R., Mussi, G., and Gisin, N., "On the characterization of optical fiber network components with optical frequency domain reflectometry," *IEEE Journal of Lightwave Technology*, Vol. 15, 1997, pp. 1131–1141.

[41] Von der Weid, J. P., Passy, R., Forno, A. O. Dal, Huttner, B., and Gisin, N., "Return loss measurements of WDM filters with tunable coherent optical frequency-domain reflectometry," *IEEE Photonics Technology Letters*, Vol. 9, 1997, pp. 1508–1510.

[42] Von der Weid, J. P., Passy, R., and Gisin, N., "Coherent reflectometry of optical fiber amplifiers," *IEEE Photonics Technology Letters*, Vol. 9, 1997, pp. 1253–1255.

[43] Passy, R., Gisin, N., and Von der Weid, J. P., "High-sensitivity coherent optical frequency-domain reflectometry for characterization of fiber-optic network components," *IEEE Photonics Technology Letters*, Vol. 7, 1995, pp. 667–669.

[44] Mantz, . W., "A review of spectroscopic applications of tunable semiconductor lasers," *Spectrochimica Acta*, Vol. 51A, 1995, pp. 221–236.

[45] Sonnenfroh, D. M., and Allen, M. G., "Observation of CO and CO_2 absorption near 1.57 μm with an external-cavity diode laser," *Applied Optics*, Vol. 36, 1997, pp. 3298–3300.

[46] Chou, S.-I., Baer, D. S., and Hanson, R. K., "Diode laser absorption measurements of CH_3CL and CH_4 near 1.65 μm," *Applied Optics*, Vol. 36, 1997, pp. 3288–3293.

[47] Popov, A., Sherstnev, V., Yakovlev, Y., Mücke, and Werle, P., "Single-frequency InAsSb lasers emitting at 3.4 μm," *Spectrochimica Acta Part A*, Vol. 52, 1996, pp. 863–870.

[48] Werle, P., "A review of recent advances in semiconductor laser based gas monitors," *Spectrochimica Acta Part A*, Vol. 54, 1998, pp. 197–236.

[49] Herve, D., Ainguet, B., Pinel, S., Coquille, R., Poudoulec, A., and Delorme, F., "Narrow-band WDM spectrum analyser without mechanical tuning," *Electronics Letters*, Vol. 32, 1996, pp. 838–839.

[50] Sandel, D., and Nòe, R., "Optical network analyzer applied for fiber Bragg grating characterization," *23rd European Conference on Optical Communications (ECOC '97)*, pp. 186–189 (volume 3), Edinburgh, U.K., 1997.

[51] Koelink, M. H., Slot, M., Mul, F. F. M. De, Greve, J., Graaff, R., Dassel, A. C. M., and Aarnoudse, J. G., "Laser Doppler velocimeter based on the self-mixing effect in a fiber-coupled semiconductor laser: Theory," *Applied Optics*, Vol. 31, 1992, pp. 3401–3408.

[52] Dopheide, D., Faber, M., Reim, G., and Taux, G., "Laser and avalanche diodes for velocity measurement by laser Doppler anemometry," *Experiments in Fluids*, Vol. 6, 1988, pp. 289–297.

Appendix A

Refractive Index of InGaAsP

This appendix provides the refractive index of $In_{1-x}Ga_xAs_yP_{1-y}$ in the long-wavelength regime. While a rather complete treatment has been presented by Adachi [1], we follow a semitheoretical treatment based on a modified single-effective-oscillator method [2–4] to provide a graphical and analytical representation of the refractive index. In addition, a good agreement has been found with measurements, so these data are particularly well suited for our purpose.

Restricting the analysis to the transparent wavelength region, which means that the refractive indices of active regions may not be covered, the bandgap energy E_g and the single oscillator energies

$$E_0 \text{ [in eV]} = 0.595x^2(1-y) + 1.626xy - 1.891y + 0.524x + 3.391 \tag{A.1}$$

$$E_d \text{ [in eV]} = (12.36x - 12.71)y + 7.54x + 28.91 \tag{A.2}$$

are required to calculate the refractive index for the photon energy E:

$$n(E) = \sqrt{1 + \frac{E_d}{E_0} + \frac{E_d E^2}{E_0^3} + \frac{\eta E^4}{\pi} \ln \left(\frac{2E_0^2 - E_g^2 - E^2}{E_g^2 - E^2} \right)} \tag{A.3}$$

where

$$\eta = \frac{\pi E_d}{2E_0^3(E_0^2 - E_g^2)} \tag{A.4}$$

Using the wavelength and bandgap wavelength instead of E and E_g by way of (2.23), respectively, the refractive index of $In_{1-x}Ga_xAs_yP_{1-y}$ lattice-matched to InP is plotted in Figure A.1(a). Here the dependence of E_g on the mole fractions x and y is taken from (2.22), and lattice-matching links the mole fractions by (2.21).

The refractive index for photon energies near and below the bandgap energy may be obtained from [5, 6]. Using the experimental data in [6], where ellipsometry was used to determine the optical constants, the refractive index of InGaAsP at the bandgap energy is around 3.5 to 3.58, with typical values of 3.52 for λ_g =1,300 nm and 3.57 for λ_g =1,550 nm. It should be noted that the refractive index very close to E_g is somewhat

(a)

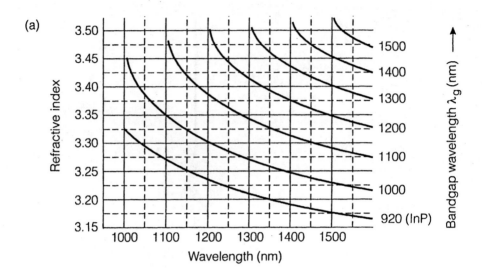

(b)

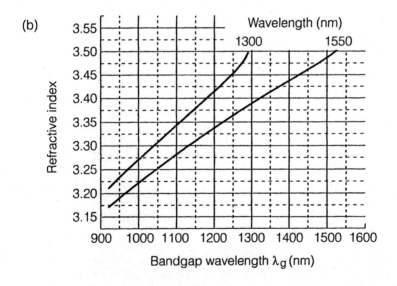

Figure A.1   Refractive index of InGaAsP lattice-matched to InP versus wavelength in the transparent wavelength region (a). Parameter is the bandgap wavelength $\lambda_g[\text{nm}] = 1240/E_g[\text{eV}]$. Refractive index of InGaAsP lattice-matched to InP versus bandgap wavelength for fixed wavelengths of 1,300 nm and 1,550 nm (b).

uncertain because of the strong disperion near the absorption edge. For most semiconductor materials, including Ga(Al)As, the refractive index at $h\nu \approx E_g$ is between 3.5 and 3.6 [6–8].

The effects of doping and carrier injection on the refractive index is not considered. In practice, however, it turns out that most InGaAsP waveguides and laser structures can be designed reasonably accurately with the present data.

In usual design work, one frequently needs the refractive index at fixed wavelengths of 1,300 nm and 1,550 nm as a function of the bandgap wavelength as shown in Figure A.1(b).

REFERENCES

[1] Adachi, S., "Refractive indices of III-V compounds: key properties of InGaAsP relevant to device design," *Journal of Applied Physics*, Vol. 53, 1982, pp. 5863–5869.

[2] Afromowitz, M. A., "Refractive index of $Ga_{1-x}Al_xAs$," *Solid State Communications*, Vol. 15, 1974, pp. 59–63.

[3] Utaka, K., Suematsu, Y., Kobayashi, K., and Kawanishi, H., "GaInAsP/InP integrated twin-guide lasers with first-order distributed Bragg reflectors at 1.3 μm wavelength," *Japanese Journal of Applied Physics*, Vol. 19, 1980, pp. L137–L140.

[4] Broberg, B., and Lindgren, S., "Refractive index of $In_{1-x}Ga_xAs_yP_{1-y}$ layers and InP in the transparent wavelength region," *Journal of Applied Physics*, Vol. 55, 1984, pp. 3376–3381.

[5] Buus, J., and Adams, M. J., "Phase and group indices for double heterostructure lasers," *Solid-State and Electron Devices*, Vol. 3, 1979, pp. 189–195.

[6] Burkhard, H., Dinges, H. W., and Kuphal, E., "Optical properties of $In_{1-x}Ga_xP_{1-y}As_y$, InP, GaAs, and GaP determined by ellipsometry," *Journal of Applied Physics*, Vol. 53, 1982, pp. 655–662.

[7] Chandra, P., Coldren, L. A., and Strege, K. E., "Refractive index data from $Ga_xIn_{1-x}As_yP_{1-y}$ films," *Electronics Letters*, Vol. 17, 1981, pp. 6–7.

[8] Kokubo, Y., and Ohta, I., "Refractive index as a function of photon energy for AlGaAs between 1.2 and 1.8 eV," *Journal of Applied Physics*, Vol. 81, 1997, pp. 2042–2043.

Appendix B

The Slab Waveguide

The one-dimensional multi-layer slab waveguide is an important example for dielectric waveguide properties, both in its own right and for use in effective refractive index calculations. Here we outline the basic theory for TE polarized waves where the electric field is parallel with the layer structure. For more details, and for treatment of the TM case, refer to specialized texts such as [1].

The geometry used is shown in Figure B.1. TE modes have three field components: The electric field has a y-component only, E_y, and the magnetic field has components in the x- and z-directions. The magnetic field components can be derived from the electric field component.

For a wavelength λ, free-space propagation constant $k_0 = 2\pi/\lambda$, and a time factor $\exp(j\omega t)$, the wave equation reads

$$\frac{\partial^2 E_y(x,z)}{\partial z^2} + \frac{\partial^2 E_y(x,z)}{\partial x^2} + n^2(x)k_0^2 E_y(x,z) = 0 \tag{B.1}$$

Looking for a wave propagating in the z-direction with a propagation constant β, we have

$$E_y(x,z) = E(x)\exp(-j\beta z) \tag{B.2}$$

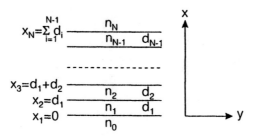

Figure B.1 One-dimensional slab waveguide. The refractive index varies in the x-direction only, the electric field is in the y-direction (TE mode), and propagation is in the z-direction.

giving

$$\frac{d^2E(x)}{dx^2} - (\beta^2 - n^2(x)k_0^2)E(x) = 0 \tag{B.3}$$

where $n(x)$ is constant within each layer.

This constitutes an eigenvalue equation for the x-dependence of the field. From the eigenvalue β, we define the modal (or effective) refractive index n_{eff}:

$$\beta = n_{\text{eff}}k_0 \tag{B.4}$$

We note that (B.3) may have several solutions, corresponding to several transverse modes. Each mode is characterized by its effective refractive index and the corresponding field distribution.

For the multilayer slab waveguide, we can immediately write the general solution for the field distribution in layer number i where $x_i < x < x_{i+1}$:

$$E_i(x) = A_i \exp\left(q_i(x - x_i)\right) + B_i \exp\left(-q_i(x - x_i)\right) \tag{B.5}$$

where

$$q_i = \sqrt{\beta^2 - n_i^2 k_0^2} \tag{B.6}$$

The values of the coefficients A_i and B_i are determined by the boundary conditions, which require the transverse electrical field to be continuous:

$$E_{i+1}(x_{i+1}) = E_i(x_{i+1}) \tag{B.7}$$

and the transverse magnetic field H_z, which is proportional to dE_y/dx, to be continuous, leading to

$$\left.\frac{dE_{i+1}}{dx}\right|_{x=x_{i+1}} = \left.\frac{dE_i}{dx}\right|_{x=x_{i+1}} \tag{B.8}$$

(TM modes, where the only component of the magnetic field is in the y-direction, can be treated in a similar way, except for the boundary conditions.)

The boundary conditions give

$$A_{i+1} + B_{i+1} = A_i \exp\left(q_i d_i\right) + B_i \exp\left(-q_i d_i\right) \tag{B.9}$$

and

$$A_{i+1}q_{i+1} - B_{i+1}q_{i+1} = A_i q_i \exp\left(q_i d_i\right) - B_i q_i \exp\left(-q_i d_i\right) \tag{B.10}$$

Since the field must vanish at $\pm\infty$, we have

$$E_0 = A_0 \exp\left(q_0 x\right) \tag{B.11}$$

and

$$E_N = B_N \exp\left(-q_N(x - x_N)\right) \tag{B.12}$$

that is, $B_0 = 0$ and $A_N = 0$.

The field is then found by providing a start-guess for β and setting $A_0 = 1$. The field coefficients are found by recursive use of the boundary conditions (with $d_0 = 0$):

$$A_{i+1} = \frac{1}{2}\left(A_i \exp\left(q_i d_i\right)\left(1 + \frac{q_i}{q_{i+1}}\right) + B_i \exp\left(-q_i d_i\right)\left(1 - \frac{q_i}{q_{i+1}}\right)\right) \tag{B.13}$$

$$B_{i+1} = \frac{1}{2}\left(A_i \exp\left(q_i d_i\right)\left(1 - \frac{q_i}{q_{i+1}}\right) + B_i \exp\left(-q_i d_i\right)\left(1 + \frac{q_i}{q_{i+1}}\right)\right) \tag{B.14}$$

Iterations are then carried out until a value of β that gives $A_N = 0$ is found.

When the field has been found, we can calculate the confinement factor (power fraction) for each layer:

$$\Gamma_i = \frac{\int_{x_i}^{x_{i+1}} |E_i|^2 dx}{\int_{-\infty}^{\infty} |E_i|^2 dx} \tag{B.15}$$

The simplest case is the three-layer symmetrical slab with $n_2 = n_0$. We introduce the parameters u and w:

$$u^2 = (n_1^2 - n_{\text{eff}}^2)\left(\frac{k_0 d_1}{2}\right)^2 \tag{B.16}$$

$$w^2 = (n_{\text{eff}}^2 - n_2^2)\left(\frac{k_0 d_1}{2}\right)^2 \tag{B.17}$$

This allows us to treat the problem in terms of normalized parameters, with the normalized frequency v defined by

$$v^2 = u^2 + w^2 = (n_1^2 - n_2^2)\left(\frac{k_0 d_1}{2}\right)^2 \tag{B.18}$$

and the normalized propagation constant b defined by

$$b = \frac{n_{\text{eff}}^2 - n_2^2}{n_1^2 - n_2^2} \tag{B.19}$$

or

$$n_{\text{eff}} = \sqrt{bn_1^2 + (1 - b)n_2^2} \tag{B.20}$$

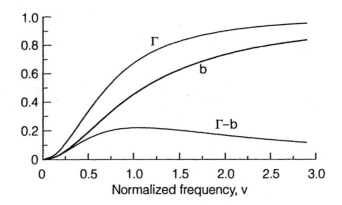

Figure B.2   The normalized propagation constant b, the confinement factor Γ, and $\Gamma - b$ as functions of the normalized frequency v for a symmetrical three-layer slab waveguide.

Using these parameters, matching the field and its derivative at $x = 0$ and at $x = d_1$, and requiring the field to vanish at infinity, we find the following equation (the characteristic equation):

$$v\sqrt{1 - b} = \arctan \sqrt{\frac{b}{1 - b}} + M\frac{\pi}{2} \tag{B.21}$$

where M is the mode number ($M = 0$ for the fundamental mode).

The advantage of the normalized parameters is that b is a function of v only, regardless of the specific structure. This means that for a given structure we first calculate v, from this value we can find the value of b, and then the effective refractive index follows from (B.20).

Using the normalized parameters in the definition of the confinement factor (B.15) it can be shown, after some algebra, that the confinement factor can be expressed in terms of v and b:

$$\Gamma = b + (1 - b)\frac{v\sqrt{b}}{1 + v\sqrt{b}} = b + \frac{v}{2}\frac{db}{dv} \tag{B.22}$$

It is clear that b and Γ cannot be expressed directly as simple functions of v. However, there are a couple of very good approximate expressions [2, 3]:

$$b \approx 1 - \frac{1}{2v^2} \ln(1 + 2v^2) \tag{B.23}$$

and

$$\Gamma \approx \frac{2v^2}{1 + 2v^2} \tag{B.24}$$

In Figure B.2, we show b, Γ, and $\Gamma - b$ as functions of v.

It should be noted that all of the theory described above, and all the equations with the exception of (B.23) and (B.24), remain valid if the refractive indices are complex (i.e., in the presence of gain or loss). The parameters b and v as well as the field coefficients A_i and B_i may become complex, but the confinement factor Γ remains real.

From (B.20), we can find the change in the effective refractive index caused by a perturbation in the refractive index n_1 of the center layer. Taking into account that the normalized propagation constant b depends on n_1 (through v), and using the second part of (B.22), we find

$$\frac{dn_{\mathrm{eff}}}{dn_1} = \frac{n_1}{n_{\mathrm{eff}}}\Gamma \tag{B.25}$$

If the refractive index difference $(n_1 - n_2)$ is small, this gives

$$\Delta n_{\mathrm{eff}} \approx \Gamma \Delta n_1 \tag{B.26}$$

For the general multilayer structure, a perturbation of the refractive index of layer i gives

$$\Delta(n_{\mathrm{eff}})^2 = \Gamma_i \Delta(n_i)^2 \tag{B.27}$$

leading to

$$\Delta n_{\mathrm{eff}} = \Gamma_i \frac{n_i}{n_{\mathrm{eff}}}\Delta n_i \approx \Gamma_i \Delta n_i \tag{B.28}$$

If we consider the imaginary part of the refractive index (which describes gain or loss) as a perturbation, we obtain, with g_i being the gain of layer i:

$$n_{\mathrm{eff}}g_{\mathrm{eff}} = \Gamma_i n_i g_i \tag{B.29}$$

For the case of small index variations, this gives

$$g_{\mathrm{eff}} \approx \Gamma_i g_i \tag{B.30}$$

For dispersive material the group index is given by

$$n_g = n - \lambda\frac{dn}{d\lambda} \tag{B.31}$$

The effective group index for a multilayer structure is given by

$$n_{\mathrm{eff}}n_{g,\mathrm{eff}} = \sum_{i=0}^{N} \Gamma_i n_i n_{g,i} \tag{B.32}$$

For small index variations this simplifies to

$$n_{g,\text{eff}} \approx \sum_{i=0}^{N} \Gamma_i n_{g,i} \tag{B.33}$$

Note that even in the absence of material dispersion the effective group index differs from the effective index because of waveguide dispersion (i.e., the fact that the waveguide properties are wavelength dependent even when the refractive indices are constant).

Numerical Example: We consider a three-layer symmetrical slab waveguide corresponding to a laser. With $n_1 = 3.6$, $n_2 = 3.2$, $n_{g,1} = 4.5$, $n_{g,2} = 3.4$, and a confinement factor of 0.3, we find an effective refractive index of about 3.26 and an effective group index of about 3.8. For a passive waveguide with $n_1 = 3.35$, $n_2 = 3.2$, $n_{g,1} = 3.65$, $n_{g,2} = 3.4$, and a confinement factor of 0.3, we have an effective refractive index of about 3.22 and an effective group index of about 3.5. The higher dispersion of the active material in the laser structure leads to a higher value of the group index. In the various numerical examples in this book, we have used group index values of 4 for laser structures and 3.5 for passive waveguides.

As an example of the use of normalized waveguide parameters, we consider the change in operating wavelength of a distributed feedback (DFB) laser due to a change in the thickness of the active layer. Starting from

$$\frac{d\lambda}{dd_a} = \frac{d\lambda}{dn_{\text{eff}}} \frac{dn_{\text{eff}}}{db} \frac{db}{dv} \frac{dv}{dd_a} \tag{B.34}$$

we use

$$\frac{d\lambda}{dn_{\text{eff}}} = \frac{\lambda}{n_{g,\text{eff}}} \tag{B.35}$$

$$\frac{dn_{\text{eff}}}{db} = \frac{n_1^2 - n_2^2}{2n_{\text{eff}}} \approx \Delta n = n_1 - n_2 \tag{B.36}$$

$$\frac{db}{dv} = (\Gamma - b)\frac{2}{v} \tag{B.37}$$

and

$$\frac{dv}{dd_a} = \frac{v}{d_a} \tag{B.38}$$

This gives

$$\frac{\Delta\lambda}{\lambda} \approx 2(\Gamma - b)\frac{\Delta n}{n_{g,\text{eff}}} \frac{\Delta d_a}{d_a} \tag{B.39}$$

It should be noted that in most practical cases a DFB laser is not a symmetrical three-layer structure; (B.39) should therefore be considered as an approximate result.

Numerical Example: For $v \approx 0.4$, we have $\Gamma - b \approx 0.1$, and with $\Delta n \approx 0.4$ and $n_{g,\text{eff}} = 4$ we find the coefficient 0.02 used in (3.69). Similarly for the sensitivity to the width we use $v \approx 1.5$ giving $\Gamma - b \approx 0.2$, and with $\Delta n \approx 0.1$ and $n_{g,\text{eff}} = 4$, we find the coefficient 0.01 used in (3.71).

REFERENCES

[1] Adams, M. J., *An introduction to optical waveguides*, Chichester, U.K., Wiley, 1981.

[2] Chen, K.-L., and Wang, S., "An approximate expression for the effective refractive index in symmetric DH lasers," *IEEE Journal of Quantum Electronics*, Vol. 19, 1983, pp. 1354–1356.

[3] Botez, D., "Analytical approximation of the radiation confinement factor for the TE-0 mode of a double heterojunction laser," *IEEE Journal of Quantum Electronics*, Vol. 14, 1978, pp. 230–232.

Appendix C

Transfer Matrices

A transfer matrix relates the right- and left-propagating waves at one end of a structure to the right- and left-propagating waves at the opposite end of the structure. These matrices form a powerful tool for the analysis of structures consisting of several concatenated sections, where each section is described by a transfer matrix. The transfer matrix for the complete structure is then found as the matrix product of the individual matrices. In Figure C.1, we show the case for a structure with two sections. If $\mathbf{F_1}$ is the transfer matrix for section 1 and $\mathbf{F_2}$ is the transfer matrix for section 2, we have

$$\begin{pmatrix} E_r^{(2)} \\ E_s^{(2)} \end{pmatrix} = \mathbf{F_1} \begin{pmatrix} E_r^{(1)} \\ E_s^{(1)} \end{pmatrix} \tag{C.1}$$

and

$$\begin{pmatrix} E_r^{(3)} \\ E_s^{(3)} \end{pmatrix} = \mathbf{F_2} \begin{pmatrix} E_r^{(2)} \\ E_s^{(2)} \end{pmatrix} \tag{C.2}$$

hence

$$\begin{pmatrix} E_r^{(3)} \\ E_s^{(3)} \end{pmatrix} = \mathbf{F_2} \mathbf{F_1} \begin{pmatrix} E_r^{(1)} \\ E_s^{(1)} \end{pmatrix} \tag{C.3}$$

Note that the order of the matrices is reversed relative to the figure.

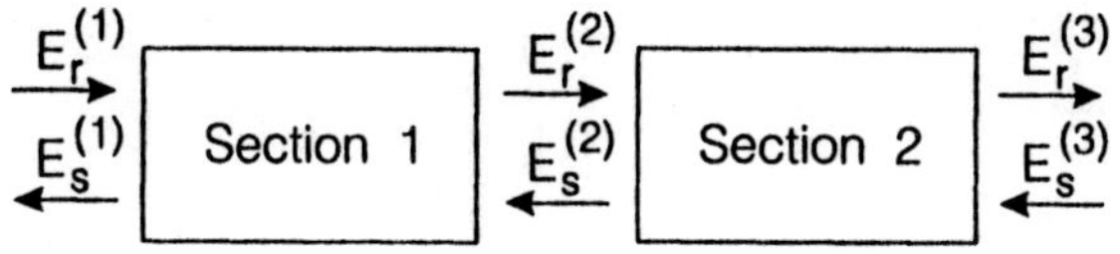

Figure C.1   Right- and left-propagating waves in a two-section structure.

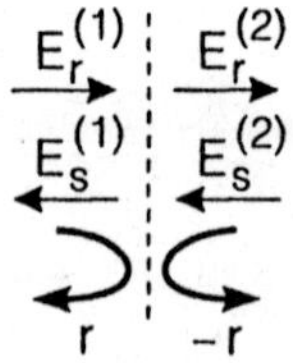

Figure C.2   Reflection at a discontinuity.

To use this method, we need to build up a "library" of matrices for some specific structures. If a section is simply a homogeneous material of length L, and if the propagation constant is β, then

$$E_r^{(2)} = \exp(-j\beta L)E_r^{(1)} \tag{C.4}$$

$$E_s^{(2)} = \exp(j\beta L)E_s^{(1)} \tag{C.5}$$

giving

$$\mathbf{F}_{\text{hom}}(\beta L) = \begin{pmatrix} \exp(-j\beta L) & 0 \\ 0 & \exp(j\beta L) \end{pmatrix} \tag{C.6}$$

If a "section" is a discontinuity with a field reflection coefficient r when seen from the left, and $-r$ when seen from the right (see Figure C.2), then

$$E_s^{(1)} = rE_r^{(1)} + (1-r)E_s^{(2)} \tag{C.7}$$

$$E_r^{(2)} = -rE_s^{(2)} + (1+r)E_r^{(1)} \tag{C.8}$$

This is seen by setting $E_r^{(1)}$ and $E_s^{(2)}$ equal to zero in turn, and using the continuity condition at the interface. This leads to the transfer matrix

$$\mathbf{F}_{\text{dis}}(r) = \begin{pmatrix} 1/(1-r) & -r/(1-r) \\ -r/(1-r) & 1/(1-r) \end{pmatrix} \tag{C.9}$$

It is important to note that we can use the matrix elements "the other way around," and express the reflection in terms of matrix elements:

$$r = -\frac{(\mathbf{F}_{\text{dis}})_{21}}{(\mathbf{F}_{\text{dis}})_{22}} \tag{C.10}$$

If the discontinuity is caused by the transition from a material with index n_1 to one with index n_2, then

$$r = \frac{n_1 - n_2}{n_1 + n_2} \tag{C.11}$$

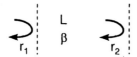

Figure C.3   Fabry–Perot laser as two reflectors and a homogeneous gain region of length L.

and using (C.9), the transfer matrix becomes

$$\mathbf{F}_{\text{dis}} = \begin{pmatrix} 1 + (n_1 - n_2)/2n_2 & -(n_1 - n_2)/2n_2 \\ -(n_1 - n_2)/2n_2 & 1 + (n_1 - n_2)/2n_2 \end{pmatrix} \tag{C.12}$$

We can use the transfer matrix description to analyze a laser with N sections

$$\mathbf{F} = \mathbf{F}_N \mathbf{F}_{N-1}, \dots, \mathbf{F}_1 \tag{C.13}$$

In a laser, there are no incoming fields, and it follows from $E_s^{N+1} = E_r^{(1)} = 0$ that we must have $F_{22} = 0$, corresponding to an infinite reflectivity. This can be used to derive the oscillation condition. We consider the simplest possible Fabry–Perot laser, which can be modeled as an amplifying, homogeneous medium placed between two reflectors, as shown in Figure C.3.

In this case, the whole structure consists of only three sections, and the transfer matrix is

$$\mathbf{F}_{\text{fp}} = \mathbf{F}_{\text{dis}}(r_2) \mathbf{F}_{\text{hom}}(\beta L) \mathbf{F}_{\text{dis}}(r_1) \tag{C.14}$$

Carrying out the matrix multiplications and using the oscillation condition $(\mathbf{F}_{\text{fp}})_{22} = 0$ leads to

$$-r_1 r_2 e^{-2j\beta L} = 1 \tag{C.15}$$

Except for the sign, this is the same result as (2.39). The reason for the sign change is that in the derivation of (2.39) we were looking at the facets from inside the cavity, whereas in Figure C.3 we are looking at the left facet from outside, consequently, the sign of the field reflection coefficient r_1 is reversed.

As an additional transfer matrix, we recall the result for a periodic structure from Section 3.2.2:

$$\mathbf{F}_{\text{per}} = \begin{pmatrix} \left(\cosh(\gamma L) - \frac{j\Delta\beta}{\gamma} \sinh(\gamma L) \right) & -\frac{j\kappa}{\gamma} \sinh(\gamma L) \\ \frac{j\kappa}{\gamma} \sinh(\gamma L) & \left(\cosh(\gamma L) + \frac{j\Delta\beta}{\gamma} \sinh(\gamma L) \right) \end{pmatrix} \tag{C.16}$$

There is an interesting formula for a structure consisting of N identical substructures, each characterized by the matrix $\mathbf{F}$. It is, of course, possible to use the relation

$$\mathbf{F}_{\text{tot}} = \mathbf{F}^N \tag{C.17}$$

but using the Lagrange–Sylvester formula [1] for a 2 by 2 matrix, we have directly

$$F^N = \frac{\lambda_1^N - \lambda_2^N}{\lambda_1 - \lambda_2}F + \frac{\lambda_1\lambda_2^N - \lambda_2\lambda_1^N}{\lambda_1 - \lambda_2}\mathbf{1} \tag{C.18}$$

where λ_1 and λ_2 are the eigenvalues of F, and $\mathbf{1}$ is the unit matrix.

The eigenvalues are found from

$$\text{Det}\begin{pmatrix} F_{11} - \lambda & F_{12} \\ F_{21} & F_{22} - \lambda \end{pmatrix} = 0 \tag{C.19}$$

which gives

$$\lambda^2 - (F_{11} + F_{22})\lambda + (F_{11}F_{22} - F_{12}F_{21}) = 0 \tag{C.20}$$

We can therefore write the eigenvalues as

$$\lambda = \frac{F_{11} + F_{22}}{2} \pm \sqrt{\left(\frac{F_{11} + F_{22}}{2}\right)^2 - D} \tag{C.21}$$

where D is the determinant of F.

We recall that the reflection from a single element is given by (C.10); for a structure with N identical elements we have

$$\left(F^N\right)_{21} = \frac{(\lambda_1^N - \lambda_2^N)F_{21}}{\lambda_1 - \lambda_2} \tag{C.22}$$

and

$$\left(F^N\right)_{22} = \frac{(\lambda_1^N - \lambda_2^N)F_{22} + (\lambda_1\lambda_2^N - \lambda_2\lambda_1^N)}{\lambda_1 - \lambda_2} \tag{C.23}$$

This gives

$$r_N = \frac{-F_{21}}{F_{22}}\left(1 - \frac{\lambda_1^{N-1} - \lambda_2^{N-1}}{\lambda_1^N - \lambda_2^N}\frac{\lambda_1\lambda_2}{F_{22}}\right)^{-1} \tag{C.24}$$

REFERENCES

[1] Barnett, S., *Matrices: Methods and Applications*, Oxford, U.K., Clarendon Press, 1990.

Appendix D

Thermal Response of a Laser Diode

The dynamics of thermal heating in laser diodes leads to time-dependent refractive index changes that in turn dynamically change the laser wavelength. As it is the effective refractive index of the transverse laser mode under investigation that determines the laser wavelength, we investigate the effect of the heat generation in the tuning region on the effective refractive index. In the time domain, the pulse response of the wavelength change is calculated by considering the heat generation in the tuning region, which occurs unintentionally following a steplike tuning current change. In the frequency domain, we calculate the frequency modulation (FM) response for a sinusoidal time dependence of the heat generation in the tuning region.

D.1 PULSE RESPONSE IN THE TIME DOMAIN

An analytical solution can be obtained if we assume that the thermal conductivity is constant within the laser chip and that the chip is mounted upside-up onto an ideal heat sink kept at constant temperature. In this case, we obtain the simplified schematic cross-section shown in Figure D.1(a), where for the sake of convenience the heat sink temperature is taken zero and the heat conduction of the ambient air ($y > 0$) is neglected. Assuming a longitudinal homogeneous structure, such as a TTG or DFB laser, the heat source can be approximated as an infinitely thin line source at the origin. The laser stripe geometry can be transformed into the entire $x - y$ plane by using the method of mirror heat sources and sinks as shown in Figure D.1(b), whereby because of the mapping into the upper plane, the strengths of the sources and sinks becomes doubled with respect to the single heat source placed in the origin of Figure D.1(a). Now we use polar coordinates to calculate the contribution of each source to the temperature in the mode area, which is described in Figure D.1 by a cylinder of radius R_0 around the origin. Owing to symmetry, the temperature distribution caused by any source or sink depends only on the distance from this particular source or sink, respectively.

In polar coordinates, the differential equation for the temperature distribution due to an infinitely thin line source at $r = 0$ reads

$$\frac{\partial T}{\partial t} = k_{\text{therm}} \frac{1}{r} \frac{\partial}{\partial r} \left(r \frac{\partial T}{\partial r} \right) + \frac{q(t)}{c_v} \frac{\delta(r)}{2\pi r} \tag{D.1}$$

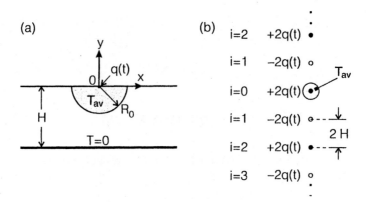

Figure D.1   Schematic cross-section of upside-up mounted stripe-geometry laser diode with constant heat conductivity and a line heat source q in the origin (a). The cross-section area of the lasing transverse mode is approximated by the semicircle of radius R_0 ($R_0 \ll H$). At $y = -H$, an ideal heat sink provides constant temperature $T = 0$. The laser chip cross-section is mapped onto the entire $x - y$ plane by using an infinite set of mirrored heat sources and sinks (b).

where k_{therm} is the thermal diffusivity (dimension cm²/s), which is related to thermal conductivity χ (dimension W/cmK) and volume heat capacity c_v (dimension Ws/cm³K) as

$$k_{therm} = \frac{\chi}{c_v} \tag{D.2}$$

and $q(t)$ is the time-dependent heat-source power per unit length with dimension W/cm.
     Supplying a δ-pulse at $t = 0$:

$$q(t) = Q\delta(t) \tag{D.3}$$

where Q is the heat energy per unit length of the δ-pulse, the solution of (D.1) reads [1]

$$T(r, t) = \frac{2Q}{4\pi\chi t} \exp\left\{-\frac{r^2}{4k_{therm}t}\right\} \tag{D.4}$$

where the factor of two in the denominator stems from the doubling of the source strength from the mapping (c. f., Figure D.1).
     To study the effect of all heat sources and sinks on the transverse mode, we calculate the temperature in the mode area. To this end we treat the heat source in the origin differently from the other sources and sinks, because it is placed in the center of the mode so that the strong temperature variation around $r = 0$ (c. f., (D.4)) leads to a strongly inhomogeneous heating of the mode area. As a consequence, we average the temperature over the mode area for this particular source. Owing to the large H/R_0 ratio (typ. 50–100), the variations of the temperature contributions within the mode area from all other sources and sinks, on the other hand, can be neglected and we may simply use the corresponding temperature contributions at the mode center (origin) using (D.4).

The spatial averaging over (D.4) yields for the temperature contribution of the source in the origin

$$T_{av} = \frac{1}{\pi R_0^2} \int_0^{R_0} T(r,t) 2\pi r \, dr = \frac{2Q}{\pi c_v R_0^2} \left[1 - \exp\left\{ -\frac{R_0^2}{4k_{therm}t} \right\} \right] \tag{D.5}$$

The effect of a step heat source at $t = 0$ with heat power per unit length q_0

$$q(t) = \begin{cases} 0 & t < 0 \\ q_0 & t \geq 0 \end{cases} \tag{D.6}$$

can be obtained by replacing Q in (D.4) and (D.5) by q_0 and integrating over time. This yields for the source in the origin

$$T_{av} = \frac{2q_0 t}{\pi \chi \tau_{therm}} \left[1 - E_2 \left(\frac{\tau_{therm}}{4t} \right) \right] \tag{D.7}$$

and for all other sources

$$T_i = \frac{q_0}{2\pi\chi} E_1 \left(\left(\frac{r_i}{2R_0} \right)^2 \frac{\tau_{therm}}{t} \right) \tag{D.8}$$

where E_1 and E_2 are exponential integrals [2], $\tau_{therm} = R_0^2/k_{therm}$, and $r_i = 2iH$ is the distance of the source i ($i = 1, 2, \ldots$) from the origin. The total time-dependent spatially averaged temperature of the mode volume is obtained by summation of all sources and sinks yielding

$$T(t) = T_{av} + 2 \sum_{i=1}^{\infty} (-1)^i T_i \tag{D.9}$$

where the factor $(-1)^i$ takes into account that even and odd indices are for sources and sinks, respectively.

The asymptotic case $t \to \infty$ is obtained by using the limiting values of the exponential integrals for small arguments

$$\lim_{x \to 0} E_1(x) = -\gamma - \ln(x) \tag{D.10}$$
$$\lim_{x \to 0} E_2(x) = 1 + x \left[\ln(x) + \gamma - 1 \right] \tag{D.11}$$

where γ is Euler's constant. Performing the summation for $t \to \infty$ thus yields

$$T(\infty) = \frac{q_0}{\pi\chi} \left[\ln\left(\frac{4H}{\pi R_0} \right) + 0.5 \right] \tag{D.12}$$

Evaluating (D.9) using (D.7) and (D.8) and normalizing with (D.12) finally leads to (4.23).

From (D.12), we may derive the DC thermal resistance R_{therm}:

$$R_{\text{therm}} = \frac{T(\infty)}{q_0 L} = \frac{1}{\pi \chi L} \left[\ln \left(\frac{4H}{\pi R_0} \right) + 0.5 \right] \tag{D.13}$$

which compares well with the results obtained with conformal mapping for a stripe-geometry laser with stripe-width $w = 2R_0$ [3]

$$R_{\text{therm}} = \frac{1}{\chi L} \frac{K}{K'} \approx \frac{1}{\pi \chi L} \ln \left(\frac{8H}{\pi R_0} \right) \tag{D.14}$$

where K and K' are the complete elliptic integrals for argument $\exp(-\pi w/2H)$, and the approximation holds for $H/w \gg 1$.

Numerical Example: Taking $R_0 = 1\,\mu\text{m}$, $w = 2R_0$, $H = 100\,\mu\text{m}$, $L = 300\,\mu\text{m}$, and $\chi = 0.7\,\text{W cm}^{-1}\,\text{K}^{-1}$, (D.13) yields $R_{\text{therm}} = 81\,°\text{K/W}$ and (D.14) gives $R_{\text{therm}} = 84\,°\text{K/W}$. As can be seen, the two values agree to within 4%. The weak (logarithmic) dependence of the thermal resistance on the stripe-width makes total R_{therm}-values (including the contribution of the heat sink) around $100\,°\text{K/W}$ for 300-μm-long devices reasonable (c. f., Numerical Example in Section 3.5.2).

D.2   RESPONSE IN THE FREQUENCY DOMAIN

The thermal FM response in the frequency domain $S_{\text{therm}}(\omega)$ is defined as the frequency dependent wavelength change under sinusoidal heating normalized to the DC response. Because the wavelength changes are proportional to the temperature changes, we may write

$$S_{\text{therm}}(\omega) = \frac{\tilde{T}(\omega)}{\tilde{T}(0)} \tag{D.15}$$

where $\tilde{T}$ denotes the Fourier transform (4.26) of the temperature variation.

$\tilde{T}$ is obtained by solving the Fourier transform of (D.1) with a δ-pulse heat source (D.3) at $t = 0$, yielding the ordinary differential equation:

$$j\omega \tilde{T} = k_{\text{therm}} \frac{1}{r} \frac{d}{dr} \left(r \frac{d\tilde{T}}{dr} \right) + \frac{Q}{c_v} \frac{\delta(r)}{2\pi r} \tag{D.16}$$

The solutions of (D.16) are Bessel functions. The boundary conditions of the present problem require an outward heat flow for $r \to \infty$, which corresponds to Hankel's function $H_n^{(2)}$. As we have no azimuthal variations, the index n is zero and the contribution of source i is

$$\tilde{T}_i = -\frac{jQ}{2\chi} H_0^{(2)} \left(\sqrt{-j \frac{\omega}{k_{\text{therm}}}} r_i \right) = -\frac{jQ}{2\chi} H_0^{(2)} \left(2i \frac{H}{R_0} \sqrt{-j\omega \tau_{\text{therm}}} \right) \tag{D.17}$$

where we considered that the total heat flux supplied by the line source must be equal to the heat flux $-\chi d\tilde{T}/dr$ at $r \to 0$ integrated over the circle $2\pi r$.

As before in (D.5), we have to average over the mode area for the source in the origin, yielding

$$\tilde{T}_{av} = \frac{Q}{\chi \omega \tau_{therm}} \left[\sqrt{-j\omega\tau_{therm}} H_1^{(2)} \left(\sqrt{-j\omega\tau_{therm}} \right) - \frac{2j}{\pi} \right] \tag{D.18}$$

The total temperature is now obtained by summing over all sources and sinks according to (D.9). For the normalization we require the response for $\omega = 0$, which is obtained by approximating Hankel's functions for small arguments as [2]

$$\lim_{x \to 0} H_0^{(2)}(x) = 1 - \frac{2j}{\pi} \left[\ln \left(\frac{x}{2} \right) + \gamma \right] \tag{D.19}$$

$$\lim_{x \to 0} H_1^{(2)}(x) = \frac{x}{2} + \frac{j}{\pi} \left[\frac{2}{x} - x \ln \left(\frac{x}{2} \right) \right] \tag{D.20}$$

yielding

$$\tilde{T}(0) = \frac{Q}{\pi\chi} \left[\ln \left(\frac{4H}{\pi R_0} \right) + \gamma \right] \tag{D.21}$$

Performing the normalization to $\tilde{T}(0)$ using (D.15) finally yields (4.28).

REFERENCES

[1] Luikov, A. V., *Analytical heat diffusion theory*, New York, NY, Academic Press, 1968.

[2] Abramowitz, M., and Stegun, I. A., *Handbook of mathematical functions*, New York, NY, Dover Publications, 1964.

[3] Carslaw, H. S., and Jaeger, J. C., *Conduction of heat in solids*, Oxford, U.K., Clarendon Press, 1990.

List of Symbols

A_i	field amplitude coefficient for layer i
a	gain parameter
B	bimolecular recombination coefficient
B_i	field amplitude coefficient for layer i
b	normalized propagation constant
b_a	gain curvature (gain in the active layer)
b_g	gain curvature (mode gain)
C	Auger recombination coefficient
C	coupling matrix
c	vacuum speed of light
c_v	volume heat capacity
D	dispersion parameter
d	layer thickness
d_a	thickness of active layer
d_g	thickness of grating
d_i	thickness of layer i
E	electric field; total energy
$E_{c,v}$	band edges of conduction and valence band
E_F	Fermi energy
E_{Fc}, E_{Fv}	quasi-Fermi levels for conduction and valence band
E_g	bandgap energy ($E_g = E_c - E_v$)
E_i	exponential integral ($i = 1, 2$)
$E_{J,I}$	field distribution for mode J in region I
E_y	y component of electrical field

e	unit charge
F	dispersion factor for coupler
$\mathbf{F}$	transfer matrix, various subscripts
$F(t)$	Langevin force
f	frequency; data rate
f_r	resonance frequency
f_{red}	reduction factor for coupling coefficient
$G(z, z')$	Green's function
g	optical (power) gain
g_0	gain for field (half the power gain)
g_a	gain in the active layer
g_c	cavity (roundtrip) gain ($g_c = g_{\text{net}} - \alpha_m$)
g_{eff}	mode gain ($g_{\text{eff}} = \Gamma g_a$)
g_{net}	net mode gain ($g_{\text{net}} = g_{\text{eff}} - \alpha_i$)
g_p	peak gain, occurs at the wavelength λ_p
g_α	gain (or loss) perturbation
$H_N^{(2)}$	Hankel's function of order N
h	Planck's constant
I	current; optical field intensity (optical power per unit area)
I_t	tuning current
I_{th}	threshold current
J	current density
J_N	Bessel function of order N
j	imaginary unit
K, K'	complete elliptic integrals of the first kind
K_{therm}	ratio of thermal tuning and tuning via the plasma effect
k	(electron) wave vector
k_0	free-space propagation constant
k_B	Bolzmann's constant
k_g	grating vector
$k_{\text{pl}}, k_{\text{IVBA}}$	derivative of optical loss with respect to carrier density for plasma effect (subscript pl) and intervalence band absorption (subscript IVBA)

k_{therm}	thermal diffusivity
L	length, various subscripts
L_c	coupling length for codirectional coupler
L_{eff}	effective length of periodic structure
L_f	filter length
L_g	sub-grating length
L_s	sampling period
M	grating order; mode number
$\mathbf{M}$	propagation matrix for one period in a coupler
m_e, m_h	effective masses of electrons and holes
N	(longitudinal) mode number; electron density, various subscripts
N_c, N_v	effective carrier densities of conduction and valence band
N_s	number of sampling periods
$n = n' + jn''$	complex refractive index, n' and n'' denote the real and imaginary parts
n_a	refractive index of active layer
n_{eff}	effective (modal) refractive index
n'_{eff}	real part of effective refractive index
n_g	group index
$n_{g,\text{eff}}$	effective (modal) group index
n_i	refractive index of layer number i
$n_I(x)$	refractive index profile in region I
n_R	modal refractive index for mode R
n_{sp}	spontaneous emission coefficient
n_S	modal refractive index for mode S
P	optical power; hole density
Q	heat energy per unit length of δ-pulse line heat source
$Q(z)$	auxillary function (Section 3.2.1)
$q(t)$	heat power per unit length of line heat source
q_i	auxillary parameter (transverse propagation constant) for layer i (Appendix B)
R	recombination rate; power reflectivity; resistance; object distance
$R(z)$	modal amplitude, right going wave

R_d	differential diode resistance
R_I	modal amplitude, region I
R_{sp}	spontaneous emission rate into one cavity mode
R_x	filter width to modespacing ratio for structure x
R_{therm}	thermal resistance
R_0	effective (circular) waveguide radius
r	field reflectivity, various subscripts; radius (in cylinder coordinates)
S	photon density
$S(\omega)$	frequency modulation (FM) response
$S(z)$	modal amplitude, left going wave
S'	photon number
S_I	modal amplitude, region I
S_N	photon density for mode N
S_{therm}	thermal FM response
S_{tot}	total FM response
SSR	side-mode suppression ratio
T	temperature
$\mathbf{T}$	propagation matrix
T_x	tuning enhancement for structure x
t	time
U	voltage, various subscripts
V	volume, various subscripts
ν	normalized frequency
ν_g	group velocity
$W(f)$	spectral (noise) power density, various subscripts
w	stripe width; width of active region
x, y, z	transverse, lateral and longitudinal coordinates
α	optical (power) loss coefficient; connectivity
α_0	field loss coefficient (half the power loss coefficient)
α_H	linewidth enhancement factor
α_i	internal loss
α_m	end loss (sometimes referred to as mirror loss or facet loss)

α_{tot}	total loss
β	propagation constant or wave number, respectively
β_0	Bragg propagation constant
$\beta_{J,I}$	propagation constant for mode J in region I
β_{pl}	derivative of refractive index with respect to carrier density
β_R	propagation constant for mode R
β_S	propagation constant for mode S
Γ	confinement factor
Γ_i	confinement factor for layer or region i
γ	eigenvalue; Euler's constant ($\gamma = 0.57721\ldots$)
Δf	frequency shift (excursion) in FMCW radar
Δg	amplitude of gain variation
Δg_c	cavity gain difference
ΔL_s	sampling length difference
Δn	refractive index step
Δn_t	refractive index change in tuning region
Δx	variation of the parameter x
$\Delta\beta$	deviation from β_0
$\Delta\lambda_B$	shift of Bragg wavelength
$\Delta\lambda_c$	shift of comb-mode spectrum
$\Delta\lambda_{el}$	electronic wavelength tuning (excluding accompanying thermal contribution)
$\Delta\lambda_{f,x}$	filter width for structure x
$\Delta\lambda_i$	change in wavelength for mode i with tuning
$\Delta\lambda_m$	longitudinal mode spacing
$\Delta\lambda_{max,x}$	maximum tuning range for structure x
$\Delta\lambda_p$	change in gain peak wavelength with tuning
$\Delta\lambda_s$	modespacing corresponding to the length L_s
$\Delta\lambda_{therm}$	thermal wavelength tuning
$\Delta\lambda_{tune}$	tuning range
$\Delta\nu$	linewidth
$\Delta\phi$	phase change of optical field due to noise processes, various subscripts

δ	detuning
$\delta(x)$	Dirac's delta function
δ_I	detuning in region I
$\delta\lambda_c$	change in coupling wavelength
ϵ	overlap integral
ϵ_0	free-space permittivity
η	efficiency
η_d	differential efficiency
η_t	tuning efficiency ($\eta_t = d\lambda/dI$)
θ	facet phase angle
κ	coupling coefficient
Λ	grating period
Λ_m	"mark" length in grating
Λ_s	superperiod
λ	wavelength
λ_B	Bragg wavelength
λ_c	coupling wavelength
λ_g	bandgap wavelength ($\lambda_g = hc/E_g$)
λ_N	wavelength for mode number N
λ_p	gain peak wavelength
μ_e, μ_h	mobility of electrons and holes
μ_0	free-space permability
ν	frequency
$\rho(t)$	autocorrelation function, various subscripts
$\rho(z)$	local (field) reflection
$\sigma(z)$	reflection parameter
τ_d	differential lifetime
τ_s	lifetime for spontaneous emission
ϕ	phase of reflected wave; phase of optical field
$\phi(z)$	phase variation of grating
ϕ_0	phase of optical field without phase noise ($\phi_0 = \omega t$)
χ	thermal conductivity

ψ	phase shift in grating
ω	angular frequency
ω_e	angular frequency change per electron-hole pair
$< \dots >$	ensemble average
$\tilde{U}$	Fourier transform of U
$\bar{n}$	average of n

Superscripts

A, B	region A or B
long	longitudinal
t	transpose
$'$, $''$	real or imaginary part
*	conjugate complex
3d	three-dimensional

Subscripts

a	active region (layer)
av	average
B	Bragg region
if	intermediate frequency
lat	lateral
max	maximum
pl	plasma effect
STH	Schawlow-Townes-Henry
t	tuning region (layer)
th	threshold
therm	thermal
tot	total
trans	transverse

List of Acronyms

ACA	active-coupler-absorber
AM	amplitude modulation
AR	antireflection
ASK	amplitude shift keying
ATM	asynchronous transfer mode
BH	buried heterostructure
BIG	bundle integrated guide
BJ	butt joint
CW	continuous wave
DBR	distributed Bragg reflector
DFB	distributed feedback
DFC	distributed forward coupling
DPSK	differential phase shift keying
EAM	electroabsorption modulator
EDFA	Erbium doped fiber amplifier
FM	frequency modulation
FMCW	frequency-modulated continuous wave
FP	Fabry–Perot
FSK	frequency shift keying
FWHM	full-width at half-maximum
GAC	grating assisted coupler
GCSR	grating coupled sampled reflector
GG	gain-guided
HR	high reflection

IG	index-guided
IRSN	injection-recombination shot noise
IVBA	intervalence band absorption
LO	local oscillator
MAGIC	multistripe array grating integrated cavity
MBE	molecular beam epitaxy
MGC	multichannel grating cavity
MOVPE	metal-organic vapor-phase epitaxy
MQW	multiquantum well
MTTF	mean time to failure
MZ	Mach–Zehnder
MZI	Mach–Zehnder interferometer
OEIC	opto-electronic integrated circuit
PIC	photonic integrated circuit
PPL	phase locked loop
PSK	phase shift keying
QCSE	quantum confined Stark effect
QIG	quasi-index-guided
QW	quantum well
RW	ridge waveguide
SCH	separate confinement heterostructure
SG	sampled grating
SL	strained layer
SOA	semiconductor optical amplifier
SSG	superstructure grating
SSR	side-mode suppression ratio
STH	Shawlow-Townes-Henry
TE	transverse electric
TM	transverse magnetic
TTG	tunable twin-guide
VCF	vertical coupler filter
VCSEL	vertical cavity surface emitting laser

| VMZ | vertical Mach–Zehnder |
| WDM | wavelength division multiplexing |

Index

About the Authors

Markus-Christian Amann is professor of Semiconductor Technology at the Walter Schottky Institute of the Technical University of Munich. He has been engaged in the fields of optoelectronics and laser diode technology since 1976 including more than 10 years experience in industrial R&D as deputy director at Siemens Corporate Research and Development. During this period he developed the MCRW laser, which is now a commercial product, and the first transversely integrated tunable laser (TTG laser). From 1994 to 1997 he was professor of Technical Electronics at the University of Kassel, where he continued the research on laser diode technology and design. Prof. Amann holds the Dipl.-Ing. and Dr.-Ing. degrees in electrical engineering, both from the Technical University of Munich. He is a senior member of IEEE and a member of the German Informationstechnische Gesellschaft (ITG).

Jens Buus has worked on diode lasers and related topics for over 20 years, and has published about 120 journal and conference papers in these areas. He was a PhD student and postdoctoral fellow at the Technical University of Denmark, then a scientist with GEC-Marconi Materials Technology (formerly Plessey Research Caswell), and since the start of 1993 he has been an independent consultant (Gayton Photonics). He is also a visiting professor at Aston University. During the last 10 years he has worked as project manager for several collaborative projects, partly supported by the European Union through the RACE and ACTS programs. Dr. Buus holds MSc, PhD, and DSc degrees from the Technical University of Denmark. He is a fellow of the IEEE and a member of OSA, IEE, and the Danish Physical Society.

The Artech House Optoelectronics Library

Brian Culshaw and Alan Rogers, *Series Editors*

Optical Measurement Techniques and Applications, Pramod Rastogi

Optical Network Theory, Yitzhak Weissman

Optoelectronic Techniques for Microwave and Millimeter-Wave Engineering, William M. Robertson

Reliability and Degradation of LEDs and Semiconductor Lasers, Mitsuo Fukuda

Reliability and Degradation of III-V Optical Devices, Osamu Ueda

Semiconductor Raman Laser, Ken Suto and Jun-ichi Nishizawa

Smart Structures and Materials, Brian Culshaw

Tunable Laser Diodes, Markus-Christian Amann and Jens Buus

Wavelength Division Multiple Access Optical Networks, Andrea Borella, Giovanni Cancellieri, and Franco Chiaraluce

For further information on these and other Artech House titles, including previously considered out-of-print books now available through our In-Print-Forever™ (IPF™) program, contact:

Artech House	Artech House
685 Canton Street	Portland House, Stag Place
Norwood, MA 02062	London SW1E 5XA England
781-769-9750	+44 (0) 171-973-8077
Fax: 781-769-6334	Fax: +44 (0) 171-630-0166
Telex: 951-659	Telex: 951-659

e-mail: artech@artech-house.come-mail: artech-uk@artech-house.com

Find us on the World Wide Web at: www.artech-house.com